LADLING MOLTEN METAL

The ladle full of molten metal is carried by a crane to the desired positions above the ingot
molds and there is teemed out of the bottom of the ladle into the different molds.

Courtesy of Carnegie-Illinois Steel Corporation

METALLURGY

BY CARL G. JOHNSON

Associate Professor of Mechanical Engineering
Worcester Polytechnic Institute
Consultant and Member of American Society for Metals
and American Welding Society

CHAPTER XVII
"Titanium, Zirconium, Indium, and Vanadium"

BY WILLIAM R. WEEKS

Assistant Professor of Industrial Technology
Western Michigan College of Education

FOURTH EDITION

AMERICAN TECHNICAL SOCIETY
CHICAGO, U.S.A.

PREFACE

EVERY person engaged in manufacturing of any type, as well as the machinist and foundryman, should be familiar with the basic concepts of metallurgy. Knowledge of metals and their alloys is basic to almost every fabrication process.

The use, the how, and the why of metallurgy are explained in this book. As a teaching device, the book makes the reader *think through* problems by effectively explaining guiding principles, defining terms and outlining manufacturing processes. Discussion of theories is in the light of the *best shop practices,* making the book an accurate source of valuable information for the student as well as the practical man in industry.

The authors discuss and weigh theories against their applications in the shop so that the book is an organized authoritative aid to the technical man. Clear writing and carefully selected illustrations will appeal to the many persons in industry who have had little opportunity to study metallurgy.

A new chapter of this Fourth Edition of *Metallurgy* on the metals Titanium, Zirconium, Indium, and Vanadium, provides a source of information that is difficult to find elsewhere. The properties of these four, newest of the metals to receive widespread industrial use, are fully and clearly explained and illustrated. The addition of this new material greatly increases the value of the book as a text and as an important source of information.

The Quiz Questions at the end of each chapter provide a valuable home-study guide as well as an invaluable aid in the classroom. In industry and in the classroom, *Metallurgy* has already found widespread acceptance. To readers of this newest edition it will prove to be of even more value.

THE PUBLISHERS

ACKNOWLEDGMENTS

THE CORRECTNESS and practicality of this book have been ensured by the liberal use of accurate illustration material and authoritative sources of information. This has been made possible by the individuals, groups, publishers, and corporations who granted permission to use illustrations and data supplied by them.

The authors and publishers wish to express their sincere appreciation to the following who contributed so generously to this volume:

Ajax Electrothermic Corporation

Ajax Metal Company

Allegheny Ludlum Steel Corporation

Allis-Chalmers Company

Aluminum Company of America

American Foundrymen's Association

American Institute of Mining Engineers

American Iron and Steel Institute

American Machine and Metals, Inc., Riehle Testing
   Machine Division

American Society for Metals

American Society for Steel Treating

American Society for Testing Materials

Amplex Division, Chrysler Corporation

Bausch and Lomb Optical Company

Bethlehem Steel Company

A. M. Byers Company

Carnegie-Illinois Steel Corporation

Chrysler Corporation

The Colonial Steel Company

Constable and Company

The Engineering Foundation

"Engineering and Mining Journal"

Ford Motor Company

Gathmann Engineering Company

The Indium Corporation of America

International Nickel Company, Inc.

"Iron Age"

Tracy Jarrett

Massachusetts Steel Treating Corporation

McGraw-Hill Book Company

Metallurgical Dept., Research Laboratories of
General Motors Corporation

Norton Company

Ohio Crankshaft Company

Republic Steel Corporation

Revere Copper and Brass, Inc.

Shore Instrument & Manufacturing Company, Inc.

Society of Automotive Engineers

F. J. Stokes Machine Company

Tinius Olsen Testing Machine Company

Titanium Metals Corporation of America

United States Steel Corporation

The University Press

Vanadium Corporation of America

Wedge Mechanical Furnace Company

Westinghouse Electric and Manufacturing Company

Wilson Mechanical Instrument Company, Inc.

Wyman-Gordon Company

Zirconium Metals Corporation of America

CONTENTS

BLAST FURNACES OF CARNEGIE-ILLINOIS STEEL CORPORATION
Courtesy of United States Steel Corporation

CHAPTER I

Properties of Metals and Tests to Determine Their Uses

DEFINITION AND SCOPE. The art of metallurgy includes the deriving of metals from their ores, or the condition in which they are found in nature; their purification, or their admixture with other metals; and finally their manufacture into shapes and forms usable in industry. The science of metallurgy includes the study of these processes with a view to their control and improvement, and the development of new metal mixtures or alloys and of new test methods.

Because of this wide scope the field of metallurgy may be divided into two parts. The first part deals with the melting and refining of metals, and has been designated as **Process** or **Chemical Metallurgy.** The second deals with the physical and chemical behavior of the metals during shaping and treating operations, and their behavior in the service of man. This phase is termed **Physical Metallurgy.**

The scope of Physical Metallurgy is wide and is of interest to more people than the field of Process Metallurgy. For example, only a few individuals will be engaged in the operation of a melting and refining furnace, whereas a hundred men will be employed in the rolling or forging of the metal so produced, and thousands of individuals will work at manufacturing the rolled or forged metal into automobiles, bridges, ships, airplanes, buildings, wire goods, tools, and a multitude of useful articles. This book, therefore, treats principally of Physical Metallurgy.

Everyone comes in contact with metals through their many everyday uses; therefore the term **metal** is well known. Not everyone realizes, however, that metals have been known for so long a time that there is some uncertainty as to the origin of the term; and despite this age-long acquaintance with metals, comparatively little is known about their real nature and the reasons for their varied behaviors.

During the last fifty years, men have tried diligently to search out reasons for metallic behavior. In this book, some of the results of this search will be examined, beginning with consideration of the uses of the metals and the properties which especially fit them for these uses. The way in which the metals are obtained from their ores will be studied briefly, together with how they are alloyed to make new materials possessing properties suited to the particular applications in which they are used. Some attention will be given also to the methods of manufacturing metals into the many shapes in which they are used, such as rails, tools, and machine parts. Finally the composition of alloys, and the theory and practice of heat treatment of both metals and alloys will be considered.

PROPERTIES OF METALS AND THEIR CONSEQUENT USES

Let us consider why metals have come to play so large a part in man's activities. Wood and stone are both older in use, yet to a considerable extent they have been supplanted by the metals. The reason for the increased use of metals is to be found in their characteristic properties. Most important of these properties is their strength, or ability to support weight without bending or breaking, combined with toughness, or the ability to bend rather than break under a sudden blow. Resistance to atmospheric destruction, plasticity, and the ability to be formed into desired shapes add to the remarkable combination of properties possessed by no other class of materials. Some metals also have special additional properties, two of which are the power to conduct electric current and the ability to be magnetized.

Metals can be cast into varied and intricate shapes, weighing from a few ounces to many tons. Their plasticity, or ability to deform without rupture, makes them safe to use in all types of structures, and also allows their formation into required shapes through forging and other operations. Metals also possess the important property of being weldable. Of all the engineering materials, only metals are truly weldable and repairable. Other materials used in engineering construction, including glass, stone, and wood, usually are discarded when the structure is no longer usable. On the other hand, an obsolete bridge, ship, or boiler made of metal usually is cut into easily handled sections, put into a furnace, remelted, cast, and finally worked into the making of a new ship, bridge, or boiler.

SELECTION FOR USE. The selection of the proper metal or alloy for a given use is an important part of the practice of metallurgy. Because iron and steel are used in larger quantities than any of the other metals, it is common practice to divide metallurgical materials into ferrous, or iron-bearing, and nonferrous, or those containing no iron or only small proportions of iron.

Strength, Shaping, Cost. Strength, ease of shaping, and relatively low cost are of greatest importance for major structural purposes. For these purposes, steel is ideally suited. Steel is used for the structural members of buildings, for rails, locomotives, and ships. For automobile parts, and wherever greater strength and toughness are required, more expensive special steels are used. As a general rule, if strength alone is the main consideration, nonferrous alloys would not be used. However, where the requirement is for strength combined with resistance to rusting, aluminum-bronze or monel metal may be used. There are purposes for which strength is not so important as ease of machining. In making screws, for instance, another kind of steel, or perhaps a brass, may be used. Where the finished form is to be produced by casting, and great strength is not required, cast iron or cast brass are employed.

The steel that is used in tools might be called the master metal of them all. This steel can be made soft enough for machining, or for cutting or forming to the desired shape, and then by heat treatment it can be properly hardened for use as a tool. Steel is made soft or hard by practice of a heat treatment which, in primitive form, is as old as man's knowledge of the metals.

Metals Light in Weight. For making airplane parts, and in other applications where strength must be combined with light weight, metals such as aluminum or magnesium and their alloys are used.

Softness, Ease in Bending. For uses requiring softness and ease
in bending, as in cable sheathing or plumbers' pipe, and where certain
chemical properties are needed, lead and its alloys may be employed.

Susceptibility to Corrosion. Metals vary greatly in their susceptibility to atmospheric and chemical corrosion. The rusting of iron
is the commonest example. A list of the elements in the order of their
susceptibility to attack would start with potassium, which actually
catches fire in contact with water, and would end with platinum and
gold, which are unattacked by almost all chemical reagents. Such a
list, known as the electromotive or electrochemical series, is as follows:

a) Potassium	*g*) Zinc	*m*) Copper
b) Sodium	*h*) Iron	*n*) Mercury
c) Calcium	*i*) Nickel	*o*) Silver
d) Magnesium	*j*) Tin	*p*) Platinum
e) Aluminum	*k*) Lead	*q*) Gold
f) Manganese	*l*) Hydrogen	

The electromotive series is an arrangement of the metals in the
diminishing order of their tendency to oxidize or corrode. Hydrogen
is not a metal, but is included in this series to show its activity in relation to that of the various metals.

Oxidation or corrosion of those metals at the top of this list takes
place at ordinary temperatures. Such activity decreases from top
to bottom. Copper and those below it do not oxidize at ordinary
temperatures when exposed to pure dry air.

Metals above hydrogen are difficult to obtain free in nature as
they unite readily with other elements. Such metals are rarely found
in the native state. Metals below hydrogen are found free in nature
because they combine with other elements with difficulty. Hence,
they do not corrode and are not easily oxidized.

Although the list indicates the varying effects or lack of effect of
corrosion, it is misleading in practice, since both aluminum and zinc
form protective coatings in the early stages of oxidation and are not
further destroyed; whereas, iron or steel, if unprotected, will rust
completely through. For this reason iron or steel, when used in exposed positions, is protected by paint or by a thin coat of zinc (galvanized sheet) or tin. If greater resistance to corrosion is required, cop-

Table 1. Some Properties of Metallic Elements
(Arranged in order of melting point)

Metal	Melting Point Deg. F.	Specific Gravity	Electrical Conductivity Percentage[a]	Linear Coef. of Thermal Expansion[b]
Tin	449	7.3	11.3	11.63
Bismuth	520	9.8	1.1	9.75
Cadmium	610	8.7	21.2	16.6
Lead	621	11.3	7.6	16.4
Zinc	787	7.2	26.0	18.0–12.8[c]
Magnesium	1204	1.7	35.5	14.3
Aluminum	1215	2.7	53.0	13.3
Arsenic	1497	5.73	4.6	2.14
Silver	1761	10.5	100.0	10.5
Gold	1945	19.3	66.0	8.0
Copper	1981	8.9	94.0	9.1
Manganese	2268	7.2	....	12.8
Beryllium	2345	1.85	....	6.8
Silicon	2600	2.4	....	1.6–4.1
Nickel	2646	8.9	11.8	7.6
Cobalt	2714	8.9	16.3	6.7
Iron	2795	7.87	17.7	6.6–
Palladium	2831	12.0	....	6.4
Platinum	3224	21.45	16.4	4.3
Chromium	3275	7.14	....	4.5
Molybdenum	4748	10.2	32.2	3.0
Tungsten	6098	19.3	28.9	2.2

[a]Silver=100% conductivity.
[b]Thermal expansion per degree Fahrenheit at room temperature. Value $=(\times10^{-6})$.
[c]18.0 for hot rolled zinc with grain; 12.8 for hot rolled zinc across grain.

per or its alloys, brass, bronze, or nickel silver are used. Where real permanence is required, the precious metals must be chosen.

The development of stainless steels (steels containing varying percentages of carbon, chromium, and nickel) has made it possible to use this material without protective coating against corrosion.

Electrical Conductivity. Copper and aluminum are used for conducting electricity since they offer less resistance to the passage of the current. Silver offers even less resistance but is too expensive for commercial use. Copper offers less resistance than aluminum for the same size wire, but aluminum, due to its lighter weight, offers less resistance per unit of weight. Despite this fact, from a cost standpoint the advantage is still with copper. In the passage of current through a conductor, resistance results in the giving off of heat; the

Table 2. Mechanical Properties of Some Metals and Alloys*

Metal	Composition	Tensile Strength Pounds per Square Inch		Elongation Per Cent 2 In.	Brinell Hardness	Modulus of Elasticity —Tension
		Yield Point	Ultimate			
Aluminum	Al	8,000	12,500	20	21–24	10,000,000
Brass, 70–30, annealed	70 Cu-30 Zn	18,000	46,000	64	70	12,000,000
Brass, 70–30, cold-worked	70 Cu-30 Zn	45,000	92,000	3	170	12,000,000
Brass, 95–5, annealed	95 Cu-5 Sn	13,000	46,000	67	74	11,000,000
Bronze, 95–5, cold-worked	95 Cu-5 Sn	59,000	85,000	12	166	15,000,000
Bronze—manganese	Cu+Zn+Mn	13,000	70,000	33	93	15,000,000
Copper, annealed	Cu	5,000	32,000	56	47	14,000,000
Copper, cold-drawn	Cu	38,000	56,000	6	104	16,000,000
Chilled cast iron	Fe+C+Si+Mn	.....	35–80,000	..	400–700	33,000,000
Duralumin, heat-treated	Al+Cu+Mg+Mn	48,000	56,000	18	95	10,000,000
Gray cast iron	Fe+C+Si+Mn	.....	20–60,000	1	150–225	15–20,000,000
Iron, commercial, pure	Fe	19,000	42,000	48	69	30,000,000
Lead	Pb	.....	3,000	406	...	....
Magnesium	Mg	1,200	32,500	6	41	6,700,000
Magnesium—aluminum alloy	Mg+Al	26,000	44,000	14	55	6,250,000
Malleable cast iron	Fe+C+Mn	37,500	57,000	22	110–145	25,000,000
Molybdenum	Mo	.....	150,000	5	...	....
Monel metal	Ni+Cu	50,000	90,000	40	166	25,000,000
Nickel	Ni	25,000	70,000	48	85	32,000,000
Steel, structural	Fe+C	35,000	60,000	35	120	30,000,000
Steel, high-carbon, heat-treated	Fe+C	150,000	275,000	5	550	30,000,000
Steel alloy, heat-treated	S.A.E. 2340	174,000	282,000	8	488	30,000,000
Steel alloy, heat-treated	S.A.E. 4140	116,000	140,000	16	250	30,000,000
Steel alloy, heat-treated	S.A.E. 5150	210,000	235,000	13	455	30,000,000
Tin	Sn	200	2,000	43	...	6,000,000
Tungsten wire	W	.....	230,000	3	...	60,000,000
Wrought iron	Fe+Slag	30,000	50,000	35	100	27,000,000
Zinc, rolled sheet	Zn	5,000	24,000	35	...	12,000,000

*The data in this table are based on tests made in several materials testing laboratories.

greater the resistance, the greater the heat for the passage of a given current. Hence for electrical heating, metals with high electrical resistance are needed. These are found in the alloys; among the best are alloys of nickel and chromium. The relative conductivity of some metals is shown in Table 1. Note that copper is 94% of that for silver, while iron is only 17.7% of that for silver.

Resistance to Heat. The relative electrical resistances of metals may be seen in Table 1. The resistance to the flow of heat is of the same order as the resistance to electricity; hence, ordinarily we use copper for boiler tubes, heating coils, and soldering irons. For cooking utensils, aluminum is used because of the combination of high-heat conduction with resistance to attack by foodstuffs. In magnetic properties, iron and its alloys stand alone.

Tables 1 and 2, listing the most important physical constants of various metals, will be helpful in selecting the proper metal for a given job.

MELTING POINT. The melting point is the temperature at which a substance passes from a solid to a liquid condition. For water this is 32° F. Pure substances have a sharp melting point, that is, they pass from entirely solid to entirely liquid form in a very small temperature range. Alloys usually melt over a much wider temperature interval. The melting points and other temperatures in Table 1 are expressed in degrees Fahrenheit. According to this scale, water melts at 32° and boils at 212°. In metallurgy, temperatures are expressed frequently in degrees centigrade. To convert degrees centigrade to degrees Fahrenheit, use the following formula:

$$\text{Deg. F.} = (\text{Deg. C.} \times \tfrac{9}{5}) + 32$$

COEFFICIENT OF EXPANSION. With few exceptions, solids expand when they are heated and contract when cooled. They increase not only in length, but also in breadth and thickness. The number or factor which shows the actual increase in unit length of a solid when it is heated one degree is called its **coefficient of linear expansion.**

SPECIFIC GRAVITY. Sometimes it is an advantage to compare the density of one metal with that of another. For such a purpose, we need a standard. Water is the standard which physicists have selected with which to compare the densities of solids and liquids.

Hence, the weight of a substance compared to the weight of an equal volume of water is called its **specific density** or **specific gravity.**

If we weigh one cubic foot of copper, we find that it weighs 549.12 pounds. One cubic foot of water weighs 62.4 pounds. If we divide 549.12 by 62.4, we get 8.9, which we call the specific weight of copper. The specific weight or gravity of the common metals is listed in Table 1. It is obvious that if we wish to find the weight of a cubic foot of any of these metals, then all we have to do is to multiply 62.4 by the specific gravity as listed in the table.

ELECTRICAL RESISTANCE. The opposition to electric current as it flows through a wire is known as the resistance of the wire. In order to have a standard of comparison, an arbitrary resistance unit has been agreed upon internationally. This unit is called the **ohm.** The resistances of metals are expressed in terms of millionths of an ohm, or **microhms** of resistance in a cube of metal one centimeter on each side.

The resistance of an electric circuit is a property of the conductor forming the circuit and depends upon the length, cross-sectional area, temperature, and upon the material, whether copper, iron, brass, etc. Silver, as has been stated, is the best conductor known; in other words, it offers the least resistance to the passage of an electric current. Copper, gold, and aluminum are next in order.

MECHANICAL PROPERTIES. Generally we are very much concerned with the mechanical properties of metals and alloys. The mechanical properties, such as hardness, tensile strength, compressive strength, ductility, etc., are those measured by mechanical methods. These properties will be discussed in some detail in the next section and in the treatment of the individual metals or alloys.

TESTING OF METALS TO DETERMINE USE

A knowledge of the properties of specific metals or alloys enables us not only to determine whether or not such materials are suitable for certain definite uses, but also to modify the thermal and mechanical treatments of such materials in order to obtain them in the most desirable form. Testing methods, in general, enable us to take a small portion of material, and from it to predict with some certainty how the material will behave in actual service.

COMPOSITION. The composition of metals and alloys is important in the effect it has on their mechanical, electrical, or magnetic properties. Even a very minute amount of some elements exerts a profound influence, and the chemical analysis of alloys thereby becomes a matter of great consequence. The methods of chemical analysis, however, are too lengthy and complicated to describe briefly; they are a part of chemical engineering.

Strength and Plasticity. Strength with plasticity is the most important combination of properties a metal can possess. Strength is the ability of a material to *resist* deformation; plasticity is the ability to *take* deformation without breaking. If metals having this combination of properties are used in vital parts of structures and for tools and machines that may become overloaded in service, serious trouble will be avoided. For example, should a member of a bridge structure become overloaded, plasticity allows the overloaded member to flow, so that the load becomes redistributed to other parts of the bridge structure.

Elasticity. Loading a material causes a change in form. Elasticity is the ability of a material to return to its original form after removal of the load. Theoretically, the elastic limit of a material is the limit to which a material can be loaded yet recover its original form after removal of the load. In reality, we find that metals are not entirely elastic even under slight loads; therefore, an arbitrary method of determining the commercial elastic limit must be used.

TENSILE TESTS. Tensile tests may be made on the machine illustrated in Fig. 1. This machine measures the load placed upon the specimen, and by dividing the load required to break the specimen by its area, the ultimate tensile strength of the material is obtained. Tensile strength accordingly is expressed in pounds per square inch (p.s.i.) or in kilograms per square millimeter.

If an accurate gage is clamped to the specimen and its elongation measured and plotted against the load, the point at which the elongation ceases to be proportional to the load, see Fig. 2, is known as the **proportional limit.** The **elastic limit** is the greatest load which may be applied, after which application the material will return to its unstrained condition. For practical purposes the elastic limit is the same as the proportional limit. This is an important factor in designing, as it is usually of more importance to know what load will deform a structure than what load will cause rupture. Some materials, notably steel, indicate what is known as a **yield point.** This is the load at which the material will continue to elongate even though the load is not being increased. It is indicated by a dropping of the weighing beam and is somewhat greater than the elastic limit.

Fig. 1. Universal Testing Machine for Determining Tensile Strength; Equipped with Electronic High Magnification Recorded for Drawing Stress-Strain Diagram

Courtesy of Tinius Olsen Testing Machine Co., Philadelphia, Pa.

Both lever and hydraulic types of tensile testing machines are in use for pulling standard test pieces, either flat or round, bolts and medium sized bars, rods, and wire. The hydraulic type of machine is far superior and is rapidly replacing the lever type. Large hydraulic machines are needed for testing large pieces, full-sized units, and assembled machines. Lever and spring-actuated machines are more useful for light loads.

Ductility. The plasticity exhibited by a material under tension loading is known as its **ductility** and is measured by the amount a material can be permanently elongated. This ability to elongate permits a metal to be drawn from a larger size to a smaller size of wire.

Malleability. The ability of a metal to deform permanently under compression without rupture is known as its **malleability.** It is this

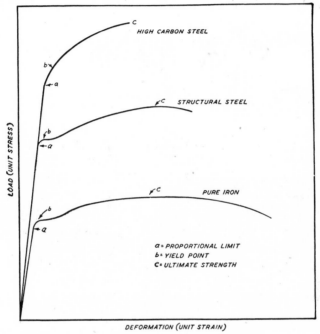

Fig. 2. Stress-Strain Curves for Three Materials

property which allows the hammering and rolling of metals into thin sheets.

Toughness. Although there is no direct and accurate method of measuring the toughness of metals, it may be assumed that a tough metal is one possessing high strength and the ability to deform* permanently without rupture. Often the impact resistance or shock resistance of a material is taken as an indication of its inherent toughness.

*An explanation of this term can be found under *Deformation of Metals.*

Brittleness. Brittleness is the property opposite to plasticity. A brittle metal is one that cannot be visibly deformed permanently; that is, it lacks plasticity. The hard metals, such as fully hardened tool steel, may exhibit very little plasticity and may therefore be classified as brittle; yet hardness is not a measure of plasticity. A brittle metal usually develops little strength upon tensile loading, but may be safely used in compression. Brittle metals show very

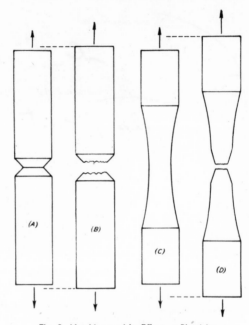

Fig. 3. Notching and Its Effect on Plasticity

little shock or impact strength. There are no values for brittleness, and a brittle metal will fail without any warning of impending failure.

On the other hand, a ductile metal may fail without any visible deformation if the load becomes concentrated, due to a notched effect, as shown in Fig. 3. The test specimen A in Fig. 3 has a sharp reduction in cross section, and, when pulled apart, ruptures with a brittle fracture; see specimen B. Specimen C, made from the same metal but with a gradual reduction in cross section, behaves as a plastic material, elongating noticeably before rupture; see specimen D.

The student of metallurgy should remember this example and apply its principles by the omission, in all design work, of such factors as sharp corners, notching, or sudden changes in cross section.

Shock Resistance. The behavior of metals under impact loads, or shock, may oftentimes be quite different from their behavior under loads slowly applied. The resistance of metal to shock is measured by means of a pendulum-type machine, shown in Fig. 4. If the pendulum is allowed to swing freely, it will swing through a known angle; if we interpose a specimen which the pendulum breaks, some energy

Fig. 4. Pendulum-Type Impact
Testing Machine

*Courtesy of Tinius Olsen Testing
Machine Co., Philadelphia, Pa.*

Fig. 5. Fatigue Fracture of Grinding Machine Spindle

will be used up and it will swing through a smaller angle. This machine enables us to measure the angle through which the pendulum swings, and thus to calculate the energy consumed in breaking the specimen. This is usually reported in foot-pounds. The energy consumption for a piece of cast iron (which is very fragile) will be low, and we say that the shock resistance is small; while for a piece of wrought iron, energy consumption will be high and shock resistance correspondingly large.

Standard tests exist in which notched specimens are fractured by a single impact in order to check for any tendency toward brittle behavior. Two of the most common tests are the Izod and the Charpy. In the former test, a square notched bar is gripped vertically in a vise, and a measure is made of the number of foot-pounds necessary to break the bar by a blow struck just above the notch. In the Charpy test, the specimen, usually square, is supported freely at its ends and is hit at a point just behind the notch at the middle of the span. In both cases the blow is applied by a freely swinging pendulum.

Fatigue. When a sample is broken in a tensile machine, a certain definite load is required to cause that fracture. However, the same material will fail under a much smaller load if that load is applied and removed many times. In this way, an axle may break after months of use, even though its loading has not been changed. Such a failure is pictured in Fig. 5. The part breaks with no sign of deformation. The final part to fracture is usually quite coarse grained with adjacent sections showing signs of having rubbed together for quite some time. The fracture above shows concentric rings of sections which have rubbed together during the period of time prior to ultimate failure. The coarse grain of the final fracture has often led to the erroneous statement that the part failed due to crystallization in service. All such failures are known as **fatigue** or **progressive failures,** and in designing parts subjected to varying stresses, the fatigue limit of a material often is more important than its tensile strength or its elastic limit. The **fatigue limit** is that load, usually expressed in pounds per square inch, which may be applied during an infinite number of cycles without causing failure. In fatigue testing it is assumed, ordinarily, that a load which can be applied 100,000,000 times without failure can be applied indefinitely without failure. Fig. 6 shows typical diagrams for fatigue tests of metals.

A number of types of fatigue-testing machines are available. In the most common type, a round test bar is rotated horizontally with a load applied by means of a weight hung on one end, and the stresses are calculated from the applied load and the dimensions of the test bar. In such a test, the load varies from a tensile stress to a compressive stress of equal magnitude. In another type of machine, a bar is alternately compressed and elongated. For testing samples of sheet metal, Professor H. F. Moore, University of Illinois, has developed a machine in which the flat specimen is clamped to one end of a calibrated spring and the other end to a shaft from an eccentric.

Stress in the specimen is calculated from the movement of the calibrated spring.

Much knowledge has come to us in recent years which enables us to use metals in a safe and economical way and to meet the rigid

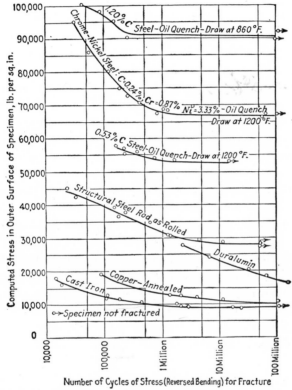

Fig. 6. Typical S-N (Stress-Cycle) Diagrams for Fatigue Tests of Various Metals

Reprinted by Permission from *Materials of Engineering* by Moore, Published by McGraw-Hill Book Co., Inc., New York, N.Y.

requirements for metals in our modern machines. Of prime importance for high fatigue life is the smoothness and lack of stress-raising imperfections on metals used. Fatigue limit increases with the tensile strength and, in ductile steels, is approximately 50 per cent of the tensile strength. Lack of surface uniformity, such as decarburization, lowers the fatigue limit. Further, roughened, notched, or threaded surfaces serve to decrease pronouncedly the fatigue limit. Damaging corrosive conditions will greatly decrease the fatigue strength of a metal at even small stresses.

In figuring allowable stresses under repeated stress, it must be remembered that stresses above the yield strength of the metal will cause elastic failure. The designer and user of steel parts must be on guard against both elastic and fatigue failure. Machinists, machine operators, and inspectors share the responsibility of keeping stress raisers out of parts and assemblies.

It is a known fact that offsets, slots, holes, notches, and sharp re-entrant angles build up stresses excessively when they are loaded. Use of generous fillets, rounding off the ends of keyways and slots, smoothing out corners and shoulders, and avoiding sharp tool cut marks will do much to eliminate stress raisers. Any sharp grooves or notches may so change the distribution of stresses as to alter greatly the usual physical properties of the material and cause the part to react to loading in a wholly unexpected way.

Hardness. Hardness is the property of a metal which gives it the ability to resist being permanently deformed when a load is applied. The greater the hardness, the greater the resistance to deformation. Because the definitions for ultimate strength and hardness are somewhat synonymous, in general it can be assumed that a strong metal is also hard. A simple though crude method of measuring relative hardness is to determine whether or not one material will scratch another. For minerals this is about the only way of determining hardness; a scale, the **Mohs scale,** ranges from very soft talc with a hardness of 1 to diamond with a hardness of 10. The same method is applied to hardened steel, for when the steel cannot be filed it is pronounced "file hard" and considered to be in the hardest possible state. A small fine-toothed file is an extremely convenient tool for testing hardness, especially case-hardened objects, quenched shapes, and surface-hardened pieces that should be hard. Despite the personal equation of the man handling the file and other variables such as the force applied, it is possible to make close comparisons to Rockwell hardness readings of the steels tested. Such measurements are difficult to evaluate quantitatively; other methods therefore are necessary for more exact measurement of hardness.

One way of measuring the hardness of a metal is to determine its resistance to the penetration of a nondeformable ball or cone, or to determine the depth to which such a ball or cone will sink into the metal under a given load. The **Brinell hardness test** is made by pressing a hardened steel ball, usually 10 millimeters in diameter, into the test material by weight of a known load—500 kilograms for soft ma-

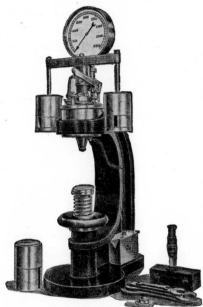

Fig. 8. Vickers Pyramid Hardness Tester

Fig. 7. Brinell Hardness Tester

Courtesy of American Machine and Metals, Inc., Riehle Testing Machine Division, East Moline, Ill.

terials such as copper and brass, and 3000 kilograms for materials such as iron and steel—and measuring the diameter of the resulting impression. The hardness is reported as the load divided by the area of the impression, and tables are available from which the hardness may be read, once the diameter of the impression is obtained. A small microscope is used for measuring these impressions.

Fig. 7 shows a Brinell hardness tester. The specimen is placed upon the anvil, which is raised or lowered by means of the screw. The anvil is then raised until the specimen is in contact with the steel ball. The load is then applied by pumping oil; the handle of the oil pump is shown directly under the dial. The load is applied for 30 seconds; then the diameter of the resulting impression is measured. The Brinell hardness of annealed copper is about 40, of annealed tool steel about 200, and of hardened tool steel about 650.

The **Vickers** hardness testing method is almost the same as the Brinell method. The penetrator used in the Vickers machine is a diamond pyramid, and the impression made by this penetrator is a dark square on a light background. This impression is more easily read than the circular impression of the Brinell method. There is also the advantage that the diamond point does not deform. In making the Vickers test, a predetermined load is applied to the specimen. After removal of the load the ratio of the impressed load to the area of the resulting impression gives the hardness number. The operation of applying and removing the load is controlled automatically. Several loadings give practically identical hardness numbers on uniform material; this is much better than the arbitrary changing of scale with the other hardness testing machines. Although the Vickers tester is thoroughly precise and very adaptable for testing the softest and hardest materials under varying loads, its cost precludes its use where a Rockwell suffices and is far more rapid. The Vickers machine, Fig. 8, is limited definitely to size and shape of the object to be tested, and is extremely well suited to very hard materials. The hardness is given by the relation

$$H = \frac{P}{A}$$

where P is the load in kilograms and A the area in square millimeters of the surface of indentation.

Hardness as determined by the Vickers method is about the same as the Brinell hardness numbers up to a value of 500.

The **Rockwell hardness tester,** illustrated in Fig. 9, measures the resistance to penetration as does the Brinell test, but the depth of impression is measured instead of the diameter, and the hardness is indicated directly on the scale attached to the machine. This scale is really a depth gage graduated in special units. In testing soft materials a $\frac{1}{16}''$ steel ball with a 100-kilogram load is used, and the hardness is read on the B scale; for testing hard materials, a diamond cone is used with a 150-kilogram load, and the hardness is read on the *C* scale. The advantages of the Rockwell tester are that the test can be made quickly; that only a small mark is left on the sample; and that very hard materials can be tested with the diamond cone.

The Rockwell superficial hardness tester employs a light load, causing very little penetration of the diamond cone. This superficial hardness tester does not differ in principle from the standard machine. The hardness number is based on the additional depth to

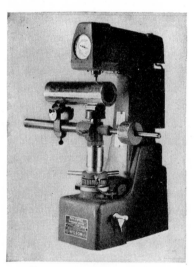

Fig. 9. Rockwell Hardness Tester
Courtesy of Wilson Mechanical Instrument Co., Inc., New York, N.Y.

Fig. 10. Model D Shore Scleroscope Testing Hardness of Standard Test Block
Courtesy of Shore Instrument & Mfg. Co., Inc., Jamaica, N.Y.

which a test point penetrates the material under a given load beyond the depth to which the penetrator has been driven by a small initial load. The initial load is 3 kilograms, while the major load varies and may be 15, 30, or 45 kilograms, depending on the thickness of the hard surface. The machine is very useful in testing exceptionally high surface hardness, such as case-hardened or nitrided surfaces. Thus, sections of razor blades, clock springs, etc. react favorably to this method of testing.

With the **Shore scleroscope,** Fig. 10, the hardness is measured by the height of rebound of the diamond-pointed hammer after it has been dropped on the sample. The harder the material used, the greater the rebound. The height of rebound is read on the gauge. The scleroscope can be used for large sections; it is portable; and the indentation made by the test is very slight, an advantage where surface finish is important. The amount of rebound is a factor more of the elastic limit of the specimen than of its tensile strength, and therefore the machine does not measure exactly the same type of hardness as do the indentation methods. The specimen must be solidly held in a horizontal position, and the hammer must fall exactly vertically. The smallness of the impression made by the Shore scleroscope leads to variations in reading, thus necessitating a range of readings rather than any single one. More than one penetration should not be made on the same spot. Because of its portability, it can be transported to the work and tests can be made on specimens too large to be taken conveniently to the other machines.

Another useful hardness-testing machine is called the **Monotron.** This tester measures the indentation made by pressing a hard penetrator into the material under test. The difference between it and other testing machines is that the depth of impression is made constant instead of the pressure. Two dials at the top of the machine enable the operator to read depth of impression on one and pressure on the other. Pressure is applied until the penetrator sinks to the standard depth, 9/5000 inch; the amount of pressure so needed is read on the upper dial. The penetrator used is a diamond having a spherical point about 0.025 inch in diameter. One advantage for this method, based on constant depth of impression, is that the same amount of cold work is performed regardless of whether the material tested is extremely hard or comparatively soft. Because of this, a wider range of materials can be tested without making any change in the penetrator or the methods of the tests.

There are several other hardness-testing machines that are satisfactory for hardness testing of metals. However, they all yield comparative values for hardness only. There is no definite relationship between hardnesses as measured by the different methods, or between hardness and strength. However, tests have been carried out and various conversion tables have been constructed which are useful when approximate conversion values are needed. See Table 3.

PROPERTIES OF METALS 21

Table 3. Hardness Conversion Table for Alloy Constructional Steels
(Approximate)

Vickers or Firth Diamond Hardness Number	BRINELL		ROCKWELL HARDNESS		Shore Hardness	Tensile Strength 1000 lbs./ sq. in.
	Diameter of Impression for 3000 kg. Load and 10 mm. Ball	Hardness Number	C Scale 150 kg., 120° Diamond Cone	B Scale 100 kg., 1/16″ Ball		
	MM.					
1220	2.20	780	68	..	96	...
1114	2.25	745	67	..	94	...
1021	2.30	712	65	..	92	354
940	2.35	682	63	..	89	341
867	2.40	653	62	..	86	329
803	2.45	627	60	..	84	317
746	2.50	601	58	..	81	305
694	2.55	578	56	..	78	295
649	2.60	555	55	..	75	284
608	2.65	534	53	..	73	273
587	2.70	514	51	..	71	263
551	2.75	495	50	..	68	253
534	2.80	477	48	..	66	242
502	2.85	461	47	..	64	233
474	2.90	444	46	..	62	221
460	2.95	429	44	..	60	211
435	3.00	415	43	..	58	202
423	3.05	401	42	..	56	193
401	3.10	388	41	..	54	185
390	3.15	375	39	..	52	178
380	3.20	363	38	..	51	171
361	3.25	352	37	..	49	165
344	3.30	341	36	..	48	159
335	3.35	331	35	..	46	154
320	3.40	321	34	..	45	148
312	3.45	311	32	..	43	143
305	3.50	302	31	..	42	139
291	3.55	293	30	..	41	135
285	3.60	285	29	..	40	131
278	3.65	277	28	..	38	127
272	3.70	269	27	..	37	124
261	3.75	262	26	..	36	121
255	3.80	255	25	..	35	117
250	3.85	248	24	100	34	115
240	3.90	241	23	99	33	112
235	3.95	235	22	99	32	109
226	4.00	229	21	98	32	107
221	4.05	223	20	97	31	105
217	4.10	217	18	96	30	103
213	4.15	212	17	95	30	100
209	4.20	207	16	95	29	98
197	4.30	197	14	93	28	95
186	4.40	187	12	91	27	91
177	4.50	179	10	89	25	87
171	4.60	170	8	87	24	84
162	4.70	163	6	85	23	81
154	4.80	156	4	83	23	78
149	4.90	149	2	81	22	76
144	5.00	143	0	79	21	74
136	5.10	137	—3	77	20	71

Courtesy of The International Nickel Company, Inc., New York, N. Y.

CORROSION TESTS. The ability of metals to resist atmospheric corrosion, or corrosion by liquids or gases, often is of primary importance. Common types of corrosion are the pitting or localized type, the direct chemical or solution type, and electrolytic or galvanic corrosion. Accelerated corrosion tests have been devised whereby the behavior of the materials in actual service may be deduced from conditions applied for weeks, instead of for years as in actual use. Corrosion may be measured by determining the loss of tensile strength of specimens, by loss of weight in materials which dissolve in the corroding medium, or by gain in weight when a heavy coating of rust is formed. In applying such tests, it is important to know just what the service will be, for a given material might be attacked rapidly by fruit acids and not by nitric acid, for instance; while with another material the reverse might be true.

Although no standard tests for corrosion exist, many tests now exist which have proved to be of great practical value. A few of these tests are discussed briefly in the following material. In all such tests, it is of utmost importance to see to it that corrosion test conditions nearly duplicate the conditions of service.

Salt-Spray Test. One of the most generally accepted tests is the salt-spray test. For this test, specimens that have been thoroughly cleaned are placed in a specially prepared box or chamber and exposed to a fog or spray of salt water for a designated number of hours. The concentration of the spray and the exposure period vary depending on the severity of the service required. Such a test is suitable for testing the corrosion resistance of all of the coatings used on steel. Coated steel will withstand the attack for varying periods depending on the protection the coating affords. More resistant coatings will withstand attack for some hundreds of hours.

Test for Intergranular Corrosion. Attacking a metal with the so-called Strauss solution and microscopic examination for precipitation of carbides are two of the tests employed in looking for intergranular corrosion. In the former test, the steel is boiled in the Strauss solution for about 24 hours. The solution usually consists of 47 milliliters of concentrated sulphuric acid and 13 grams of copper sulphate crystals per liter. If intergranular corrosion is present, the attacking reagent will cause the metal to lose its metallic resonance, cause a considerable decrease in the electrical conductivity, or cause the metal to develop cracks following a bend test.

In the test employing microscopic examination for precipitation of carbides, one side of the specimen is polished and then electrolytically etched in an oxalic acid or sodium cyanide solution. Such an etch causes precipitated carbides to appear as black particles. If carbides are found, the specimen is given an embrittlement test.

Mercurous Nitrate Test. Brass and bronze objects are tested by dipping in a 40 per cent solution of nitric acid, followed by immersion in a solution containing 1 per cent nitric acid and 1 per cent mercurous nitrate. After a few minutes, the specimens are removed, cleaned, and dried. Upon low power microscopic examination, if no cracks are visible, the specimens will probably not crack because of internal stresses.

Weathering Test. An accelerated weathering or exposure test uses intermittent watering and drying to simulate the effect of sunshine and moisture in producing corrosion. Cabinets with suitable heating and watering units are needed for this test.

MICROSCOPIC TESTS. Metals, as ordinarily fabricated, are composed of very small particles which are visible only with the microscope. Since Dr. H. C. Sorby's pioneer work with the microscope (1863–64), the use of that instrument in the metal industry has contributed inestimably to the development of the industry. For the student of metallurgy the microscope is of utmost importance. Microscopic examination will show, for example, whether or not the most desirable structure has been produced, and if the material contains an excessive amount of dirt or nonmetallic inclusions. Such studies not only determine whether the best possible material has been produced, but they also teach us how to modify the manufacturing processes to obtain more desirable metals or alloys.

In order to present the true structures of metals, it is important that the samples be carefully prepared. For such examinations, small samples are selected, representing as nearly as possible the entire piece. One side of each sample is smoothed by means of a file or an emery wheel. This side, which is to be examined, is then ground with several emery papers of different coarseness, beginning with coarse and ending with a very fine paper. The sample is held so the scratches made by each emery paper are at right angles to the ones made in the preceding operation. The sample is then polished on a rotating moist cloth, using very fine alumina or rouge as a polishing agent. After this preparation, the sample should be nearly flat, free from pitting, and almost free from scratches when viewed through the microscope.

Several types of automatic polishing machines are now available for the grinding and polishing of specimens; one is shown in Fig. 12.

Fig. 12.   Jarrett Polishing Machine

Courtesy of Dr. Tracy Jarrett

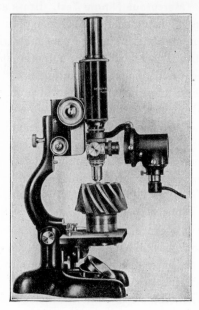

Fig. 13. Metallurgical Microscope

Courtesy of Bausch and Lomb Optical Co., Rochester, N.Y.

Specimens to be ground and polished on this machine are first mounted in bakelite, six bakelite mounts being used each time. These mountings are then placed in a fixture, and the fixture with the specimens is rotated in one direction, in contact, progressively, with stone, pitch, wax, and cloth laps, which rotate in the opposite direction to the fixture and specimens. Abrasive is fed to the face of the laps during each operation. After the last lap, which is a cloth disc with a finely levigated alumina abrasive, the specimens are removed from the fixture. Examination will reveal a highly polished surface, free from scratches, and flatter than those usually obtained by hand grinding and polishing. Time is saved by keeping the specimens rather small. Too much care cannot be taken in the selection and preparation of specimens for microscopic examination. Each cutting, grinding, and polishing operation may alter the surface structure of the metal so as to destroy the evidence wanted in the analysis.

A microscope suitable for the examination of metallic specimens is shown in Fig. 13. This microscope differs from those used in view-

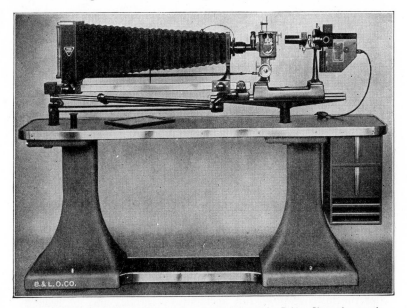

Fig. 14. Large Metallurgical Microscope with Attachment for Taking Photomicrographs
Courtesy of Bausch and Lomb Optical Co., Rochester, N.Y.

ing transparent substances in that a vertical illuminator is placed just above the objective, which is the lens next to the specimen. By means of this vertical illuminator, light from the small lamp is thrown onto the specimen through the objective. The vertical illuminator may consist either of a thin piece of glass or a half mirror. Both types are mounted so they may be rotated by a small disc; in examining specimens it is important to adjust the illuminator for the best view.

A microscope designed especially for metallographic work and equipped with an attachment for taking photomicrographs is shown in Fig. 14. In this machine the image of the specimen is projected on ground glass at the end of the bellows, just as the portrait camera projects the image of a person onto a ground glass. To record the magnified image, a photographic plate or film is substituted for the ground glass and exposed for the proper length of time. With such a machine, magnifications ranging from 10 to 10,000 may be obtained. The magnifications most used are 75, 100, 200, and 500, although it is frequently necessary to use higher magnifications to see the finer structures.

Fig. 15. Photomicrograph of Grey Cast Iron, Unetched, Showing the Flakes of Graphitic Carbon; Magnified 200 Times

Fig. 16. Same as Fig. 15, Etched; Magnified 200 Times

When a polished but otherwise untreated sample is examined under the microscope, a few accidental scratches may be seen, together with some dirt or nonmetallic impurities, such as slag and manganese sulphide in iron. If an alloy is examined which consists of two or more constituents, one of which is appreciably softer than the other, the softer element will have eroded away somewhat in polishing, and the eroded space will appear black. An example of this is shown in Fig. 15, a photomicrograph of a polished but otherwise untreated sample of grey cast iron magnified 200 times. Grey cast iron consists of a mixture of iron, throughout which there are flakes of graphite. These graphite flakes are eroded away on polishing, and the areas these flakes occupied show black in the micrograph.

To reveal the structure, it is necessary in most cases to etch the polished samples. Fig. 16 is the same specimen as shown in Fig. 15, except that it has been etched in dilute nitric acid. The light structural background in Fig. 15 has now darkened and is revealed as a structural component called **pearlite.** This pearlitic structure is a very fine lamellar structure consisting of layers of ferrite and cementite (Fe_3C), as shown at higher magnifications in Fig. 17. Fig. 18 is a photomicrograph of malleable cast iron magnified 500 times. In etching, the sample is immersed in a dilute acid or other reagent which will dissolve a portion of the surface or tarnish the different

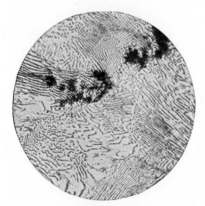

Fig. 17. Same as Fig. 16, but Magnified 500 Times

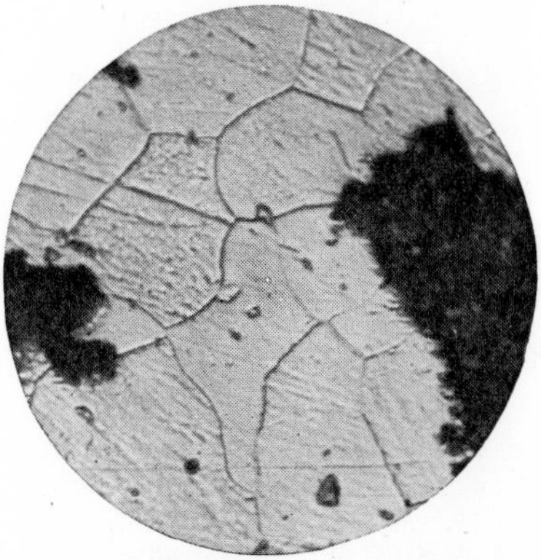

Fig. 18. Malleable Cast Iron Magnified 500 Times. Graphite Nodules (Dark) in a Matrix of Ferrite (Etched)

constituents selectively. Fig. 19 shows a sample of iron which has been etched with a dilute solution of nitric acid in alcohol. As the micrograph shows, the material consists of minute and regularly shaped grains. The nitric acid etch has attacked the crystalline structure of the iron in such a manner as to develop a difference in level of the individual grains, so that the crystals or grains are easily seen with the aid of the microscope.

Investigations have indicated that the size of these grains—for other metals as well as for iron—has a profound influence on the physical properties of the material. In some instances, therefore, the grain size of metals is determined as a routine test. An example of a structure made visible through the staining or tarnishing of some parts of the specimen is shown in Fig. 20, which is of ordinary soft sheet brass. In this instance the etching solution of ammonia and hydrogen peroxide has stained the grains in varying amounts, depending upon their orientation.

FRACTURE TEST. The fracture test is made simply by notching a suitable specimen and then breaking it. If the specimen is relatively small in cross section, and not very ductile, it may be fractured without notching. Although no concrete values of the properties of a metal are obtained through this test, it does reveal many character-

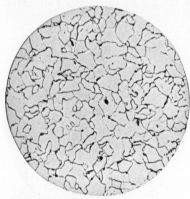

Fig. 19. Photomicrograph and Typical Chemical Analysis of Pure Open-Hearth Iron. Carbon .015%; Manganese .020%; Phosphorus .005%; Sulphur .035%; Silicon .005%; Total Metalloid .080%

Fig. 20. Photomicrograph of Cartridge Brass Annealed at 1200° F.; Magnified 100 Times

Courtesy of A. M. Byers Co., Pittsburgh, Pa.

istics, such as grain size, lack of soundness, case depth in casehardened steel, etc. The fracture test is probably the oldest of the methods used in the inspection and testing of metals. The earliest specifications for metals probably included a requirement for soundness, and doubtless the check for soundness, or the examination for defects that would contribute to unsoundness, was made by the fracture test. A fracture will usually follow the path of least resistance and thus uncover any previous cracks or defects in the metal, which would make it unsound. Fig. 21 shows a standard grain-size test as developed by Shephard in which the standard consists of a series of ten steels of varying grain sizes. The test is made by comparing fractures with these actual standards.

Fig. 21. Standard Grain Size Test as Developed by Shephard

Reprinted by Permission, from *Visual Examination of Steel* by Enos, Published by American Society for Metals, Cleveland, Ohio

From the examination of fractures, it is possible to tell whether a bar is high- or low-carbon steel. A fractured casting will also show whether it is grey cast iron, white cast iron, wrought iron, or malleable cast iron.

When fracturing, **low-carbon steel** will bend and be quite tough. The fracture will be light grey, and often the grain size can be noted if the fracture has not been distorted badly. If heated to a bright red heat, about 1500° Fahrenheit, and quenched in water, not much change in properties can be noted upon fracturing after this treatment.

High-carbon steel will fracture more easily than low-carbon steel since it is more brittle and so will stand less bending. The fracture will glisten more, and the grain size will be readily seen. If heated to a red heat, 1425° Fahrenheit, and quenched in water, marked changes in properties occur. The steel becomes very hard and brittle, and the fracture will be very fine and silky in appearance after this treatment.

Grey cast iron cannot be forged, but sometimes it becomes necessary to distinguish it from white or malleable cast iron. The grey iron will fracture very easily, and the metal will be soft and brittle. The fracture is coarse grained and dark grey in appearance.

White cast iron will fracture very easily and is very hard and brittle. The fracture will show the grain size and be very white in color. White cast iron cannot be forged or machined, except by grinding.

Malleable cast iron cannot be forged or worked cold, but it will be found hard to fracture, being much tougher and more ductile than either white or grey cast iron. The fracture has the appearance of a case and core. The case at the edge of the fracture has the appearance of low carbon steel, and the core or interior of the fracture is similar to grey cast iron but somewhat darker in color.

Wrought iron is very tough and hard to fracture. Heating and quick cooling, as of low carbon steel, have little or no effect. Due to streaks of slag that often can be seen on the surface after cleaning off the scale, the fracture seems fibrous and darker than low-carbon steel. This fibrous condition and streaks of slag are the outstanding characteristics of this material.

TESTING BY MACRO-ETCHING. In testing metals, certain characteristics which may not be apparent to the naked eye often can be brought out by deep etching of the specimen. Although a good surface finish is desired for this type of test, it is possible to deep etch a specimen that has been machined or ground, without resorting to the fine grinding and polishing necessary in preparing a specimen for microscopic examination. Deep etching with a 10% solution of nitric acid in alcohol will be found useful in revealing soft spots in hardened steels, case depth in casehardened steel, welds, and small

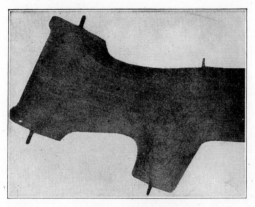

Fig. 22. Axle Forging, Sectioned and Etched to Show
Proper Flow of Fiber

cracks. A drastic deep etching may be obtained with a 50% solution of hydrochloric acid in water. This solution, which is heated to 160°–175° F., will disclose the fiber or flow lines in a forging, as well as segregation, blowholes, cracks, seams, pipes, dendritic structures, etc. A deep etched forging showing the flow lines or direction of forging is illustrated in Fig. 22, while Fig. 23 shows the effect of deep etching a sectioned cast ingot of steel.

MAGNETIC TESTING. This type of test method may be used with the magnetic metals, such as iron, nickel, cobalt, and their alloys. The test may be used to determine the presence of any defects that would affect the soundness and mechanical properties of the metal. This type of test, being nondestructive, can be applied to all the material instead of to a specimen.

Two types of magnetic test are used: one to discover defects such as cracks, seams, blowholes, etc., and the other to determine variations in structure and properties of a metal as compared with a standard specimen that is known to be satisfactory.

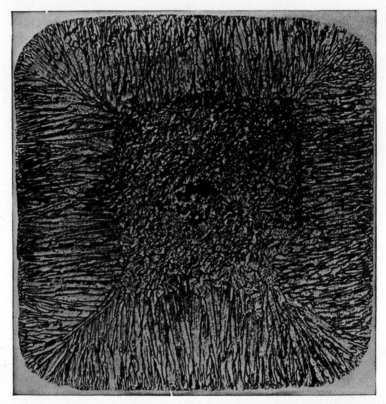

Fig. 23. Horizontal Fracture of Steel Ingot Showing Dendritic Outer Surface and Normal Free Crystal Inner Structure (Note Cleavage Planes at Corners and Central Pipe)

Courtesy of Gathmann Engineering Co., Baltimore, Md.

In the Sperry test, cracks and other flaws in rails may be uncovered by the passage of a heavy direct current longitudinally through both rails, by means of a test car that moves along the rail at about six miles an hour. Any flaw greater than 1% of the cross section of the railhead causes an abrupt change in the magnetic field induced by the current. Both rails may be completely inspected at the same time. Periodic inspection also is possible by this method.

Magnaflux Testing. A powder (Magnaflux) method of magnetic inspection is used a great deal to detect defects on or just below the surface of steel forgings. Such defects might be revealed by the macro-etching method, but at the same time they will be destroyed by the deep etching; whereas, by the Magnaflux method, indications

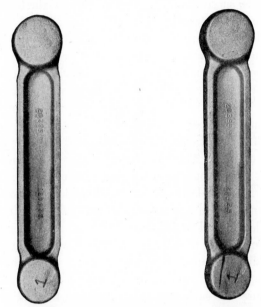

Fig. 24. Magnaflux Test on Defective Forging; Forging Crack before Magnaflux Test, Left; After, Right

Courtesy of Wyman-Gordon Co., Worcester, Mass.

of defects remain intact and may be examined under the microscope to identify their character and extent. Parts to be examined must first be magnetized, then coated with finely divided iron powder or magnetic iron oxide. The powder may be dusted onto the magnetized specimen or applied by immersion in a solution of kerosene and carbon tetrachloride containing the magnetic iron oxide powder. A deposit of the magnetic powder will adhere to any defects which may be present; see Fig. 24. This test has been used successfully to reveal fatigue cracks developing in machinery in service. Where safety is all important, as in aircraft, this test has become very popular.

In the use of magnetic tests for checking variations in structure and mechanical properties of metal parts, it is assumed that any two identical metal parts having identical mechanical properties should show identical magnetic properties. Unfortunately there appear to be many factors that upset this assumption, so this phase of the test has not been so successful. The simplest form of the test consists in comparing the characteristics of the unknown material with those of an acceptable or standard test sample, on the theory that comparison of the magnetic properties of each one will reveal any differences between them. This method is used to check large quantities of similar materials, such as razor blades, bar stock, wire, and tubing.

SPARK TEST. When the chemistry of steel is unknown, the spark test may be used to determine its identity. This is revealed by a study of the sparks formed when the steel is held against a high-speed grinding wheel. This test does not replace chemical analysis, of course, but it is very convenient when supplies of steel become mixed, and when a fast, nondestructive method of identification is needed.

When any form of iron or steel is held against a grinding wheel, small particles, heated to red or yellow heat, are released from the metal and hurled into the air. Upon contact with the oxygen in the air they oxidize, or burn. If an element such as carbon is present, rapid burning occurs, resulting in a bursting of the particles. The "spark picture" of each type of steel should be studied carefully. The best way to master this method of identification is to obtain a series of sample pieces of steel of known analyses and become familiar with the spark picture of each. By comparing the spark picture of the unknown with that of the known steel, a fairly accurate identification may be obtained. One of the big advantages of this test is that it can be applied to metals in practically all stages of production —billet, bar stock in racks, machined forgings, or finished parts. Inasmuch as the test can be made on pieces directly, expensive sampling with possibilities of mixing samples is avoided.

Different theories have been advanced to explain the forking or bursting in the spark picture. It seems reasonable to believe that these forks or bursts are due to the carbon in the steel. There are some observations to support this contention, for if particles of the metal ground off are collected and examined, they are found to be hollow spheres with one side completely blown away. Evidently the solid carbon present in the incandescent fragment on coming in contact with the oxygen of the air is burned to gaseous carbon dioxide. Sudden escape of this gas from the interior of the nearly molten globule would create the tiny explosion and account for the eggshell-like hollow spheres.

A very practical and useful spark-testing layout may be set up at very little cost. A grinder, with a rather coarse and hard wheel, mounted in the left front of a sturdy wooden cabinet about 3½ feet long, 3 feet wide, and 3 feet deep should prove suitable for use. This cabinet, painted a flat black inside, should be placed on top of a bench or table at a convenient height.

When using a cabinet such as the one just described, the operator should hold the piece to be tested against the wheel in such a way as to throw a horizontal spark stream about 1 foot long at right angles to his line of vision. Wheel pressure is extremely important. Too much pressure will raise the temperature of the spark stream and give what appears to be a picture of higher carbon content. Observation should be made of the spark picture nearest and around the wheel, the middle of the spark stream, and how the incandescent particles react at the end of the spark stream. By experience and observation, the operator will soon be able to fix and correlate spark images in such a manner as to enable him to distinguish between steels of different chemical analyses. A 0.15% carbon steel shows sparks in long streaks with some tendency to burst with a sparkler effect; a carbon tool steel exhibits pronounced bursting; and a steel in the neighborhood of 1.00% carbon shows brilliant and minute explosions or sparklers. As the carbon content ranges from a very low to a high percentage, the intensity of the bursting increases.

Spark bursts will vary in intensity, size, number, shape, and distance from the wheel or ends of the carrier lines. The burst is the characteristic spark of carbon. Other alloying elements may have some influence on the spark picture, thus permitting identification. However, steels alloyed differently but having the same carbon content are not always so easily distinguished from each other.

X-RAY TESTS. X rays are rays of much shorter wave length than ordinary light rays. The fact that they will pass through materials impervious to ordinary light, such as metals, makes them valuable in searching for internal defects. When used for this purpose, a photographic plate is placed on one side of the specimen or part to be examined, and the source of X rays on the other side. The X rays penetrating the sample are registered on the photographic plate. If the sample has blowholes or large inclusions, for example, such defects will allow more rays to pass through and will be identified by dark spots on the photographic plate. This method has been used to find defects in small castings.

X rays are also used in studying the crystal structure of metals and alloys. In this use, the atoms deflect the rays in such a way that it is impossible to determine just how the individual atoms are built up to form metallic crystals. Such studies have conclusively demonstrated the crystalline arrangement of metals.

MEASURING TEMPERATURES. In metallurgical work, temperatures are usually measured with a thermoelectric pyrometer. Such an instrument may consist of two dissimilar wires welded together at one end, called the thermocouple, with the opposite ends connected to a millivoltmeter. The welded ends of the thermocouple are placed in the furnace where temperature is to be measured. As this end becomes heated, an electromotive force (emf) or voltage is generated and a current flows through the thermocouple wires. The voltage generated depends upon the temperature reached by the hot end of the thermocouple, and is known, so that a millivoltmeter may be used to read the voltage generated and the temperature may be determined from that voltage. The scale reading on the millivoltmeter usually indicates the temperature in degrees, so that it may be read as easily as the common mercury thermometer. Instruments (usually termed recorders) are available, which register the temperature on a roll of slowly moving paper, thereby furnishing a record of the temperature throughout the day.

The metals and alloys most used for thermocouples are iron with constantan, chromel with alumel, and platinum with a platinum-rhodium alloy. Platinum and platinum alloy, due to their high cost, are used only for measuring very high temperatures.

For measuring temperatures higher than those for which thermo-couples are adapted, such as steel furnace temperatures, a pyrometer of the optical or radiation type may be used. In the optical type of pyrometer, a lamp filament located in the instrument is heated by means of a variable current to the same brightness as the hot substance being measured for temperature. Temperature is then determined from the current necessary to heat the filament to the same brightness as the hot object. In using this instrument, however, it must be remembered that all bodies do not show the same brightness at a given temperature. As furnished by the makers, these instruments are calibrated for "black body" conditions, such as the inside of an empty furnace muffle. For other conditions a correction must be applied which will be found in handbooks under the "emissivity" of bodies.

While the optical pyrometer measures the intensity of a narrow spectral band of radiation emitted by a glowing object, the radiation pyrometer measures the intensity of all wave lengths, light and heat waves combined. Actually the energy of all wave lengths radiated by the source is forced to fall upon the hot junction of a small thermocouple. The temperature which this thermocouple reaches is approximately proportional to the rate at which energy falls upon it; which, in turn, by the Stefan-Boltzmann law, is proportional to the fourth power of the absolute temperature of the source. This rise in temperature generates a current which may be measured and converted to read in temperatures. Radiation pyrometers, like ordinary thermocouple instruments, may be fitted with automatic temperature recording.

QUIZ QUESTIONS

1. Name the two important divisions in the study of Metallurgy. Which is the more important to men who work in the metal industries?

2. What are some of the most important properties included in the combination of properties possessed by metals?

3. Metals are divided into what two large groups?

4. What common means are employed to resist corrosion?

5. What metals offer least resistance to the passage of electric current?

6. Describe briefly how a tensile test is made on a specimen.

7. *Define or explain the following terms:*

strength	ductility
plasticity	malleability
elasticity	toughness
proportional limit	brittleness
elastic limit	hardness
yield point	

8. *What is meant by "progressive failure"? How can the designer and others connected with the metal industries help to eliminate such failure?*

9. *Name and describe briefly the important methods for testing hardness.*

10. *List the most common types of corrosion and give a brief description of the most generally accepted test.*

11. *Describe briefly the steps taken in the preparation of a specimen for microscopic analysis. Why is etching often necessary?*

12. *From the fracture tests describe the following:*

low-carbon steel	grey cast iron
high-carbon steel	white cast iron
wrought iron	malleable cast iron

13. *How is the fracture method used in testing for grain size?*

14. *Why are electric and magnetic tests applied?*

15. *Describe briefly Magnaflux testing.*

16. *What is meant by spark testing of metals?*

17. *What is a thermoelectric pyrometer?*

CHAPTER II

Chemical Metallurgy

SOME metals are mined in the native state. Among these are gold, silver, tin, mercury, platinum, and copper. Native metals need little refining to make them useful, either in pure form or alloyed with other metals. However, even in native metals there are impurities, such as rock, gravel, and sand, which require removal.

Most metals, however, are found as oxides (metal combined with oxygen). This oxide, which may be mined with commercial profit, is called ore. Not all ores are found in oxide form; some of the most important occur as sulphide ore (metal combined with sulphur), or as carbonates (oxide of metal combined with CO_2). Carbonate ores of iron, copper, and zinc are important; some principal ores of copper and zinc occur as silicates. Ores of different metals are put through various refining processes to obtain pure metal.

ALLOYS

Pure metals, as they come from the smelter reduced from their ores, are seldom suitable for manufacturing. Copper for electrical uses is an exception. For most uses, several metals are combined in an alloy with properties differing from those of any constituent. Exact alloy-making methods are discussed under individual metals; only general procedure is considered here.

In making an alloy, one metal, generally that with the highest melting point, is melted first, and others are added. This procedure might be reversed, or all constituents might be put in at once. The simplest melting procedure is the crucible method, used for some steels and in most smaller brass and aluminum foundries. Fig. 1 shows a crucible of steel being lifted from the furnace after the melt. Such crucibles, holding from 50 to 150 pounds, are made from graphite, mixed with a clay binder.

Fig. 1. Removing Crucible of Steel from Furnace
Courtesy of The Colonial Steel Co., Pittsburgh, Pa.

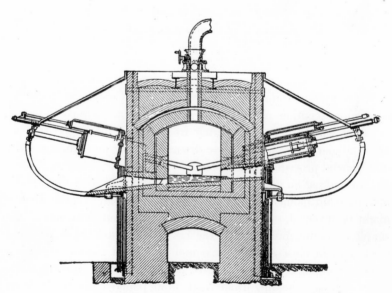

Fig. 2. Section of Pure-Arc Type of Electric Steel Furnace
Courtesy of the "Engineering and Mining Journal"

Where a large quantity of metal is to be melted continuously, the shaft furnace or cupola may be used. Since its use is chiefly confined to cast iron, it is described under that heading.

In making larger amounts of alloys, other than cast iron, electric furnaces of either the arc or the induction type are used. Figs. 2 and 3 are diagrams of arc-type electric steel furnaces. Fig. 4 illustrates the Héroult type of furnace for melting steel and other alloys with high melting points. In the arc furnace, graphite or carbon electrodes

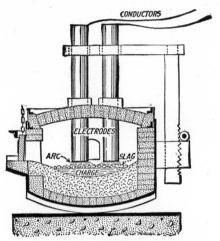

Fig. 3. Diagram of Arc-Type Electric Steel Furnace

Reprinted by Permission, from *Materials of Engineering* by Moore, Published by McGraw-Hill Book Co., . Inc., New York, N.Y.

are used and the heat is generated by electric current passing through the air separating the electrodes from the bath. The electrodes are burned up in this process and must be fed forward as the furnace is operated. For melting brass on a large scale, the Ajax-Wyatt low frequency induction furnace is used most frequently. Such a furnace is shown in Fig. 5. The heat in an induction furnace depends on the fact that if an alternating current is passed through a coil with a metal core in the center, the core will be heated by the eddy currents induced into it. In this type of furnace the molten metal is in the shape of a ring, and the induced current flows around it, thus heating it more readily. Enough metal must be left in the furnace to form the ring.

Fig. 4. Heroult Type of Electric Steel Furnace
Courtesy of the "Iron Age"

Fig. 5. Ajax-Wyatt Induction Furnace
Courtesy of The Ajax Metal Co., Philadelphia, Pa.

The linings of both these types of furnaces are tamped into place from pulverized refractory material; their preparation is the greatest single problem in the operation of such furnaces.

Where iron alloys, or other alloys of high melting point, must be melted under very close control, the Ajax-Northrup high frequency furnace is used. Such a furnace is shown in Fig. 6. The material is placed in a crucible which is heated by currents induced from a water-

Fig. 6. Ajax-Northrup High Frequency Furnace
Courtesy of The Ajax Electrothermic Corp., Ajax Park,
Trenton, N. J.

cooled coil surrounding the crucible. Metal melted in this furnace is oxidized or burnt much less, and is subject to much closer control than that melted in the arc-type furnace.

For metals with low melting points, such as aluminum or lead, ordinary cast-iron or steel pots or kettles, heated by gas, oil, or coal, may be used.

In the field of nonferrous alloys, the art of crucible melting and alloying is very old. As far as we know, this process was used before the dawn of history. However, we believe that iron and steel, as we know them today, were made by a process involving a long exposure of iron ore to the action of carbonaceous fuels such as charcoal. This was a sort of roasting process that reduced the ore and impregnated carbon into the iron, thus producing the alloy of iron and carbon which we know as steel. This process, used long before recorded history, continued until Benjamin Huntsman, in about 1740, devised the method of melting steel in small covered crucibles, or pots. The alloying with carbon was accomplished by the addition of wood or charcoal to the crucible. The iron absorbed the carbon necessary to produce steel. Today, by far the largest tonnage of steel is produced by the open-hearth process.

PRODUCING NONFERROUS METALS

One way in which the nonferrous metals differ from iron is in the manner of their occurrence. Iron oxide occurs in large and comparatively pure deposits; the other metals and compounds from which metals are derived are scattered through large volumes of rock, such as limestone or quartz. Since it would be difficult and costly to smelt these large amounts of barren rock, recourse is had to concentration or "ore dressing" by which the metals or metallic compounds are partially separated from the "gangue," or worthless material, before smelting. As the methods of ore dressing are rather general, we consider them here, rather than under the specific metals.

METHODS OF ORE DRESSING. Gravity. The simplest method of ore dressing depends on the fact that in general the metallic compounds have a higher specific gravity than the gangue, and hence settle faster in a stream of water. Gold panning is the simplest illustration of the procedure. On a larger scale, it is carried on in jigs where the ore is placed on a screen and a pulsating stream of water forced through the screen, causing the lighter gangue to be washed out. Another form of gravity concentrator is the "table," consisting of a surface with longitudinal ridges, which is given a jerking end-to-end motion while a stream of water flows across it laterally. By this means the heavy ore is shaken over the end while the gangue washes off the front.

Oil Flotation. A method of ore separation coming into greater use is oil flotation. This process is based on the following: if a finely ground mixture of ore minerals and gangue is mixed with water, a little of certain oils added, and the whole stirred violently to produce a froth, the metallic mineral will be found in the froth. This method is capable of removing the last traces of mineral from the gangue, and hence is used to supplement the gravity process.

In discussing the metallurgical treatment of nonferrous ore, it should be understood that we refer to metallic mineral which has been concentrated by one of these methods. We shall also consider briefly the kinds of furnaces used for nonferrous smelting.

FURNACES. Reverberatory. The simplest of these is the reverberatory furnace. In this type the melting pot or hearth is long and narrow, and the charge is heated by a flame directed over the top of the material to be melted, so that much of the heating is indirect. The hearth has a slight tip toward the end of the furnace away from the firing end; the molten metal or alloy, and the slag if any, are drawn off here.

Slags are molten glassy materials which are purposely formed in certain metallurgical furnace operations for several reasons: first, impurities in the ore and the ash of the fuel must be removed and prevented from contaminating the metal. The slag layer over the metal also prevents excessive oxidation. Thus for lead ores, with silica as an impurity, iron oxide is added as a slag-former or flux. The silica and the iron oxide combine to form a glassy molten slag at the temperature of working. If the iron oxide were not added, the silica would combine with lead oxide, and lead would be left in the slag.

These reverberatory furnaces vary greatly in size and are used for a variety of purposes, such as copper matte smelting, lead fire refining, etc. They may be fired with gas, coal, or oil; powdered coal is coming into increasing use. Powdered coal is used in the 115' copper matte furnaces at Anaconda.

Blast Furnace. The other type of furnace principally used in nonferrous smelting is the blast furnace, similar to the steel blast furnace except that it is much smaller and the blast is not heated. In the blast furnace the material to be melted is mixed with the fuel, usually coke, the heat for melting being obtained by combustion of the fuel when a blast of air is blown through the charge. Blast furnaces are taller than their cross section, and the charge is fed in near the top. As this charge travels through the furnace, the coke is burned and the metal reduced and melted. The metal is drawn off at the bottom; the slag, formed from the ash of the coke and the impurities in the ore together with added fluxes, is drawn off from a layer immediately above the metal. A blast furnace for treating copper ore is shown in Fig. 7.

Roasting Furnace. In certain smelting processes it is necessary to oxidize the sulphide ore by roasting before smelting. Roasting consists in heating the ore in air until most of the sulphur is driven off and the sulphides are converted to oxides. For this purpose, various forms of furnaces are used. Fig. 8 shows the Wedge multiple hearth furnace. In this, the ore is raked through the various hearths by means of rotating rabble arms, and the hot oxidizing gases travel upward through the furnace.

Collection of Fume. In all smelting operations a considerable amount of fume is given off. The collection of this fume is important, both because of the damage it would do to surrounding vegetable and animal life, and because considerable metallic materials would be wasted. Bag houses or Cottrell treaters are used for collection of this fume.

Bag houses are rooms filled with long cotton bags through which the smelter smoke passes. The solid material is retained by the bags, which are periodically shaken to remove the dust. The dust is treated to recover the metallic values.

The Cottrell treater takes advantage of the fact that if a gas with suspended solid matter is passed between two electrodes, between which is passing a high voltage discharge or "corona," the dust will agglomerate and fall to one of the electrodes. This electrode is arranged so that it may be shaken and the dust recovered.

REFINING OF NONFERROUS METALS. Copper. The most important use of metallic copper is in the form of wire and bars as electrical conductors. It is also used in tubes and boilers because of its property of heat conduction. Copper is one of the comparatively few metals which are found in nature in the free state. Native copper is found mainly in the mines of Upper Michigan. It occurs elsewhere, also, but the Michigan mines are the only ones where the ore is obtained in commercial amounts. Native copper now being mined yields about 0.5% copper. Copper ores have been found which yield as much as 40% copper, but the average is around 2%.

Most copper ore is first concentrated, either by the flotation or

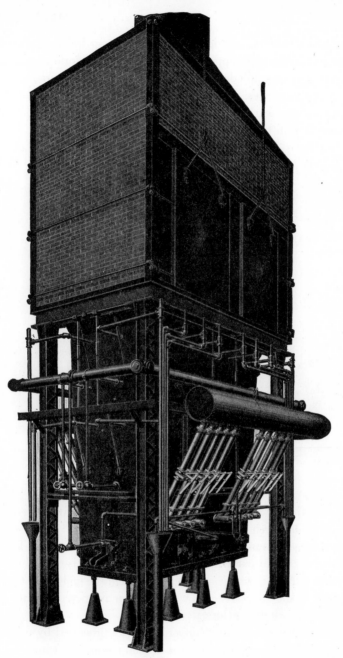

Fig. 7. Water-Jacketed Blast Furnace for Smelting Copper Ores
Courtesy of Allis-Chalmers Co., Milwaukee, Wis.

the gravity method, to yield 20 to 25% copper before it is refined. The most important copper ores are found in the form of a sulphide mixed with iron sulphide, although large amounts are found as oxides, carbonates, silicates, arsenides, and in other forms. Gold and silver are present in nearly all copper ores, and their extraction is one important step in the reduction of copper ores.

Fig. 8. Multihearth Mechanical Roasting Furnace
Courtesy of Wedge Mechanical Furnace Co., Bethlehem, Pa.

Smelting is accomplished either in a reverberatory or a blast furnace. One such blast furnace appears in Fig. 7. This smelting does not result in pure copper but in an alloy called **matte.** The next operation, that of oxidizing the sulphur and iron, is carried out in a converter, Fig. 9, where air is blown through the molten matte. The product of the converter, known as **blister** copper, contains many impurities, including gold and silver.

This blister or impure copper is further processed by partial refining in a furnace, after which the molten metal is cast into the form of plates, about 3′x4′x1″, called **anodes.** The metal anodes are then electrically refined by immersion in a solution of copper sulphate, after which they are placed in close contact with thin sheets of pure copper. An electric current is then passed through the solution. The copper dissolves from the anodes and is deposited on the thin plates or starting sheets. The impurities remain in the form of a sludge, which falls to the bottom of the tank. Gold and silver are removed

Fig. 9. View of Two of the Great Falls Converters at Anaconda; Converter at Left Is Blowing, Converter at Right Is at Finish of Pour

from this sludge by a separate process. The deposited copper is stripped from the starting sheets from time to time, and fresh anodes are put in the cell as the old ones are used up. Since this is a very slow process requiring about one month for an anode to dissolve completely, tanks containing a very large number of anodes are used. Fig. 10 shows an electrolytic copper refinery.

The copper taken from the cathode sheets is remelted and cast into wire bars or cakes for rolling or drawing into wire or tubes. In this remelting process, the copper first is oxidized to remove impurities. Impurities, particularly arsenic, antimony, iron, and tin must not be present, since they lower the conductivity of the copper.

The copper is then reduced by wooden "poles" until it contains .04 to .06% oxygen. If further reduced, it becomes porous on casting. The remaining oxygen might be removed by the addition of phosphor

Fig. 10. Electrolytic Vats (Top) and Copper Anodes (Below)
Courtesy of "Engineering and Mining Journal"

copper without seriously affecting the physical properties; however, this would lower its conductivity. Fig. 11 diagrams a method of extracting and refining copper. Copper containing .05 to .06% oxygen is cast into wire bars and hot-rolled to 1/4" rod.

Fig. 12 shows the process of rolling copper rod. The ¼″ rod is pickled in sulphuric acid to remove the oxide, then reduced to wire of any desired size by drawing. Drawn copper wire is hard, and has a tensile strength of 46,500 to 70,000 lbs. per sq. in. The electrical conductivity is lowered some 2 to 3%; nevertheless, this kind of wire

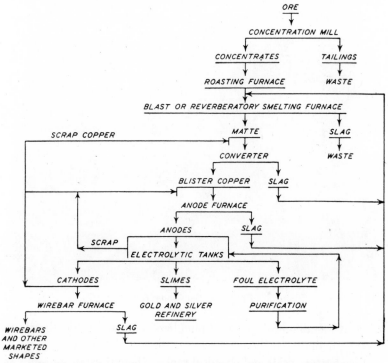

Fig. 11. Flowsheet of Common Method of Copper Extraction and Refining

is preferred for line wire, where strength is important. For other uses, the wire is annealed. This brings back its conductivity while decreasing its strength to about 35,000 lbs. per sq. in. The annealing treatment is given in an atmosphere of steam, in order to leave the wire bright.

For castings and other uses where high electrical conductivity is not important, copper is usually deoxidized with phosphor copper to give a sound casting. For casting purposes as well as for fabrication processes other than wire drawing, copper alloys are to be preferred to pure copper.

Lead. Both lead and the alloys of which it is the major constituent are characterized by softness, pliability, and low melting temperature. Pure lead melts at 621° F. Lead exhibits a high degree of resistance to atmospheric corrosion and to attack by chemicals, particularly sulphuric acid. These properties determine the principal

Fig. 12. Rolling Copper Rod

uses for metallic lead, namely: plumbers' pipe and cable sheathing, where pliability combined with corrosion resistance is important; storage battery grids and chemical tanks, where resistance to sulphuric acid is vital; and solder alloys where low melting point is the paramount requirement.

Lead occurs in nature principally in the form of lead sulphide known as galena, a substance found in abundance in the United States.

Three methods are used to refine the lead ores—the blast furnace, the reverberatory furnace, and the ore-hearth method. The blast furnace is the most important method at the present time.

Lead ores are subjected to a roasting-sintering process as a preliminary step in their reduction, an important procedure in the metallurgy of lead. The object of the roasting-sintering process is to reduce the percentage of sulphur by oxidation of the sulphur to sulphur dioxide (SO_2). Fig. 13 is a drawing of a Dwight-Lloyd sintering machine used in this process.

The lead blast furnace is similar to the blast furnace used in the production of copper matte. Its operation results in a crude lead containing both gold and silver. Both a metal and a matte from

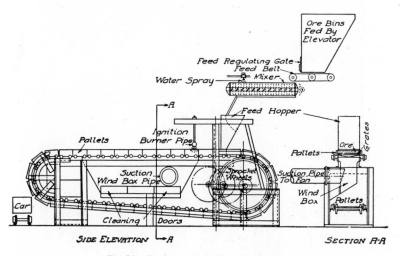

Fig. 13. Continuous Roast-Sintering Machine
Courtesy of American Institute of Mining Engineers

which lead is obtained are produced ordinarily in lead smelting. The crude lead is then cast into small bars to be further refined.

The reverberatory process of refining lead by oxidation is no longer used to any extent in the United States. However, the ore hearth is used as the simplest method of smelting ores rich in lead. The ore hearth consists of a basin to hold the melted lead and to support the charge being smelted. Fig. 14 shows an ore hearth in operation. The lead ore mixed with coke is fed on the hearth, and air is blown through the ore and passes above the surface of the molten lead. In this way the lead sulphide is reduced to metallic lead.

Lead obtained by any of these smelting methods contains the silver, copper, bismuth, arsenic, and antimony which were in the ore, and usually it must be purified. Lead from southeastern Missouri is an exception, being sufficiently pure to use without further treatment. Other leads are purified by fire or electrolytic refining.

Fire refining consists in oxidizing out the arsenic, antimony, and most of the copper by blowing air through the molten lead in a reverberatory furnace at a red heat. The lead so purified is then subjected to the "Parkes process," to remove the gold and silver and

Fig. 14. Lead Ore Hearth for Smelting Rich Ores

the remaining copper. This process consists in adding a small amount of zinc to a kettle of molten lead. The zinc does not dissolve in the lead, but melts and stays on top of the molten lead. Most of the gold and silver enter this layer of zinc, and are skimmed off with it. The zinc-silver-gold alloy then is treated to recover the gold and silver, by the process described in the section on precious metals.

In electrolytic refining, the impure lead or bullion is cast into anodes as described for copper, from which it is dissolved in a lead fluosilicate solution and redeposited as pure lead through the action of an electric current. All the impurities, including bismuth and precious metals, are collected as a slime and treated to recover the metals. The deposited lead is then remelted and cast into pigs.

Several grades of pig lead are available to the consumer: common lead; corroding lead which is used when a lead of exceptional purity is required; chemical lead, which is used in the chemical industries; and antimonial lead, containing between 6 and 7% antimony and used in the manufacture of storage batteries.

Fig. 15. Block of Zinc Retorts in Action

Zinc. Zinc is brittle in the cast form but may be rolled into sheets or drawn into tubes at 100° to 150° C. In these forms it is sometimes substituted for brass or aluminum. The principal uses of metallic zinc, however, are in galvanizing and as an alloy.

Zinc is available in several grades, depending largely on the lead content. High-grade zinc contains less than .05% lead, while the ordinary grade known as **Prime Western** may contain up to 1% lead.

Zinc occurs in nature both as oxide and sulphide. In the recovery of zinc the sulphide is roasted to oxide; the oxide may then be treated to produce zinc, either by smelting or by leaching and electrolysis.

In smelting, the oxide is mixed with coke and heated in a clay retort. The zinc distills off and is condensed in a clay condenser. Each retort produces about 50 lbs. of zinc per day. A block of zinc retorts in action is shown in Fig. 15. The flames are due to the carbon monoxide formed in the reduction burning at the end of the condenser.

In electrolytic recovery, the zinc oxide is dissolved in sulphuric acid and the zinc is removed from solution by electrolysis. The zinc deposited in this process, which accounts for a large percentage of all zinc production, is melted and cast into slabs.

The recognized commercial grades of zinc in the United States have been specified, by the American Society for Testing Materials, as follows:

Grade	Description	MAXIMUM PERCENTAGES			
		Pb	Fe	Cd	Al
1a	Special High Grade	0.007	0.005	0.005	none
1	High Grade	0.07	0.02	0.07	none
2	Intermediate	0.20	0.03	0.50	none
3	Brass Special	0.60	0.03	0.50	none
4	Selected	0.80	0.04	0.75	none
5	Prime Western	1.60	0.08	....	....

The amount and kind of impurities contained in the zinc have a profound influence on the mechanical and chemical properties of the zinc and its alloys.

Cadmium. Cadmium, which is obtained as a by-product in zinc and lead smelting, is closely related to zinc in its properties. It is sometimes used as an electroplate, and as a constituent of alloys of very low melting point. **Wood's metal,** which melts at 154° F., is composed of cadmium 14.3%, tin 19.0%, lead 33.1%, bismuth 33.6%. An alloy of copper with 1% cadmium is used as trolley wire combining high strength with good conductivity.

Nickel. Nickel owes most of its use to its resistance to atmospheric and chemical corrosion, and its ability to take a high polish. For these reasons it is used for vats and vessels in the chemical industry, and as an electroplate on a great variety of hardware. A greater amount of nickel, however, is used as an alloy in **nickel steel**

and in the important nonferrous alloys such as **nickel silver, nichrome,** and **monel metal.**

Nickel is derived principally from mixed nickel sulphide ores by a process of roasting followed by reduction with carbon in a blast furnace—the Orford or "tops and bottoms" process. The product as cast from the blast furnace solidifies in two layers, the top containing copper sulphide, and the bottom layer nickel sulphide. The cast nickel is then further refined electrically or by the Mond or carbonyl process, which consists of vaporizing the nickel in carbon monoxide and redepositing.

Nickel is produced in various forms: nickel pellets, produced by decomposition of nickel carbonyl gas without fusion; electrolytic cathode sheets; nickel shot or blocks, made by casting nickel pig molds or pouring into water without deoxidation; malleable nickel, a deoxidized cast nickel; nickel cubes, reduced from oxides; nickel salts; and nickel powders.

Aluminum. Aluminum is strictly a modern-day metal. Despite the fact that the earth's crust contains an abundance of aluminum, wresting this metal from nature and separating it from the stubborn ores with which it is associated was not accomplished until about 1886 when a young American by the name of Hall and a Frenchman by the name of Héroult simultaneously discovered a way to make aluminum cheaply. A singular fact about these two young scientists is that they were born the same year, discovered a method for obtaining aluminum the same year, and both died the same year.

The only aluminum ore used in this country is called bauxite. Aluminum occurs in this ore in the form of aluminum hydroxide. Such ores are found in Arkansas, Georgia, Alabama, and in several other states. Aside from producing aluminum, the ore is also used for manufacturing chemicals and high temperature insulating materials, and for grinding wheels and stones.

There are several different methods for refining aluminum; however, the most commonly used process was discovered by Karl Bayer. In this process, the bauxite is first crushed to a powder and then mixed in large pressure tanks with a hot solution of caustic soda. The caustic soda dissolves the aluminum hydroxide, but not the impurities. This solution is then filtered to remove the impurities and then pumped into large tanks. On slow cooling, the aluminum hydroxide settles out in the form of fine crystals. These crystals are then washed to remove the caustic soda.

The aluminum hydroxide crystals are now fed into large revolving kilns and heated until they are white hot. This heat drives off the water in the form of steam, the residue being a white powdery chemical of aluminum oxide, called **alumina.**

The last step in this process is to send the alumina through reduction plants where the aluminum is released from the oxygen with which it is now firmly combined. This separation is effected by means of an electrolytic cell. A material called cryolite fills the cell. When the electric current has melted the cryolite, the powdery alumina is dissolved in the cryolite bath. Passage of the electric current breaks up the combination of aluminum and oxygen, the oxygen being freed at the carbon electrode, while the aluminum deposits in a molten layer at the bottom of the furnace. This deposit is poured into molds and cools as a metallic aluminum called pigs. The pigs are remelted to remove any remaining impurities, and then poured to form aluminum ingots.

Aluminum is the lightest of the common metals, having a specific gravity of 2.70. Aluminum does not rust and strongly resists corrosion. Due to its high electrical and heat conductivity, as well as its chemical resistance, it finds many everyday uses.

Because of its lightness, the greatest single use of aluminum is in the field of transportation. Aluminum is also used to a very great extent for electric cables, for cooking utensils, and for protective foil for wrapping foods and other products. Its use in the building industry is of no small importance.

Aluminum lends itself readily to shaping. It is easily cast into molds of all shapes and kinds. It can be rolled hot or cold into thick plates, flexible sheets, or the thinnest of foil. In addition, it can be rolled into bars, rods, or drawn into the finest of wire.

Aluminum alloys are in common use. It alloys easily with copper, silicon, manganese, and chromium. Such alloying, with subsequent heat treatment, results in greatly increased strength and hardness.

Magnesium. Magnesium is the lightest metal now used commercially, having a specific gravity of 1.74. It is produced from minerals used as ores, the most common being magnesite and carnallite, and from concentrated brines and sea water.

In one of the many processes, the metal is obtained by first producing fused magnesium chloride, and then electrolyzing the salt. It is also produced by heating the carbonate, dissolving the oxide thus formed in a fused salt bath, and then electrolyzing.

In producing magnesium from brine, brine containing magnesium chloride, sodium chloride, and calcium chloride is first treated to bring about a separation of these chlorides. The magnesium chloride from this treatment is then subjected to a drying treatment to remove most of the water. This material is then electrolyzed, and magnesium, which collects on the cathode side, is dipped from the cells and cast into ingots.

Magnesium is now produced in great abundance from ordinary sea water. There are three essential steps in this processing. First, lime water is mixed with sea water to convert its soluble magnesium salts into milk of magnesia. This milk of magnesia is then treated with acid converting it into a molten magnesium chloride. The last step involves electrolyzing this molten product yielding solid magnesium at one electrode, and chlorine gas at the other.

Like most metals, magnesium is seldom used in the pure form for metal parts. It is most commonly alloyed with aluminum, although several other alloys are produced.

Magnesium can be forged, rolled, and extruded. It displays its best mechanical properties in the extruded form, where it attains a tensile strength of more than 25,000 pounds per square inch. As a cast material, its tensile strength is about half this amount. Cold working results in a rapid increase in hardness; therefore, it is advisable to carry on such operations at temperatures ranging between 500° to 650° F. Magnesium can be heat treated thus, resulting in a substantial increase in mechanical properties.

Magnesium stands high in the electrochemical series, its corrosion resistance being only fair for ordinary purposes. Machining qualities of this metal are excellent; however, care should be taken in handling small chips or filings as they will oxidize and burn very readily. The danger of such burning decreases as the size of the piece increases.

The greatest single use of magnesium is in the field of aircraft and general transportation, where its extreme lightness is the dominating factor. Its metallurgical value as a desulphurizer, deoxidizer, and alloying element are well known. Like aluminum, it also finds many other important everyday uses.

Tin. Tin has been extracted by the same general procedure for thousands of years, from a lode ore containing the oxide cassiterite (SnO_2). The ore is first crushed and concentrated, then smelted in a reverberatory furnace, or sometimes in a blast furnace. Further refining is then carried out by remelting, allowing the tin which melts first to flow off, then oxidizing the impurities in the molten tin. Electrolytic refining is sometimes practiced.

The best grades of tin on the market are known as Banca or Straits tin, from their places of origin. In addition to the virgin tin produced, a large amount of the tin on the market is recovered from waste and scrap metal.

Manganese. Manganese is a very hard metal, not used industrially in its pure form. It is used as an addition to various ferrous metals and alloys to render them more forgeable, which it does by combining with the sulphur present as an impurity. It is commercially available as manganese metal prepared by reduction with aluminum, or as ferromanganese, which is prepared in the electric furnace.

Chromium. Chromium is a high melting metal similar to nickel. It has recently come into use as an electroplate, replacing nickel in some applications, since it has the advantage of being harder and more resistant to corrosion. Chromium is used as a constituent of chromium steel and the nickel chromium alloys. It is prepared by reduction with aluminum.

Tungsten. Tungsten has a number of uses, important though small. Principal among these is as incandescent lamp filament. Its value here is due to its very high melting point, about 3600° C., and its ability to be drawn into fine wire. It is used also for phonograph needles and as heating elements in very high-temperature furnaces. However its chief use, from a tonnage standpoint, is as a constituent of "high-speed steel." It is available on the market as tungsten powder, wire, and as ferrotungsten.

Tungsten is a heavy metal, its density being approximately $2\frac{1}{2}$ times that of iron. It is never found free in nature, but in an ore from which an oxide is obtained. A metallic tungsten powder is made by the reduction of this tungsten oxide, either with carbon or hydrogen. It is not practical to melt down the powder to convert it to solid metal form, because of the extremely high melting point. Instead, a procedure known as Powder Metallurgy is used to change tungsten powder to the solid metal, a procedure which is discussed in a later portion of this text.

Cobalt. Cobalt is similar to nickel in nearly all its properties. It is used as a constituent of certain special steels.

Antimony. Antimony is a brittle metal with a silvery luster. The pure metal has almost no industrial uses. However, it is an important constituent of several alloys, principally those containing lead. It is available on the market as metallic antimony, much of which is imported from China, and also as antimonial lead—an alloy of lead with 15% antimony, obtained as a by-product in lead smelting.

Bismuth. Bismuth is a metal similar in appearance to antimony. It is a by-product in electrolytic lead refining. Its only use is as a constitutent of the low melting alloys mentioned in the discussion of cadmium.

Ferroalloys. Several of the metals which are difficult to produce in pure form, or can be more conveniently used when alloyed, are available as ferroalloys. These are used as additions to steel. The metals thus available are molybdenum, vanadium, tungsten, titanium, and silicon.

Precious Metals. The uses of gold and silver in coinage and jewelry are well known. Gold is the standard of value and basis of our monetary system. These metals are thus used because of their permanence and their rarity. Most of the gold and silver produced today are recovered as by-products of lead, zinc, and copper refining.

In lead refining, the gold, silver, and platinum are obtained in the zinc crust of the Parkes process. This crust is placed in a retort and the zinc distilled off. The residue is an alloy containing gold, silver, and platinum, in addition to the lead. This alloy is then cupelled, that is, heated in an oxidizing atmosphere until the lead is oxidized, leaving an alloy of the precious metals. This alloy is known as **doré bullion.** By treating with nitric acid the silver is dissolved, leaving the gold and platinum, or all three metals may be separated electrolytically.

Silver for purposes of coinage and jewelry is alloyed with 8 to 10% copper. In England the coinage standard contains 925 parts per 1000 of silver; this is known as **sterling silver.** American coinage contains 900 parts per 1000 of silver.

Gold for coinage purposes and for jewelry is usually hardened by adding copper. For coinage, an alloy of 90% gold and 10% copper is used. The purity of such alloys in jewelry is expressed in "carats." A carat is 1/24 part; hence 24-carat gold is pure, while 14-carat gold is 14 parts gold and 10 parts copper.

Platinum, palladium, and iridium also belong among the precious metals and are even more rare and expensive than gold. Platinum, due to its resistance to chemical attack and its high melting point, finds use in chemical equipment. Palladium is principally of use in dental alloys; iridium alloyed with platinum is used as pen points because of its hardness and permanence.

QUIZ QUESTIONS

1. *How is an alloy made?*
2. *What type of crucible is used in the making of alloys?*
3. *Describe the operation of the arc and induction types of electric furnaces.*
4. *Name two methods of ore dressing.*
5. *Describe the method of ore treatment called "oil flotation."*
6. *Name three types of furnaces used in refining metals.*
7. *What is the most important use of metallic copper?*
8. *What properties determine the principal uses for metallic lead and its alloys?*
9. *What is the Parkes process of purifying lead?*
10. *What are the two principal uses of metallic zinc?*
11. *List some of the important uses of nickel.*
12. *Describe briefly the Bayer process for refining aluminum.*
13. *Name some of the important uses of magnesium.*
14. *What are the best grades of tin on the market?*
15. *List the most important uses of tungsten.*
16. *What are ferroalloys?*

X

CHAPTER III

Producing Iron and Steel

ORDINARILY the terms *iron, cast iron* and *steel* in reference
to a metal in which the element iron (Fe) is the major element
do not refer to a specific metal or alloy, but are loosely used to indicate
a general type of iron alloy. The student of metallurgy, however,
should choose his terms more carefully. The term *iron* should be used
only when reference is made to the element iron (Fe). In speaking of
the commercial forms of iron, such terms as *pig iron, grey cast iron,
wrought iron,* etc., may be used. Each of these terms represents some
commercial form of the element iron, and each form may occur in
many variations of chemical composition which influence the functions within each class. Due to the tremendous production tonnage
of these metals, and to their many forms and varied uses, a detailed
study is not a simple and easy task.

STEEL. Steel, that master metal, is obtainable in great quantities,
both in wrought and cast form. Its plasticity, whether at room
temperature or at elevated temperatures, allows it to be worked
either hot or cold. Its combination of strength with plasticity makes
it the most important metal for use in large structures. By varying
the carbon content and by suitable heat treatments, we can alter the
properties from a very soft, workable steel of the type used in pressed
metal parts, wire, and similar materials to a hard, strong steel suitable
for use in tools and machinery where great strength and hardness are
required.

Essentially, steel is an alloy of iron and carbon. The carbon
content in the common types of steel ranges from approximately
0.08 to 1.40%. The percentage of carbon in steel is the most important single factor governing its properties and uses. In certain
special steels the carbon content may exceed 1.40%. Steel was made
originally by a process of adding carbon to wrought iron in the solid

state, that is, by carburizing. Today all steels are made from iron in the molten state, the carbon being added to the molten iron.

WROUGHT IRON. Wrought iron is the oldest form of iron made by man. It was originally produced by slow reduction of the metal from the ore in the forge fire. This reduction process resulted in a very impure iron which required further refining by mechanical working, that is by hammering or shaping to the form in which it was used. Wrought iron is a metal containing high purity iron and iron silicate in physical association. It is very low in carbon, and the iron silicate or slag is distributed throughout the base metal in fibers which gives it a woody or fibrous appearance when fractured.

CAST IRON. Cast iron is fundamentally an alloy whose chief elements are iron, silicon, and carbon. Cast irons are available with a wide range of properties. The American Society for Testing Materials (A.S.T.M.) specifications (-A 48) provide for classes of cast irons ranging from 20,000 to 80,000 lbs. per sq. in. minimum tensile strength. Each class has its characteristics, and within each class, controls and modifications may be desirable to adapt it to the particular design and condition of service contemplated. Pig iron, grey cast iron, white cast iron, chilled cast iron, and malleable cast iron are all referred to as cast iron, chiefly because these forms of iron are not plastic enough, even when hot, to be forgeable; therefore, they are always produced commercially by a process of melting and casting into shape. The commercial form of each of these metals is in castings.

IRON ORE. The principal iron ore is hematite (Fe_2O_3), which when pure contains 70% iron. When this oxide of iron contains water, it is called limonite, containing 60% iron when pure. Magnetite (Fe_3O_4) occurs less abundantly. Siderite ($FeCO_3$) has been used as an ore, but because of its small iron content it is not often used now.

The more common impurities in iron ore are silica, titanium, and phosphorus; the ores containing the smallest amounts of these impurities are the most valuable. Much silica and titanium are undesirable because they require extra fluxes to slag in the blast furnace, while phosphorus and sulphur are undesirable because of their adverse effect on iron and steel. The iron ores mined in Sweden are almost entirely free from phosphorus and sulphur, which explains the fame of Swedish iron and steel as high purity metals.

About three-fourths of the iron ore mined in the United States comes from the Lake Superior district. The ore from these deposits is hematite, containing as high as 68% iron. Most of the ore in this district occurs so near the surface that it can be mined cheaply, by open pit methods.

COKE. The heat required for melting ore in blast furnaces is obtained from the burning of coke. Coke is the residue left after certain soft coals have been heated in the absence of air. It is a hard, brittle, and porous material containing from 85 to 90% carbon, together with some ash, sulphur, and phosphorus. The strength, brittleness, and impurities in the coke are dependent both on the coal used and on the methods of manufacture. There are two ways of making coke. In the older, wasteful process of destructive distillation, it is made in beehive ovens with no by-products obtained from distillation. In the newer process it is made in retorts, and many by-products, such as tar, ammonia, and benzol, are obtained from the distillate.

SCRAP. Of all the materials used in the field of engineering, only the metals can be used over and over again. Other engineering materials, such as wood, glass, and concrete, become a liability when they have outlived their usefulness. However, the metals from discarded structures such as boilers, bridges, ships, automobiles, etc., become valuable scrap.

The need for scrap metals in the manufacture of both ferrous and nonferrous metals and alloys is one of the major problems facing the manufacturer, particularly in the steel industry where large quantities of selected and segregated scrap are needed. During ordinary periods of productivity, the difficulties of obtaining an amount of good scrap are not serious; however, it remains an important factor in the everyday operation of a steel mill.

Most of our scrap either comes to us as a by-product of the metalworking processes, or results from obsolescence or failure and ultimate discarding of fabricated metal products ranging from bottlecaps to battleships. The ultimate conservation of some of our metals must depend on our careful handling of the scrap sources of such metals.

Scrap metals require proper preparation and segregation in order to prove satisfactory. Preparation requirements include size, shape, segregation as to composition, etc. The segregation requirements include the separation of cast iron from steel scrap, complete separation of nonferrous from ferrous metals, separation of alloys from plain carbon steels, and the segregation of grade and composition of alloy steels, i.e., chromium, tungsten, etc.

It is not enough to segregate scrap in accordance with the grade or type of alloy, but each type must be subdivided into ranges of alloy content so that the proper estimate may be made of the alloy content in the furnace charge. The scrap that all steel companies use contains lead, antimony, zinc, cadmium, and copper. Making good steel with scrap metals requires skillful handling of the melting furnaces to work the tramp metal elements out. The problem of scrap metals is a big one and should receive extensive study by anyone interested in the production of metals and alloys.

Scrap metals receive varying treatments from the melter. A common practice is to place it in the belly of a furnace where it is fused and blended with some primary or virgin metal and then refined and cast into some useful product. Difficulties of controlling the exact composition of the final heat of the metal may be largely due to the improper segregation of the scrap charged into the furnace. With our continuing practice of using the metals over and over again, ultimately all of the scrap used will contain elements that may be undesirable in some finished product.

BLAST FURNACE. Iron is extracted from the ore by means of the blast furnace. The iron as obtained from the furnace may be remelted and cast into almost any desired shape, or it may be refined into steel or wrought iron. Present-day furnaces are usually built to produce about 500 to 1200 tons of iron a day, and due to the nature of the process, they must be kept in continuous operation.

Ore is reduced to metal in the furnace by means of coke charged with the ore, and the impurities are fluxed or slagged by means of limestone also charged with the ore. Air, blown through the furnace, is heated by stoves that constitute an important part of the apparatus of the blast furnace. The burning of the coke furnishes the necessary heat, and the carbon monoxide formed by partial combustion of the

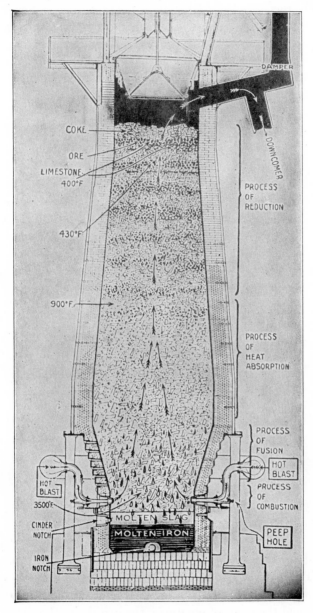

Fig. 1. Diagram of Blast Furnace
Courtesy of Republic Steel Corp., Buffalo, N. Y.

coke, together with the coke, reduces the iron. The molten iron and slag sink to the bottom of the furnace, where they are periodically drained off or tapped.

Figs. 1 and 2 may aid in visualizing the operation of the furnace. The ore, coke, and limestone are conveyed from the ground

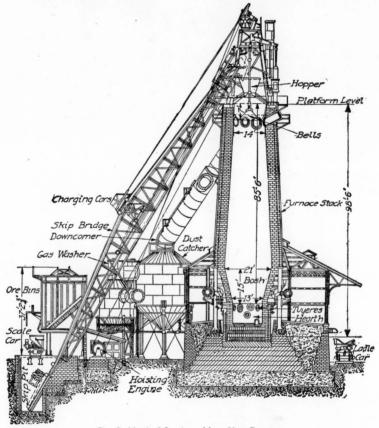

Fig. 2. Vertical Section of Iron Blast Furnace
Courtesy of "Engineering and Mining Journal"

to the top of the furnace by means of the two cars running on the skip. The materials are carefully weighed in order that they may be added in the proper proportions. These proportions vary for the furnace and the grade of ore used. The cars dump the charge into a hopper from which it is then dropped into the furnace by lowering first the upper bell, letting it fall upon the lower bell; then lowering the lower bell, allowing it to fall into the furnace proper. The use of these two bells prevents gases and flame being blown into the air from the top of the furnace every time it is charged. Hot air is blown through the tuyeres, or nozzles, near the bottom of the furnace. Exhaust gas is taken from near the top of the furnace and then through the dust catcher and washer. This gas contains nitrogen, carbon dioxide, and carbon monoxide. The carbon monoxide is combustible and can be burned to furnish power or heat. About a third of this gas is used in heating the stoves which heat the air that is blown into the furnace. These stoves consist of a steel shell containing a number of small brick flues. The burning gas heats the brick; after they are hot the gas is turned off and the air for the furnace is blown through them.

As the iron and slag are formed, they drop to the hearth at the bottom of the furnace. Since iron is heavier than the slag, it settles to the bottom, while the slag floats on the top of the molten iron. There are two holes near the bottom of the furnace. The lower hole, or iron notch from which the iron is tapped, is closed by shooting clay balls into it from an air gun. The upper hole, or cinder notch from which the slag is tapped, closes by means of a metal plug. The iron is tapped every four or five hours by digging out the clay plug; the slag is tapped two or three times between each iron tapping. Many of the impurities in the ore are collected and removed with the molten limestone in the form of slag.

The iron runs from the furnace into troughs which convey it to a ladle. One trough is equipped with a skimmer which diverts the slag to a dump car. The iron in the ladle is then cast into pigs, or else taken while molten to the steel-making furnaces. The slag is sometimes suitable for the manufacture of cement, but in most cases it is simply dumped.

Iron as obtained from the furnace contains from 3 to 4% carbon and variable amounts of silicon, sulphur, phosphorus, and manganese. The amounts of silicon and sulphur are governed to some extent by the operation of the furnace, but the phosphorus content depends solely upon the materials used. Sulphur and phosphorus are two most undesirable impurities, and as the removal of sulphur is

Table 1. Composition of Iron

Carbon Content 3.0% to 4.0%

Usage	Silicon	Sulphur	Phosphorus	Manganese
No. 1 Foundry............	2.0–3.0	under 0.035	0.5–1.0	under 1.0
No. 2 Foundry............	2.0–2.5	under 0.045	0.5–1.0	under 1.0
No. 3 Foundry............	1.5–2.0	under 0.055	0.5–1.0	under 1.0
Grey Forge..............	under 1.5	under 0.10	under 1.0	under 1.0
Malleable Bessemer......	0.75–1.5	under 0.05	under 0.2	under 1.0
Bessemer................	1.0–1.5	under 0.08	under 0.10	under 1.0
Basic...................	under 1.0	under 0.05	under 1.0	under 1.0
Basic Bessemer..........	under 1.0	under 0.05	2.0–3.0	under 0.5

rather uncertain, except through special electric refining treatments, it is important to produce iron with low sulphur content. A high phosphorus content may be desired for iron that is to be cast into intricate parts, as apparently phosphorus makes the metal more fluid, although somewhat more brittle when cold. The compositions of certain irons are given in Table 1.

Much of the sulphur in the iron comes from the coke. If charcoal is used in place of coke in a small blast furnace, a much purer iron, called charcoal iron, is the result. A certain amount of this iron is produced, bringing a higher price than ordinary iron, and used for special purposes, as in making chilled iron rolls.

BESSEMER PROCESS OF MAKING STEEL. Steels made either in a Bessemer or an open-hearth furnace are designated as either acid or basic steels, depending on the nature of the refractory linings of the furnace. Silica is an acid lining, while dolomite and magnesite are basic linings. The nature of the linings controls the slag since a basic slag could rapidly dissolve an acid lining and an acid slag would have the same effect on a basic lining. With a basic lining, a large percentage of the phosphorus and some of the sulphur can be removed, but the greater amount of iron oxide left in the steel renders basic steel inferior to acid steel. The basic Bessemer process is used extensively in Europe. In this country, where iron sufficiently low in phosphorus for acid Bessemers is still available, that process is used instead.

In making Bessemer steel, molten iron direct from the blast furnace is poured into the converter or vessel shown in Fig. 3. In the bottom of the vessel are a number of holes through which air is blown. The air first oxidizes the silicon and manganese, which, together with some iron oxide, rise to the top and form a slag. The carbon then begins to burn, and the blowing is continued until all but about 0.05% of the carbon has been eliminated. The progress of the blow can be determined from the flame coming from the vessel. The oxidation of the impurities has raised the temperature of the metal to the point

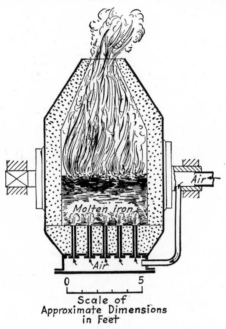

Fig. 3. Section of Round Body Bessemer Converter
with Detachable Bottom

Reprinted by Permission, from *Materials of Engineering*
by Moore, Published by McGraw-Hill Book Co., Inc.,
New York, N.Y.

where it can be cast conveniently. When the blow is completed, the amount of carbon necessary to bring the carbon content to the specified percentage, together with manganese to counteract the influence of sulphur, and silicon to degassify, are added to the molten metal. The finished steel is then poured into a ladle by tipping the vessel, and from the ladle it is poured into ingot molds for subsequent rolling or forging.

Bessemer steel is likely to be highly oxidized and dirty, and, although it is usually considered inferior to steel produced by other methods, it can compete with steels made by these other methods on jobs calling for low-carbon steel with not very high requirements for strength, ductility, and toughness. The acid process does not remove sulphur and phosphorus, with the result that these elements

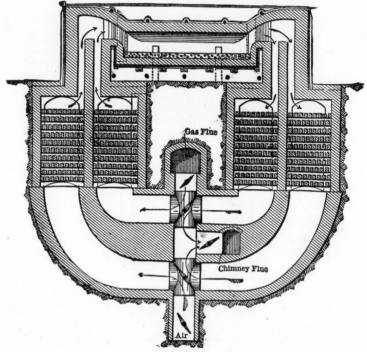

Fig. 4. Diagrammatic Representation of the Open-Hearth Steel Furnace (Called also, in Europe, the Siemens-Martin Furnace)

Reprinted by Permission, from *Engineering Metallurgy* by Stoughton and Butts. Published by McGraw-Hill Book Co., Inc., New York, N.Y.

are excessive for a good grade of steel. Because no extraneous fuel is used in the Bessemer process, and a heat of 15 to 25 tons can be made in 10 or 15 minutes, the cost of the process is low. However, the process is losing its prominence and is increasing in operational costs, due to the exhaustion of low-phosphorus iron ores. Bessemer steels find extensive use in low-grade sheets, wire, pipe, skelp for the manufacturing of pipe, and screw stock; also wherever a steel is required which is not subjected to severe loadings, and where easy machining is desirable.

A duplexing process where acid Bessemer steel is additionally refined in the basic open hearth results in a low-carbon steel inferior to that of the basic open hearth, but one which finds much use because of its cheapness. Another duplexing process takes steel produced by either the Bessemer or the open-hearth process and refines it in the electric furnace. Such steel is superior, usually, to open-hearth steel.

A triplexing process starts with steel from the Bessemer process, removes part of the phosphorus in the basic open hearth, and further refines it in the electric furnace.

OPEN-HEARTH PROCESS. The open-hearth furnace is rectangular and rather low, holding from 15 to 200 tons of metal in a shallow pool. It is heated either by gas, oil, or tar, and flames come from first one end and then the other. Waste gases pass through regenerators corresponding to the stoves of the blast furnaces. When the flame is reversed these regenerators, through which the hot gases have just been passing, heat the air and gas entering the furnace, while those at the other end begin to be reheated by the passage through them of the waste gases. The general form and operation of an open-hearth furnace are shown in Fig. 4.

The four regenerative chambers shown below the furnace proper are filled with a checker-work of brick, around which the gas and air pass. Before the furnace is first started, these bricks are heated by wood fires. The gas enters the furnace through the inner regenerative chamber on one side, while the air enters through the outer one on the same side; they meet and unite; pass through the furnace and thence to the chimney through the two regenerative chambers at the opposite end. In this way the brickwork in the out-going chambers is made still hotter by the waste heat of the furnace. The current of gas, air, and products of combustion are changed every 15 minutes; thus all four regenerators are kept continuously hot. The gas and air enter the furnace highly preheated, thus giving a greater temperature of combustion; the products of combustion go out the chimney at relatively low heat, making for fuel economy. Most of the furnaces are stationary, but some newer and very large furnaces are of the tilting type illustrated in Fig. 5. The basic open-hearth furnaces have a thick bottom and walls of sintered magnesite or dolomite, with an arched roof of silica brick. The bottom of the acid furnaces is formed from sand.

The front of the furnace, facing the charging platform, has from three to seven water-cooled and hydraulically operated doors through which the furnace is charged and melting and refining processes are

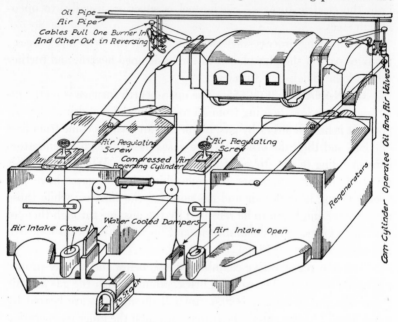

Fig. 5. Perspective Diagram of Open-Hearth Furnace
Courtesy of American Institute of Mining Engineers

observed. At the middle portion of the back of the furnace is the tap hole, tightly plugged in the stationary furnaces and loosely closed in the tilting furnaces. The basic furnaces have another hole at slag level, through which part of the first slag formed is removed. It takes from six to twelve hours to produce steel in these furnaces, depending on the furnace, its age, the fuel used, and the character of the charge. Ordinarily a large amount of scrap steel is used in making open-hearth steel. At the large steel mills where structural shapes, rails, etc., are made, about 50% scrap is used, the balance of the charge being molten iron.

A description of the making of typical basic open-hearth steel may help illustrate the fundamentals of the open-hearth process. Immediately after one heat has been produced, all traces of steel are scraped from the furnace, and calcined dolomite is thrown over the bottom and the side walls to replace that lost in the preceding heat. The furnace is then charged, limestone on the bottom, ore next, and finally the steel scrap. All large open-hearth furnaces are now charged mechanically. After about two hours, the steel scrap has begun to melt, and at this point the molten iron is added. The action of the ore upon the pig iron causes a boiling of the bath, and a thin slag is formed, part of which is removed. After the scrap is all melted, the limestone begins to decompose into carbon dioxide gas, which rises through the metal and slag, and also into calcium oxide, which comes to the surface and helps form a rather thick slag.

The action of the ore, together with the action of the slag, has lowered the carbon content of the bath so that in a properly made heat there is about 1% carbon when the limestone has all decomposed. It is now only necessary to eliminate the carbon to the desired content, depending upon the type of steel being made, and to bring the bath to the proper temperature for tapping and pouring into ingots. The carbon content will be lowered gradually by continued heating, but if it is found by tests to be too high, ore is added; if too low, additional iron—molten or solid—is added. The carbon content is judged by the fracture of test pieces which are cast in small molds, cooled, and broken. If a low carbon or soft steel is being made, as soon as the carbon content in the finished steel is at the desired percentage and the metal is hot enough, it is tapped into a ladle, and ferromanganese and ferrosilicon are added to the ladle for the purpose of deoxidizing and controlling the final chemistry of the steel. If a higher carbon steel is being made, as for rails, the carbon content is reduced to about 0.15% or 0.25%, and sufficient molten iron is added just before tapping to bring the carbon to the desired composition. Manganese and silicon are then added in the form of ferroalloys, either to the furnace, or to the steel as it runs into the ladle. The ladles from which the steel is cast into ingots are of the bottom pour type, in order to separate the steel from the slag which floats on top. In low carbon steels, small amounts of aluminum often are added to the steel in the molds, to degassify or kill the metal, thus preventing part of it from boiling over the molds as it solidifies.

In the acid open-hearth process no limestone is used, and the slag is formed from the impurities in the iron, together with part of the furnace lining. In making high carbon steels, the steel is not usually recarbonized as described above, but is tapped when the desired carbon content, as determined by rapid chemical analysis, is reached.

CRUCIBLE PROCESS. High grade tool steels and some alloy steels are still made by the crucible process, although the electric furnace is now capable of making steel equal in quality to crucible steel. In the crucible process, wrought iron or good scrap, together with a small amount of high purity pig iron, ferromanganese, the necessary alloying metals, and slagging materials are placed in a clay or clay-graphite crucible, covered with an old crucible bottom and melted in a gas or coke-fired furnace. After the charge is entirely molten, with sufficient time allowed for the gases and impurities to rise to the surface, the crucible is withdrawn, the slag removed with a cold iron bar, and the resulting fifty or one hundred pounds of steel poured into a small ingot which is subsequently forged to the desired shape. Fig. 1, Chapter II, shows a charge of crucible steel being removed from the furnace to be cast into an ingot. The crucible process differs from other steel-making in that little or no refining is included; the purity of the metal, therefore, is dependent almost entirely upon the purity of the materials charged. The chief advantage of the process is that it removes most of the impurities, including oxygen and entangled particles.

ELECTRIC-FURNACE STEEL. Electric furnaces for the melting and refining of steel had their beginning with the discovery of the carbon arc by Sir Humphrey Davy in 1800. It was not until 1878 that direct application of this method was operative when Sir William Siemens patented, constructed, and operated furnaces based on both the direct- and indirect-arc principles. Siemens had a furnace consisting of a small crucible into which a charge was introduced and subsequent fusing was brought about by the action of two carbon electrodes. In 1899, Dr. P. L. V. Héroult successfully operated a commercial direct-arc furnace in the melting of steel.

The electric furnace has proved to be an ideal melting and refining unit for the steel industry. Its advantages include the following: the nonoxidizing condition of the carbon arc, which is pure heat, makes possible a tightly closed furnace and permits maintenance of reducing atmospheres; the temperature attainable is limited only by the refractory nature of the furnace lining; close limits of regulation and control are obtainable; the efficiency of the unit is extremely high; refining and alloying are readily accomplished and controlled. The steel industry has at its command a method of producing steel, which, in competent hands, can operate on a tonnage basis and meet the most exacting specifications.

In most electric furnaces the heat is produced by means of an arc either above the bath, as in the Stassano furnace which is illustrated in Fig. 2, Chapter II, or by means of arcs between the slag and electrodes suspended above the bath, the latter being the more satisfactory and common method. The Héroult furnaces shown in Figs. 3 and 4, Chapter II, are this type. In the furnace illustrated in Fig. 4, Chapter II, there are three carbon or graphite electrodes (not shown in the picture) suspended from the roof. Each of these electrodes is connected to one phase of a three-phase current and lowered into the bath in such a manner that an arc is formed between the slag and each electrode.

The modern arc-type electric furnace is cylindrical in shape and of the standard three-phase, three-electrode service arc type as originally developed by Dr. Héroult. Basic differences of construction lie in the mechanical design. Some of these include different methods of filling, various methods of applying removable roofs to medium-sized furnaces, and arrangement and application of electrical equipment.

The greatest tonnage of tool steel made in America today is melted in the basic electric furnace. Very little steel is now made by the crucible melting process, and only small amounts are melted in the coreless induction and the basic open-hearth furnaces.

The lining of the basic electric furnace is of extreme importance and one of the principal features of the furnace. The hearth must be made from a magnesite or burned dolomite material to withstand the lime slags used in the basic process. The walls and roof may be made from a silica brick and need not be basic, but must withstand extremely high temperatures.

In making up a heat of steel, the bulk of the charge is made up of carefully selected steel scrap of such a composition that, upon melting down, the bath will contain a smaller amount of the alloying elements than is required in the finished steel. This practice permits the addition of suitable ferroalloys and carbon for proper adjustment of the chemical analysis of the steel charge. Other melting methods, such as the open-hearth, may use pig iron as a raw charge, whereas the electric furnace never starts out with a charge of pig iron. Through the use of carefully selected raw materials, a greater economy may be had in this process. The electric furnace may start with a cold charge, and the steel made this way is spoken of as **cold-melt** electric-furnace steel to distinguish it from that resulting from the practice of using a hot or molten charge previously melted in an open-hearth furnace and transferred to the electric furnace. In the manufacture of high-grade steel for tools, the slower and more expensive cold-melt method is almost always used.

When the heat of steel has been properly deoxidized or killed and is of proper chemical composition, it is ready to tap into the ladle. The melt is tapped into the ladle and subsequently poured or teemed into a mold made from cast iron. The resulting casting is called an **ingot**, and the mold used is the **ingot mold**. The tapping and pouring of the steel into the ingot molds is carried out with the greatest care. It is important that the cast ingot be as free from blowholes, shrinkage holes, segregation, etc., as is possible to insure a good ingot. No steel from an ingot is sounder than the ingot from which it was made.

A radically different type of electric furnace, sometimes used in making small tonnages of steel or special alloys, is the high-frequency induction furnace. In this, the melting method consists of a crucible furnace into which the charge is placed. An electric current is induced within the metal charge from a coil of copper tubing, carrying a high frequency current, which surrounds the crucible. The induced current is forced to flow directly through the charge, causing very rapid heating.

A fortunate phenomenon of induction furnaces insures a thorough mixing of the molten metal. This is the natural stirring action which takes place in the liquid charge, as soon as the molten state of the charge is reached. By the induction method high melting temperatures are obtained, as well as exact and controllable melting conditions. It is more economical than the electric-arc type of furnace; in some instances it may replace the open-hearth furnace, particularly when small quantities of special alloys are required.

MANUFACTURE OF WROUGHT IRON. Wrought iron is produced in lots of 300 to 1500 lbs. in what is known as a puddling furnace. This is a furnace somewhat similar to the open hearth, with combustion taking place at one end only. The furnace is lined with iron oxide in the form of mill scale or ore. Cold pig iron is charged into the furnace and, as this melts, its carbon is eliminated by the iron oxide lining. When practically all of the carbon and other impurities have been eliminated, the metal has a higher melting point and begins to form into a pasty mass. This pasty mass of metal and slag is well stirred and formed

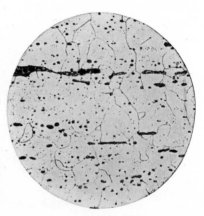

Fig. 6. Photomicrograph of Wrought Iron, Taken at 100 Magnifications, Shows the Fibrous Slag Embedded in a Matrix of Nearly Pure Iron

into a ball, which is then removed from the furnace. The bulk of the slage is then squeezed from this mass by means of a mechanical squeezer and the iron is then rolled into bars. The material is now a mixture of high purity iron and some slag (about 2 or 3%). Figs. 6 and 7 show fibrous structure of wrought iron. Bars are then cut into lengths and piled, with alternate layers at 90° angles. These stacks of bars are wired, heated to welding heat, and rolled to desired shapes. The purpose of this stacking and rolling is to get a fine and uniform distribution of the slag.

A process for manufacturing synthetic wrought iron has been developed by Professor Aston for Byers Pipe Company. This process is thought to yield a material which cannot be distinguished chemically or metallographically from puddled iron, but can be welded somewhat more easily. In this process, pig iron is melted in a cupola and blown to soft steel in a Bessemer. The steel is then poured into liquid slag, special precautions being taken to insure thorough mixing. The excess slag is then poured off and squeezed out. After this squeezing, the spongy material is rolled into bars for fabrication into pipe and similar products.

Despite the fact that many different processes have been used in the manufacture of wrought iron, the characteristics and basic prin-

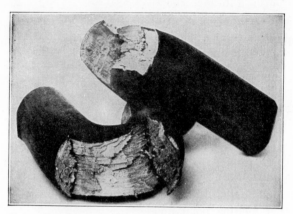

Fig. 7. Wrought Iron Bars Fractured to Show the Fibrous, Hickory-like Structure Which Is Characteristic of the Material
Courtesy of A. M. Byers Co., Pittsburgh, Pa.

ciples of metallurgy used in producing it have remained unchanged. The iron silicate or slag was at first considered an undesirable impurity; however, we know now that the slag is responsible for many of the desirable properties of wrought iron, particularly its resistance to fatigue and corrosion.

The principal value of wrought iron lies in its ability to resist corrosion and fatigue failure. Its corrosion resistance, directly attributable to the slag fibers, is also a result of the purity of the iron base metal and its freedom from segregated impurities. Because of its softness and ductility, wrought iron finds common use in the manufacture of bolts, pipe, staybolts, tubing, nails, etc.

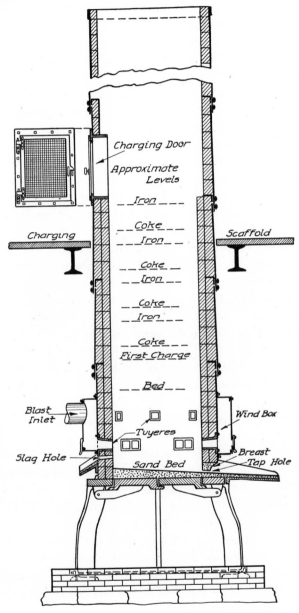

Fig. 8. Diagram of Foundry Cupola for Melting Cast Iron

FOUNDING. In the foundry, iron and steel castings of almost any desired form and size are made by casting the molten metal into sand molds.

Iron Castings. The pig iron for casting is melted in a cupola which, as illustrated in Fig. 8, is a shaft furnace, very much like a small blast furnace, in which coke and pig iron are charged at the top and air blown in near the bottom. The molten iron may be tapped periodically, or, for larger cupolas, may drain continuously into a large ladle. Cupolas vary much in size, depending on the quantity of iron used by the foundry.

The molds are made by ramming sand around a pattern in a flask. The flask is simply a box-like container of two or more sections, allowing for removal of the pattern. The pattern is removed and the space it occupied is filled with molten metal. Patterns are made of wood or metal; they are exact duplicates of the casting desired, except that they are slightly oversize to allow for shrinkage of the metal on cooling. The shrinkage of cast iron amounts to about ⅛ in. per ft.; of steel, about ¼ in. per ft. After the sand is tapped around the pattern and the pattern removed, the mold may be used without drying, in which case it is called a **green sand mold,** or it may be baked until it has the properties of soft brick, when it is called a **dry sand mold.** Molds for casting iron are washed inside with a graphite paint or dusted with lampblack in order to form smooth castings with a minimum of sand sticking to their surfaces. Steel molds are often washed with pulverized sandstone, since graphite or lampblack would be absorbed by the molten steel. The molds must be ventilated by making small holes through the sand to allow the gases to escape. When iron is cast into a metal mold, the surface is chilled very rapidly; in consequence it will be extremely hard. It will also be white in color, because of the absence of graphite. For this reason such items as crusher rolls are cast in chill molds to produce hard white iron. In the case of castings which are to have certain hard areas, the sand in the mold adjacent to the areas to be hardened is replaced with metal, causing these areas to harden by chilling. The chemical composition of the iron, as will be explained in a later section, also influences its hardness.

Malleable cast iron is cast iron of low carbon, low silicon content, which does not readily graphitize when cast in sand molds, and forms a hard white iron which, when subsequently annealed for softening, produces a structure of soft graphite and ferrite, as shown in Fig. 18, Chapter I. By such a treatment the iron is not only softened, but made somewhat malleable and therefore resistant to shock.

Steel Castings. Steel castings, the product of the steel foundry, are of more or less intricate shape and are almost exclusively cast in sand molds, although some steel is being cast centrifugally in metal molds. Steel castings range in size from light ¼-inch sections to sections up to 4 feet, weighing more than 200 tons.

Although steel is melted down in the open hearth, Bessemer converter, crucible, or electric furnace, today the electric furnace is the accepted melting medium for the steel foundry, and now dominates the foundry field in capacity and production.

A mold used for castings of steel must possess special properties, and, due to the high pouring temperatures, difficulties are encountered in trying to manufacture the perfect molding material and mold. The sands used must possess high silica content and are usually made of blended sands with bonding agents added to insure proper cohesion of the sand grains. Porosity and the formation of holes are defects which occur in steel castings because of internal shrinkage or entrapped gases, oxides, slag, etc. Some of the defects found in sand castings may be eliminated through the use of **centrifugal casting.**

Centrifugal casting is the process of casting metal, such as steel, under pressure of centrifugal force. The force is developed through rotating or spinning the molds at high speeds during the period of solidification. The centrifugal force developed within the liquid steel drives the heavy, clean metal outward to the outer surface of the casting, while the lighter impurities, such as gases, oxides, slag, etc., are driven to the inner surface of the casting. These impurities segregated at the inner surface may be removed by a rough machining operation. The centrifugal casting technique results in a casting that is sounder and cleaner than a similar casting made in a sand mold. Gun tubes, gun liners, gears, wheels, and many other parts are made by this process.

The analysis of steel castings may vary considerably, with the carbon content running from a low value of 0.10% to as much as 1.40%, and, in some special cases, as high as 2.50% carbon. However, the very high carbon content of 2.50% is in the field of cast irons. A great many steel castings are made by an alloying technique when special properties are needed. The most common steel casting is a plain carbon steel with the carbon running from 0.10% to 0.30% in the lower carbon steels, from 0.30% to 0.40% in the medium carbon range, and from 0.40% to 0.60% in a little higher carbon steel. These are the most common carbon ranges although some higher carbon steel castings are made, such as in the field of cast steel rolls, etc.

Steel castings may be subjected to heat treatments to further improve their properties. Such treatments include normalizing, annealing, relieving stress, hardening, and tempering. Information concerning these treatments may be had further along in this text.

QUIZ QUESTIONS

1. *What is the most important factor in governing the properties of steel?*
2. *What is wrought iron?*
3. *What are the chief elements of cast iron?*
4. *Name the common impurities in iron ore.*
5. *Of what importance is scrap in the manufacture of steel? What difficulties are encountered in its use?*
6. *What fuel is used in the blast furnace?*
7. *How is iron procured from a blast furnace?*
8. *How is the blast furnace charged?*
9. *What use is made of the carbon monoxide taken from the blast furnace?*
10. *What becomes of the tapped molten metal?*
11. *Describe briefly the Bessemer process of making steel.*
12. *What is meant by duplexing and triplexing?*
13. *How is steel made by the open-hearth method?*
14. *How is the carbon content of this steel judged?*
15. *Why are ferromanganese and ferrosilicon added to the ladle?*
16. *For what type of steel is the crucible process used?*
17. *Why are electric furnaces used in making steel?*
18. *Of what importance is slag in wrought iron?*
19. *What is the principal value of wrought iron?*
20. *Describe a sand mold and its use.*
21. *What is malleable cast iron?*
22. *Describe briefly the process of making steel castings.*
23. *What is centrifugal casting? What advantages has it over sand casting?*

CHAPTER IV

Physical Metallurgy

THE METALLIC STATE OF PURE METALS

THE METALS. Strength together with plasticity (ability to deform without rupture) is the combination of properties that makes metals of great importance in the mechanical and structural field. Many substances, glass for instance, have high tensile strength, but lack plasticity when loaded rapidly, as in shock; these are known as brittle substances. Brittle substances may flow slowly or exhibit plasticity under tremendous pressure. If an attempt were made to use a brittle substance such as glass in the structure of a bridge, it would fail and fall into the river when it became unevenly loaded. However, various metals are used in the construction of bridges. The structurally used metals have the ability to deform without rupture, both elastically and plastically, when subjected to overloads due to uneven alignment. This deformation occurs without loss of strength; indeed, in many cases metals so deformed become stronger.

Although the materials used in machines and structures in most cases are subjected to loads so low that the materials behave in a nearly elastic manner, a number of conditions may occur under which metals are subjected to loads so great that plastic action occurs; therefore, the behavior of the metals in the plastic range becomes of utmost importance. This is true during the shaping and fabricating operations performed upon metals in the creation of structures, or in finished structures that occasionally become overloaded. Materials that can deform plastically when overloaded are much safer structural materials than those having greater strength but lacking this property.

In addition to strength and plasticity, metals exhibit many favorable characteristics, such as resistance to corrosion, electrical and heat conductivity, a good luster, etc. The characteristics of metals are due to two structural factors: first, the atoms of which the metallic state is composed; and second, the way in which these atoms are arranged. A crude comparison can be made to a house, the character of which is in part determined by the type or quality of raw materials, such as bricks and boards (the atoms), and in part by the workmanship or assembly of the raw materials (the arrangement of the atoms).

THE SOLID OR CRYSTALLINE STATE OF METALS. When a metal freezes (changes from the liquid to the solid state), it crystallizes. During the process of solidification, the atoms of the liquid metal arrange or group themselves into an orderly arrangement, thus forming a definite space pattern. That is, the atoms regiment themselves into groups similar to a group of soldiers on parade. The pattern formed by this orderly arrangement of the atoms is known as the **space lattice,** and it is made up of a series of points in space, giving birth to a geometrical structure of atom groups. Although the atoms are too small to be seen by ordinary means, such as under the microscope, we may visualize a crystal as being made up of atoms, these atoms being arranged in space in some predetermined pattern or space lattice. The space lattice of the crystal state of metals has been determined by X-ray crystal analysis methods. By means of these X rays, the internal atomic arrangement of the crystal state may be studied, and a picture of the space lattice may be drawn as shown in Fig. 1.

There are a number of different patterns or space lattice groups into which the atoms of a crystal state may arrange themselves. A very common space lattice is that of the cubic pattern which many of the common metals, such as copper, iron, aluminum, lead, nickel, molybdenum, and tungsten, form. Some of the metals forming the cubic pattern assume the body-centered cubic pattern, an atom at the center of the cube and an atom at each corner of the cube. Other metals crystallize into the face-centered pattern having an atom in the center of the cube face and an atom at each corner, similar to C in Fig. 1. Also, some metals have the capacity of crystallizing in one form but, upon cooling, change to another form; e.g., some change from a face-centered to a body-centered pattern. The metal iron undergoes such a change of space lattice during heating and cooling within a temperature range that still maintains iron in a solid or crystal form without melting. When a metal undergoes a change from one crystal pattern to another, it is known as an **allotropic change.** When a metal undergoes an allotropic change, such as the change from a body-centered to a face-centered cubic lattice, this is accompanied by a marked change in the characteristics and properties of the metal involved in the' change. The change from a body-centered to a face-centered pattern completely rearranges the space lattice and atoms within the crystal, with the body-centered cube with 9 atoms in its pattern changing to a face-centered cube with 14 atoms in its pattern. Such a change of atomic arrangement brings about a complete change of characteristics.

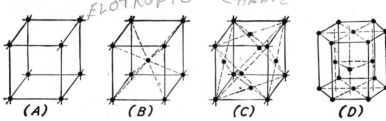

Fig. 1. The Most Common Crystal Patterns

While the cubic pattern is the most prominent with the common metals, there are many other space lattice arrangements. A rather common arrangement is the hexagonal pattern, known as the **close-packed** because of the number of atoms involved in this arrangement. Metals such as zinc, magnesium, cobalt, cadmium, antimony, and bismuth assume this arrangement upon freezing or crystallizing. This arrangement is illustrated in D of Fig. 1.

The properties of metals are dependent, in a large measure, upon the type of space lattice formed during solidification. In general, metals with the face-centered lattice lend themselves to a ductile, plastic, workable crystal state; whereas metals with the close-packed hexagonal lattice exhibit, in general, a lack of plasticity and lose their plastic nature rapidly upon shaping, such as in a cold forming operation. Hexagonally latticed antimony and bismuth are brittle.

CLEAVAGE AND SLIP PLANES. Some of the most striking effects of the crystal pattern of atoms are the directional properties created by the planes formed by the orientation of the atoms. Between the rows of atoms lies the path of rupture, so the fracture or failure of a crystal occurs by the separation of the atoms along a path parallel to the atom orientation; such a path is called a **cleavage plane.** Proof of crystallinity is obtained when a material, such as a metal, is ruptured, and the ruptured surfaces reveal facets or surfaces forming various planes, each plane being the path between the row of atoms formed by the crystals.

When an attempt is made to fracture metals of the plastic crystal state, instead of a brittle fracture taking place between the rows of atoms, the atom groups slide over one another along the planes formed by the pattern of atoms, causing a plastic flow or deformation

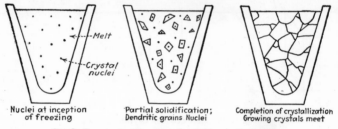

Nuclei at inception   Partial solidification;   Completion of crystallization
   of freezing   Dendritic grains Nuclei   Growing crystals meet

Fig. 2. Progressive Freezing of a Uniformly Cooled Melt

Reprinted by Permission, from *The Principles of Metallurgy* by Liddell and Doan, Published by McGraw-Hill Book Co., Inc., New York, N.Y.

to take place without rupture. This behavior leads to the plastic nature of the more common metals and allows us to change the shape of the crystals without rupture as in a forming operation such as the bending of a piece of metal. The planes along which slips occur are known as **slip planes.** The action of the plastic flow of the crystal state will be discussed more fully in the paragraph covering the deformation of metals.

As we have seen, the crystal state consists of a group of atoms arranged in some definite pattern or orientation. We will now see how a liquid cooled in a crucible or mold gives birth to the crystal state in which there are a great number of individual crystals called **grains.**

MANNER OF CRYSTALLIZATION. A crystal may be visualized as forming from a center of freezing, or nucleus, which is composed of

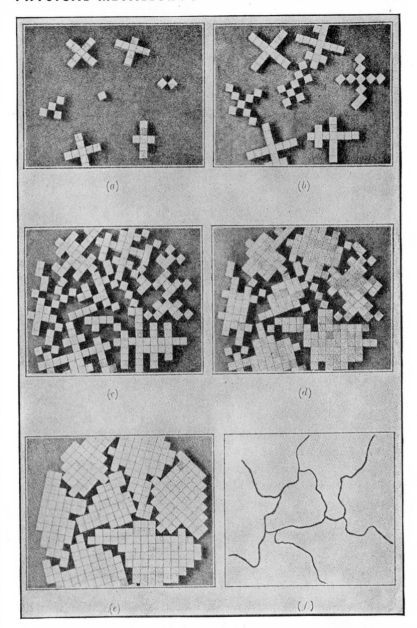

Fig. 3. Growth of Crystalline Grains (From "Introduction to Physical Metallurgy" by Dr. Walter Rosenhain)

Courtesy of American Society for Steel Treating, Cleveland, Ohio

a small group of atoms oriented into one of the common crystal patterns, Figs. 2 and 3. In the process of solidification many of these nuclei spring up, each nucleus being a potential crystal and able to grow to form a crystal large enough to be seen with the unaided eye. As each nucleus is a growing crystal, and the atoms within it are all similarly oriented, it should be appreciated by the student that no nucleus within the freezing melt may form with its planes or groups of atoms the same as those of any other nucleus. Thus, when the individual crystals have grown to the point where they have absorbed all of the liquid atoms and therefore come in contact with each other along their boundaries, they do not line up; i.e., their planes of atoms change direction in going from one crystal to another. This results in the solid state's being composed of a number of crystals of different orientation, and we have a crystal aggregate or mixed crystals. Each crystal, therefore, is composed of a group of similarly oriented atoms, but on going from one crystal through to the neighboring crystals, the orientation changes.

The nature of the crystal border is still more or less of an unknown, but we may assume that it is an interlocking border line where the atoms of one crystal change orientation from the atoms of another crystal. It may be that there are some left-over atoms along this border line separating the differently oriented crystals, such atoms not knowing to which crystal to attach themselves, and these act as a noncrystalline cement between the various crystals. This condition may account for the greater strength of the crystal boundaries as compared to the strength of the individual crystals, and for many of the actions that take place at the crystal boundaries.

In order to help in the visualization of the change from a molten state to the crystal aggregate state, Fig. 4 may be studied. A crystal nucleus forms as shown in (A) and then proceeds to send out shoots or axes of solidification as shown in (B), (C), and (D), forming the skeleton of a crystal in much the same way frost patterns form. Atoms then attach themselves to the axes of the growing crystal from the melt in progressive layers, finally filling up these axes, and thus forming a completed solid, or crystal, as shown in (E).

The student may observe the nature of crystal birth in the freezing of water, which frequently shows a surface pattern resembling a tree (trunk, branches, etc.). Also, the crystalline nature of metals is apparent to the eye in the study of the surface of galvanized iron (zinc on iron). This treelike freezing pattern is called **dendritic,** taken from the Greek word meaning treelike, and the term is frequently used in referring to a structure that has a treelike appearance.

A crystal may have almost any external shape, which is controlled by the conditions leading to its formation. The most impor-

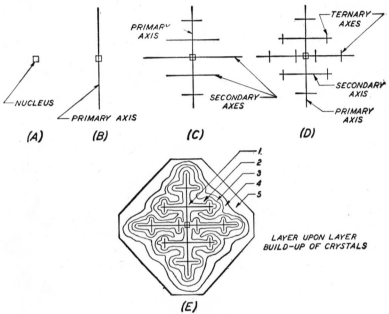

LAYER UPON LAYER
BUILD-UP OF CRYSTALS

Fig. 4. Steps in the Formation of a Crystal

tant factor affecting the external shape of any crystal is the influence of the other growing crystals which surround it. However, regardless of the external shape of the crystal, the internal arrangement of the atoms is the same. The perfect external shape would be a cube for a cubic pattern and a hexagon for a hexagonal orientation, etc. The crystals found in all commercial metals and alloys are commonly called **grains** because of this variation in their external shape. A grain is, therefore, a crystal with almost any external shape, but with an internal atomic structure based upon the space lattice with which it was born.

SINGLE VS. POLYCRYSTALLINE STATE. In commercial metals and alloys, the control of crystal size is considered very important. The reason for this is revealed in the properties exhibited by a fine-grained crystal aggregate, as compared with the properties of a coarse or larger-grained metal. A fine-grained metal is stronger and in many applications proves more satisfactory than a coarse-grained metal. A single crystal exhibits a strength characteristic of its resistance to slip or cleavage along any of its atomic planes, whereas a polycrystalline or many-crystal aggregate has no smooth, straight line

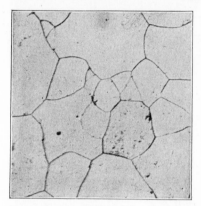

Fig. 5. Commercially Pure Iron before De-   Fig. 6. Commercially Pure Iron after Slight
            formation   Plastic Deformation

Reprinted from *Introduction to Physical Metallurgy* by Rosenhain, Published by Constable and Co., London

throughout its section for slip or fracture, due to the change of orientation taking place at each grain or crystal boundary. Thus, a fracture travelling through a polycrystalline aggregate changes direction when going from one crystal to the next. The effect of this is similar to the break in the masonry line in a brick wall. Each crystal keys to its neighbor and builds up a resistance to slip or failure. On the other hand, a coarse grain size may exhibit more plasticity than a finer-grained aggregate. The coarse grains have longer slip planes, and therefore greater capacity to slip during plastic deformation than the smaller and shorter slip planes of a finer-grained state.

DEFORMATION OF METALS. Knowing that metals are composed of many crystals or grains, and that each crystal in turn is composed of a great many atoms all arranged in accordance with some pattern, how can we visualize the plastic flow that must take place when metals are deformed during a bending operation, or during the drawing out of a piece of metal to form a long wire? This deformation may be visualized as shearing; that is, when a metal is subjected to a load exceeding its elastic limit, the crystals of the metal elongate by an action of slippingor shearing which takes place within the crystals and between adjacent crystals. This action is similar to that which takes place when a deck of cards is given a

shove, and sliding or shearing occurs between the individual cards. The mechanism of plastic deformation is illustrated in Figs. 5, 6, and 7. Fig. 5 is a photomicrograph of pure iron in the unstrained condition, and Fig. 6 shows the same iron after the occurrence of slight plastic flow. The dark lines within the grains in Fig. 6 indicate the planes on which plastic deformation took place. If deformation of the metal is continued, the

Fig. 7. Cartridge Brass Severely Deformed, Magnified 100 Times

crystals become noticeably elongated, as illustrated in Fig. 7, a photomicrograph of a section of brass that was severely deformed during plastic shaping.

This plastic flow of the metal resulting in permanent deformation of the crystals is accompanied by marked changes in the physical properties of the metal. The tensile strength, yield point, and hardness are increased, but not the scratch hardness, or difficulty of cutting, as in machine operations in a lathe. The stiffness remains about the same, though in some cases it may increase as much as 3%. With the increase in hardness and strength, the plasticity or formability is reduced. Ultimately, if deformation of the crystals is continued, the metal becomes brittle. This deformed state may retain high residual stresses and may corrode rapidly when exposed to corrosive atmospheres.

WORK HARDENING. Many attempts have been made to explain why metals become harder and stronger when permanently deformed. Two common theories are the *Amorphous Cement Theory* advanced by Rosenhain, and the *Slip Interference Theory*, by Jeffries.

The Amorphous Cement Theory explains that work hardening is caused by the formation of a hard, noncrystalline cement (amorphous, or without form), due to the rubbing together of the weak planes within the crystals; and that this cement acts as a binder, making the weak planes stronger and therefore increasing the strength of the metal as a whole.

The Slip Interference Theory explains that work hardening is caused by the action of local disorganization of the crystal structure, not necessarily until it is amorphous in nature, but having more crystal fragmentation. These crystal fragments, according to this theory, act as mechanical keys along the weak planes of the crystals, keying them together and thereby making them stronger. If we add to these effects the end resistance to slipping which is offered by the differently oriented crystals, perhaps we will have some reasonable explanation of the effects of work hardening of metals.

RECRYSTALLIZATION. The deformed or work-hardened condition found in metals that have been stressed beyond their elastic limit is an abnormal one. If the temperature of the work-hardened metal is raised above normal, the deformation begins to disappear and the metal returns to the normal condition of structure and properties. This remarkable change occurs through the recrystallization and grain growth of structure that takes place when work-hardened metals are heated to within certain temperature ranges. The process of heating work-hardened metals to temperatures where the deformed structure disappears and the properties return to normal, is called **annealing.**

If the work-hardened metal in its highly stressed state is subjected to very low annealing temperatures, the internal stresses are almost completely removed without any apparent structural change and without appreciable loss of strength or hardness; in fact, both hardness and strength may be slightly increased. This treatment, often called **stress relief,** is important industrially.

If work-hardened metals are heated to higher temperatures, the return to the normal, soft, ductile state occurs rapidly. This change is accompanied by a marked change in structure. Such a change is one of recrystallization; that is, the deformed grains crystallize over again without any melting. The action is one of new crystal nuclei forming around the boundaries and throughout the old deformed crystals, in a way similar to the formation of nuclei in a melt; and these nuclei grow at the expense of the old grains until they completely obliterate them.

The mechanism of recrystallization is illustrated in several photomicrographs, as follows: Fig. 7 is a photomicrograph of cold

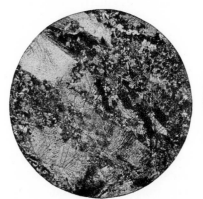 

Fig. 8. Severely Deformed Cartridge Brass, Shown in Fig. 7, Partly Recrystallized by Heating; Magnified 100 Times

Fig. 9. Same as Fig. 8, Completely Recrystallized by Heating; Magnified 100 Times

deformed brass showing that marked plastic flow has taken place; Fig. 8 shows the same specimen after heating slightly above room temperature but into the recrystallization range for this specimen, new crystals having formed in and around the old crystals; Fig. 9 shows the same specimen after heating to a temperature where complete recrystallization has occurred. The metal is now in excellent condition with a fine, strong, and highly plastic structure. The original grain structure of the metal may have been coarse, with envelopes of impurities around the grains and having the relative brittleness of the cast state, along with the internal stresses and distorted condition of the work-hardened state. This has all disappeared, resulting in the strong, tough, uniform, and stress-free condition which makes a forging so much superior to a casting for many industrial applications.

GRAIN GROWTH. If the temperature of the work-hardened metal is increased above that of the lowest temperature of recrystallization, the newborn grains grow rapidly in size by absorbing each other, as illustrated in Fig. 10. This action is known as grain growth and results in fewer but larger grains. The amount of grain growth occurring during an annealing operation depends to a great degree upon the maximum temperature and the time spent in the annealing operation. Large grains are often wanted, particularly if cold working is to be resumed after annealing, because a large crystal size does not harden as rapidly in subsequent deformation as does fine-grained metal.

Fig. 10. Cold-worked Brass, Shown in Fig. 7, Annealed at 1475° F. Magnified 100 Times

The temperature at which a metal recrystallizes after cold deformation depends upon the composition of the metal and the amount of cold deformation. The greater the amount of cold deformation, the lower the recrystallization temperature. Lead recrystallizes at room temperatures, and therefore cannot be work hardened by cold deformation.

The greater the amount of cold deformation, the finer the grain size will be after the annealing treatment. However, sometimes slight deformation (for example, 5% with iron) results in extremely large grain size after the annealing operation.

GERMINATION. The heating of cold worked metal to its recrystallization temperature usually results in a very fine grain or crystal size, due to the large number of nuclei or new centers of crystal formation. The number of nuclei that form seems to govern the size of the individual grains. Apparently, also, the greater the amount of cold work or deformation before annealing, the finer and more numerous will be the grains after annealing. As has been said, however, a slight amount of cold deformation before annealing (such as

5% with iron) results in the forming of only a few nuclei or centers, and they grow at a rapid rate, resulting in very coarse grains. This extreme growth of grain is sometimes called germination. Other conditions also contribute to extreme grain or crystal growth. Coarse or large grains weaken the metal and possibly ruin it for commercial use, as for certain shaping operations such as deep drawing in power presses. Extremely large grains may cause the metal to rupture in a deep drawing operation, or may result in such a rough surface as to make the product undesirable.

COLD CRYSTALLIZATION. Grain growth, which is commonly termed crystallization, cannot take place in steel or iron while cold. The old belief that metal sections often failed in service due to cold crystallization has been discarded. This belief developed from the fact that parts breaking in service showed at the break a relatively coarse and open grain. The assumption was that this coarse grain developed in service. The fact is that the part had a relatively coarse grain, due to poor forging or heat-treating practice, before it was put to work in the machine. This coarse grained part, when subjected to severe stresses in service, was incapable of standing up under them and failure resulted. In other words, the weak, coarse grain did not form in service, but was in the steel before it had seen any service at all. It is true that grain growth will take place below the critical range, but only with free ferrite or iron, and this free ferrite or iron must be severely distorted and heated to a red heat before any marked grain growth will take place. No grain growth will occur at room temperature.

In chains and other machine parts that are abused and become severely strained in service, there is always danger of increasing the brittleness of the material, but this brittleness is due to the cold working effect produced by severe abuse of these parts. If a coarse grain is present in these parts, failure due to extreme brittleness is certain to result. Where the chain links and other parts have not yet failed because of severe service, the brittleness can be relieved by annealing. This annealing relieves the strains and stresses, putting the parts back in shape for further service. However, if the parts have been so strained as to cause a slight failure, such as surface cracking, annealing should be prohibited, as it will not strengthen nor weld broken parts.

SUMMARY. Grain size control during cold working is one of the major problems encountered in industrial uses of commercially pure metals or their alloys. The only way in which a commercially pure metal may have its properties altered is by means of cold deformation and control of the annealing operation that may follow the cold working. Therefore, a careful study should be made of all the characteristics of commercially pure metals, particularly those involved in the cold working of these metals. This knowledge can be applied also to the behavior of the more complicated alloys.

From an industrial point of view, commercially pure metals find their greatest use in the electrical industry as conductors, and in the fields where corrosion-resistant materials are needed. With the exception of some special stainless alloys, such as stainless steel and Monel metal, pure metals are much more resistant to atmospheric corrosion than their alloys. Such metals as copper, aluminum, nickel, chromium, and cadmium are used either alone, or as a surface coating to impede corrosion of a base metal.

QUIZ QUESTIONS

1. What combination of properties makes metals of great importance in the mechanical and structural field?

2. The characteristics of metals are due to what two structural factors?

3. What is a space lattice?

4. How has the space lattice of the crystal state of metals been determined?

5. What is an allotropic change?

6. How does the type of space lattice formed during solidification affect the properties of metals?

7. What is meant by a cleavage plane?

8. Describe briefly the manner of crystallization of a metal.

9. What is meant by the term "dendritic"?

10. Why does a fine-grained metal, in many applications, prove more satisfactory than a coarse-grained metal?

11. Give a brief description of what happens when metals are deformed during a bending operation.

12. Why do metals become harder and stronger when they are permanently deformed?

13. What happens when work-hardened metals are heated to within certain temperature ranges?

14. Upon what does the temperature at which a metal recrystallizes after cold deformation depend?

15. What is germination?

16. What is cold crystallization?

CHAPTER V

The Theory of Alloys

FROM the study of the nature of pure metals, we next come to the subject of alloys. We are concerned here with a study of the properties and structural characteristics of a pure metal when atoms of a second metal or nonmetal are combined with it. Increased strength, durability, and other qualities have made alloys of much greater industrial importance than pure metals. There are many combinations of properties that can be obtained by alloying metals with each other, or with nonmetals, in various proportions. Knowledge of the properties of alloys makes it possible to determine the uses to which a specific alloy is best adapted, and to make reliable predictions as to the behavior in service of that alloy. Today is indeed the age of metals.

Alloys are much more complex in their behavior and treatment than are the nearly pure metals. A great many aspects of the behavior of our common alloys are still not clearly understood or explained. As yet we know far too little about the nature and reasons for the behavior characteristics of the metals and alloys used by industry. Most of the alloys were made by the "cut and try" method, and we have learned *how* before we have fully learned *why*. Metallurgy may be one of the oldest practices of man; but until the latter part of the nineteenth century we were concerned chiefly with the extraction and production of the metals and alloys, rather than with the reasons for the behaviors they exhibited. During all this early work, it was believed that nearly all the characteristics found in the metals were created during the refining and producing stages, and that if the manufacturing methods could be controlled, a metal or an alloy could be produced that would possess the desired properties. Shortly after the beginning of the present century, however, it became increasingly apparent that the properties of the common metals and their alloys were affected by many factors aside from methods and practices used in their manufacture. It became clearly evident that the properties of metals and their alloys were markedly affected by heat treatment, or heating followed by rapid cooling, and by the methods used in forming, such as rolling, drawing, etc. In an effort to understand and ultimately control these changes, men have engaged in active research in the field of metals. Their work in chemical research, microscopic analysis, and study of the changes taking place during the heating and cooling of metals and their alloys, has resulted in a vast amount of useful knowledge. Consideration of the changes during heating and cooling, referred to as thermic-analysis, has been especially helpful. Information gathered by this method can be assembled to form the "alloy diagram."

The difficulties encountered in the study of the characteristics of any series of alloys are lessened by use of the alloy diagram. The purpose of this study based on the alloy diagram is to simplify a difficult subject. The alloy diagram can be used by the student to predict what the normal structure of certain alloys will be. From this knowledge of the structural characteristics of any alloy, the physical and chemical properties can be predicted also. Therefore, knowledge of these alloy diagrams, representing a system that will predict the structural and physical characteristics of any alloy, is of great value to workers in the metallurgical field. Let us then consider briefly how these alloy diagrams are constructed and interpreted.

THERMAL CURVES. The alloy diagram is constructed from a series of cooling curves, which are obtained from a study of the cooling characteristics of any metal or alloy. These curves are obtainable because of the fact that bodies, while undergoing certain changes, liberate or absorb heat faster than their surroundings. Thermocouples placed in contact with the alloy, while it is being heated or cooled uniformly within a certain temperature range, provide a means for studying the changes occurring during the heating and cooling cycle.

TIME-TEMPERATURE CURVE. The simplest type of curve is obtained by taking temperature readings at fixed intervals of time, and then plotting the results with temperatures as ordinates and time readings as abscissae. So long as the metal is being raised or lowered in temperature at a steady rate, this curve follows a smooth course.

Any departure from this smoothness indicates that there has been either an abnormal absorption or evolution of heat within the specimen. Fig. 1 illustrates the common types of curves using the simple time-temperature method. Alloys when cooled from the liquid state to room temperature do not all undergo the same characteristic evolutions of heat; thus their thermal curves differ in appearance. The two most common types of alloys having different appearing thermal curves are: alloys that form a solid solution, and alloys that form eutectic or eutectoid mixtures.

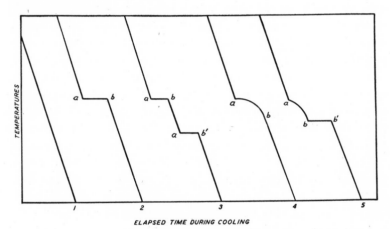

Fig. 1. Simple Time-Temperature Curves

Curve 1, Fig. 1, is the cooling curve of a metal that undergoes no change within the temperature range of the cooling curve.

Curve 2, Fig. 1, is the cooling curve of three possible metals as follows: Case 1: cooling curve of a pure metal. A pure metal changes at a constant temperature from liquid to solid, or from one form of crystal structure to another (allotropic change) at a constant temperature. Case 2: cooling curve of a compound which solidifies at a constant temperature, similar to a pure metal. Case 3: cooling curve of a particular mixture of two metals known as the eutectic or eutectoid mixture, which transforms or freezes at a constant temperature.

Curve 3, Fig. 1, is that of a mixture of two elements that do not blend or influence each other in any way, so that the solidification of each takes place at its particular freezing temperature.

Curve 4, Fig. 1, is the cooling curve of an alloy of two metals which are mutually soluble in each other in both the liquid and solid states. The freezing or transformation of such an alloy takes place over a range of temperatures, *a* to *b* on the curve.

Curve 5, Fig. 1, is a cooling curve applicable to two cases. Case 1: when two metals are soluble in each other above *a*, but have zero solubility for each other below bb^1. With this condition, a eutectic or eutectoid mixture is formed, as indicated by the horizontal arrest in the cooling curve at bb^1, the excess of either metal being separated from solution along the curve from *a* to *b*—the resultant alloy being composed of either a eutectic or eutectoid and a pure metal. Case 2: where two elements are soluble in each other above *a*, but where the solubility becomes limited below bb^1. This condition results in the separation of a eutectic or a eutectoid mixture, similar to Case 1, but instead of the excess or primary metal to freeze being pure, it consists of a saturated solid solution.

Curves similar to those in Fig. 1 can be plotted by several different methods. Other methods of study of these changes also can be used. However, the time-temperature method will serve as an elementary illustration.

THE FREEZING OF ALLOYS

THE DIAGRAM. It is difficult to discuss the changes taking place during the cooling of an alloy from the liquid state to normal temperature without the aid of a diagram. The alloy diagram is to the metallurgist what the blueprint is to the toolmaker. The alloy diagram is made up from a number of cooling curves of a series of alloys of the metals used in the investigation. The coordinates for the diagram are temperature as the ordinates, and concentration or analysis as the abscissae; if temperature-time curves are used, time is visualized in the plane perpendicular to the paper and cannot be shown on the diagram. Taking the simplest possible examples, the freezing of alloys is classified in five ways, as follows:

TYPE I ALLOYS: THE SOLID SOLUTION ALLOY SYSTEM. The single cooling curve of this type of alloy is shown in Fig. 1, curve 4. Fig. 2 illustrates this alloy system by a diagram of the copper-nickel series. The following is a brief discussion of this diagram.

The upper line is known as the **liquidus,** for the alloy is completely liquid above this line. This liquidus line indicates the lowest temperature to which a given liquid composition can be lowered without freezing. It also indicates the composition of the liquid alloy on the verge of freezing at any known temperature. The lower line of the diagram is known as the **solidus,** for all compositions in the area of the diagram below this line are in the solid state. The solidus line indicates the composition of the alloy which freezes at the given

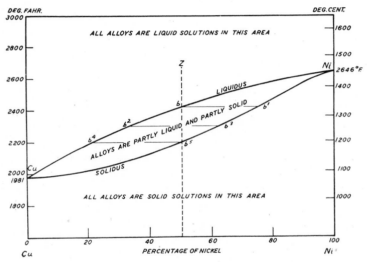

Fig. 2. Constitutional Diagram of the Copper-Nickel Alloys, Type I Alloys

temperatures within the limits represented by the solidus curve. The area between the liquidus and solidus lines represents the mushy state of the alloy, partly liquid and partly solid.

Now, let us consider briefly the changes that take place during cooling, when an alloy of 50% copper and 50% nickel is at a temperature indicated by Z, Fig. 2, and the temperature is lowered.

The alloy remains a homogeneous liquid solution until the temperature drops to a value indicated by the intersection of the liquidus line at b. Here the alloy begins to solidify, forming not pure crystals, but solid solution crystals. It is to be remembered that crystals form by progressive solidification, primary, secondary and ternary axes forming a skeleton onto which the remaining liquid solidifies. The primary axis of the crystals which form from a 50-50 liquid are not pure, but consist of a solid solution, the composition of which is found on the solidus line at b^1, 78% nickel and 22% copper.

As the mass cools, the composition of the growing crystals changes along the solidus line from b^1 to b^5, while the remaining liquid alloy varies in composition along the liquidus line from b to b^4. The solid that first solidifies from the liquid contains less copper than the liquid as a whole. The remaining liquid is thus left richer in copper than it was originally, and it therefore possesses a lower freezing

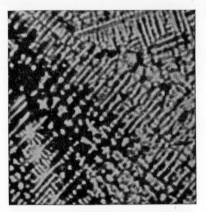

Fig. 3. Cast Monel Metal Showing the Dendritic or Segregated Structure; Magnified 25 times

point. As solidification proceeds, metal progressively poorer in nickel is deposited around the primary solid, that which solidifies last being richest in copper. The solidification, therefore, is not that of a single solution, but of an infinite number of solid solutions, and the solutions formed have a corresponding number of solidification temperatures, the result being a number of solid solutions of different chemical composition.

Hence, the structure of solid cast alloy differs from that of cast pure copper or nickel; it consists of dendritic crystals, originally so called from their branched tree-like appearance. These vary in composition, being rich nickel at the center and rich copper on the outside. Their lack of homogeneity can be corrected by diffusion if the rate of cooling is sufficiently slow, or if the alloy is rendered homogeneous by annealing at temperatures below the melting point. The rate of diffusion varies greatly for different metals, and the heterogeneous "cored" structure persists longest in alloys having the slowest rate of diffusion. It is persistent in nickel alloys. Figs. 3 and 4 illustrate this heterogeneity in a Monel metal, 67% nickel and 28% copper. Uniformity of composition of the crystal grains is assisted by mechanical work, i.e., by rolling, forging, etc., followed by anneal-

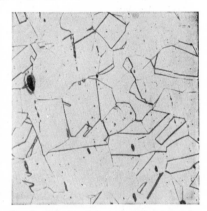

Fig. 4. Same as Fig. 3, but Magnified 100 Times; "Cored" Structure Is Very Apparent

Fig. 5. Rolled and Annealed Monel Metal; Magnified 100 Times. Compare This with Fig. 4

ing. All copper-nickel alloys in the rolled and annealed condition have a similar structure—that of a homogeneous solid solution, as indicated in Fig. 5.

TYPE II, EUTECTIC ALLOYS. These alloys are made up of two metals which are entirely soluble in each other when liquid, but insoluble in each other when solid. When solid, they form two kinds of crystals or grains. When they freeze, therefore, crystals of individual metals form; there is no solid solution. Only a few metals form alloys of this type, as a metal will rarely separate from a liquid solution in the pure state. Cadmium and bismuth, cadmium and zinc, aluminum and silicon, silver and lead are believed to represent this type of alloy.

A freezing-temperature-curve representing this Type II alloy is shown in Fig. 1, curve *5*, and the diagram of cadmium and bismuth, Fig. 6, can be used to describe this type of alloy.

The liquidus of the diagram in Fig. 6 is *AEB*, and the solidus is *ACEDB*. The line *CED* is often referred to as the **eutectic line,** and point *E* as the **eutectic point.**

If a small amount of cadmium is added to molten bismuth, the freezing point of the bismuth is lowered. If, instead, a small amount of bismuth is added to pure cadmium, the freezing point of the cadmium is lowered. It is apparent, since each metal lowers the freezing point of the other, that the lines connecting these freezing points must intersect at some point as shown by point *E* in Fig. 6. This

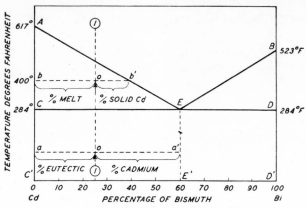

Fig. 6. Cadmium-Bismuth Diagram, Type II Alloys

point of intersection, sometimes called the eutectic point, is of the greatest importance. The composition freezing at this point is called the eutectic alloy. The alloy of this eutectic composition melts and freezes at a constant temperature, in this respect behaving as a pure metal. The eutectic alloy has the lowest melting point of any composition in the series. The eutectic is not a homogeneous alloy, but consists of crystals of nearly pure cadmium and crystals of nearly pure bismuth, approximately 40% cadmium and 60% bismuth. Point *E* of Fig. 6 informs us as to the chemical composition of the eutectic, and the extreme ends of the eutectic line, *C* and *D*, point out that the eutectic is made up of nearly pure cadmium and nearly pure bismuth crystals.

If the liquid solution contains less than 60% bismuth (the eutectic composition), when the temperature is lowered until the *AE* line is intersected, nearly pure cadmium begins to separate from the liquid solution. The separation of cadmium and the lowering of the freezing point go along the curve AE, Fig. 6, until the remaining liquid solution contains 40% cadmium and 60% bismuth. If the solution contains more than 60% bismith, then nearly pure bismuth separates from the liquid, and the separation of bismuth and the lowering of the freezing point go along the curve BE, Fig. 6, until the remaining liquid solution contains the eutectic composition.

No matter what the original analysis was, the liquid solution of cadmium and bismuth at temperature 284° F. (the eutectic temperature) always contains 40% cadmium and 60% bismuth. This so-called eutectic mixture freezes at a constant temperature, forming crystals of nearly pure cadmium and nearly pure bismuth.

STRUCTURAL COMPOSITION. From a study of the alloy diagram and through the use of the "lever law," we can determine approximately the relative amounts of each constituent present in any alloy at any selected temperature within the scope of the alloy diagram. To do this, we select an alloy, such as 75% cadmium and 25% bismuth (see Fig. 6); and if we want to know its structural composition at any temperature below 284° F., draw a constant temperature line a-o-a'. This line a-o-a' is used as a lever with the fulcrum located at the alloy in question, 75Cd-25Bi, and therefore:

$$a\text{-}o = \text{percentage of eutectic}$$
$$o\text{-}a' = \text{percentage of cadmium}$$
$$\frac{a\text{-}o}{a\text{-}a'}100 = \frac{25}{60}100 = 41.6\% \text{ eutectic by weight}$$

Also
$$\frac{o\text{-}a'}{a\text{-}a'}100 = \frac{35}{60}100 = 58.3\% \text{ cadmium by weight}$$

Also in the area $AECA$ we may find the relative amounts of melt and cadmium present by the same method. The lever is now drawn from b on the solidus line to b' on the liquidus line. Point o is the fulcrum of the lever. Therefore:

$$b\text{-}o = \text{percentage melt}$$
$$o\text{-}b' = \text{percentage of solid cadmium}$$
$$\frac{o\text{-}b'}{b\text{-}b'}100 = \frac{15}{40}100 = 37.5\% \text{ solid cadmium}$$
$$\frac{b\text{-}o}{b\text{-}b'}100 = \frac{25}{40}100 = 62.5\% \text{ melt}$$

The structural composition thus determined is one of weight percentages and may be considered fairly accurate for a volume check when the two constituents have about the same density; however, if the densities differ markedly from each other, a more general method of calculation must be used which takes into account the densities of the various constituents.

Fig. 7. The Structure Obtained if an Alloy Containing 75% Cadmium and 25% Bismuth Is Cooled from the Molten State to Room Temperature. This Alloy Contains Approximately 42% Eutectic (Wavy, Flake-like Structure) and Approximately 58% Nearly Pure Cadmium (Dark Structure)

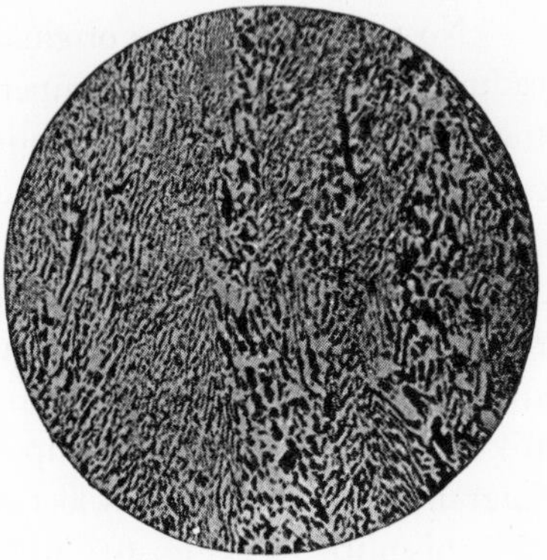

Fig. 8. An Alloy Containing the Eutectic Composition 40% Cadmium and 60% Bismuth. The Structure of This Alloy is 100% Eutectic (Wavy, Flake-like Structure). The Dark Constituent of the Eutectic Is Nearly Pure Cadmium and the Light Constituent is Nearly Pure Bismuth

Reprinted by Permission, from *Principles of Metallography* by Williams and Homerberg, Published by McGraw-Hill Book Co., Inc.

The photomicrographs in Figs. 7 to 10 show the structures developed in Type II, eutectic alloys, as illustrated by the cadmium-bismuth alloys.

You will note that in this discussion we say that the crystals which separate are "nearly" pure cadmium or "nearly" pure bismuth. Careful analysis will show that the cadmium crystals actually contain some bismuth, and the bismuth crystals some cadmium. Only in a very few instances are the crystals which separate really pure metal. In most cases the separating crystals contain more or less of the other constituent. Such crystals are called "mixed crystals" or **solid solutions,** indicating that the crystals contain more than one metal. The term "solid solutions" is to be preferred to that of "mixed crystals," since the crystals are not a mixture but a solution, in that the metals which are present in them cannot be separated by mechanical means.

Fig. 9. The Structure Developed with an Alloy Containing 20% Cadmium and 80% Bismuth. The Structural Composition Consists of Approximately 50% Eutectic and 50% Nearly Pure Bismuth (Light Constituent)

Fig. 10. The Structure Developed with an Alloy Containing 10% Cadmium and 90% Bismuth. This Alloy Contains Approximately 25% Eutectic and 75% Nearly Pure Bismuth (Light Constituent)

Reprinted by Permission, from *Principles of Metallography* by Williams and Homerberg, Published by McGraw-Hill Book Co., Inc.

As an example of this solid solution formation, let us consider the lead-antimony alloys rich in lead, which are represented in Fig. 11. If we consider the alloy represented by the point *o*, an alloy containing

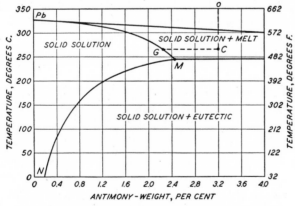

Fig. 11. High Lead End of Antimony-Lead Equilibrium Diagram
Courtesy of American Society for Metals

3.2% antimony and held at a temperature of 660° F., it is entirely liquid. If we allow it to cool to the point *C* and skim the separated crystals, we will find on analyzing them that they are not pure lead but a solid solution of antimony in lead, containing the amount of antimony which is represented by the point G. Now as we cool and skim, we find that the amount of antimony in the skimmings increases up to a definite limit, which is called the limit of solubility, represented at M. The area Pb-M-N then represents a temperature and composition range in which the entire alloy will be solid solution.

It will be noted that the limit of solubility of antimony in lead is reached at the point M, and that as we lower the temperature this solubility decreases along M-N as the temperature falls. This is analogous to the separation of salt from the "liquid" solution of it in water as a hot solution is cooled.

Now this solubility limit and the change of solubility with temperature vary with every pair of metals. In some cases the limit of solubility becomes infinite, that is, the two solid metals form solutions in all proportions, as water and alcohol form liquid solutions. Such a case is copper-nickel, Fig. 2.

TYPE III ALLOYS. Very few alloys which form perfect molten solutions crystallize into two pure metals as described in Type II solidification. Nevertheless, a large majority of the alloys which form molten solutions separate during freezing to form two kinds of crystals. These crystals are composed of the metals which are not pure, but which carry with them some part of the alternate metal in the state of solid solution. In other words, the two metals crystallize and separate, but the crystals are not pure; on the contrary, each contains some of the other metal as a solid solution.

The behavior of these alloys during freezing, and the shape of their diagrams is of an intermediate nature when compared to the diagrams of the alloys of Type I and Type II. A diagram of this type is shown in Fig. 12, the copper-silver system. Silver is capable of retaining 8.8% of copper in solid solution, and alloys in this series containing less than 8.8% copper will solidify, if slowly cooled, in a manner typical of solid solutions, Type I, and will exhibit the characteristic cooling curves of the Type I alloys.

On the other hand, those alloys of this series having compositions which place them beyond the limit of solid solubility of the metals, at either end of the series, behave in most respects very like the alloys which are entirely insoluble in one another in the solid state. The only difference is that the solid which first crystallizes is not pure metal, but a saturated solid solution of one metal in the other, similar to the saturated solid solution formed in the lead-antimony alloys. A complete diagram of such a system, therefore, is made up of three distinct parts: a central portion BC, resembling the diagram of Type II alloys, and portions AB and CD at each end, typical of the Type I alloys.

The areas AB and CD of Fig. 12, as well as the Type I alloys, Fig. 2, represent the same characteristic behavior of the alloys during

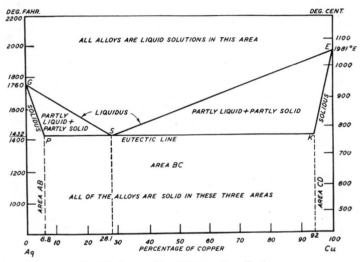

Fig. 12. Copper-Silver Diagram, Type III Alloys

solidification. Both form solid solutions upon solidification, which in the cast state are heterogeneous, with the crystals having a cored or dendritic structure. The solubility or **miscibility** of one metal in another in Types I, II, and III alloy systems, then, are as follows:

Type I. The metals are **miscible** in both the liquid and solid states; the crystals separating from the liquid contain both metals in solution.

Type II. The two metals are miscible in the liquid state but separate as nearly pure crystals of the two metals when the melt solidifies.

Type III. The two metals are miscible in the liquid state, but are only partially miscible in the solid state.

TYPE IV. ALLOYS. Not all metals are miscible in the liquid state. Thus lead and zinc or lead and copper do not mix when melted together, but form two layers, as do water and oil. This immiscibility is of commercial importance in making bearing bronze in which droplets of lead are mixed through molten copper like an emulsion of oil

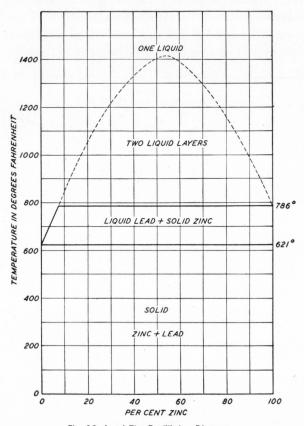

Fig. 13. Lead-Zinc Equilibrium Diagram

in water, and the whole is solidified. Two metals, however, are rarely completely insoluble. Each one dissolves some of the other, and as the temperature is increased, eventually a point is reached where any metal becomes miscible. Fig. 13 shows an equilibrium diagram for lead-zinc.

TYPE V.   COMPOUND-FORMING ALLOYS.   In the study of alloys, we find that one of the most important of all possible behaviors takes place when two metals are added to each other and they combine to form a compound.   Such a compound is called an **intermetallic compound** and is similar to the common compounds or combinations such as water or ice, H_2O, or sodium chloride, NaCl, etc.

In general, these intermetallic compounds are the principal hardeners in our industrial alloys, the compounds being hard and brittle with, frequently, little or no strength.   Such compounds or hardeners are found in alloys such as steel, aluminum alloys, and bearing metals, in which the compounds Fe_3C, $CuAl_2$, $NiCd_7$, $CuSn$, $SbSn$, etc., are found.   Some of the hardest substances known to man are formed from compounds such as WC (tungsten carbide) and B_4C (boron carbide), both of which are harder than sapphire and nearly as hard as the hardest substance known, diamond.

The alloy diagram of the compound-forming metals may take on many very different appearances.   For discussion and introduction to this type of alloy behavior, Fig. 14 may be used, and the alloys of cadmium-nickel, iron-carbon, magnesium-tin, and many others may be used as illustrations of this type of behavior among the industrial alloys.

The compound formed in the alloy diagram presented in Fig. 14 is designated as $AmBn$, and has a composition of 50% metal A, and 50% metal B.   A melt of 50% A and 50% B will solidify at temperature T to form a homogeneous solid, an intermetallic compound.   It will be seen from a study of this diagram that two Type 2 eutectic alloys are formed by this behavior.   The components of the eutectic E_1, Fig. 14, are nearly pure metal A and the compound $AmBn$; whereas, the components of the eutectic formed at E_2 are nearly pure metal B, and the compound $AmBn$.   We actually have two separate eutectic diagrams in one, and the discussion of such behavior is similar to that of a simple eutectic-forming alloy system with the intermetallic compound $AmBn$ considered as a pure substance and as one of the components of the system.   With this in mind, the significance of the various areas of the diagram becomes evident.

THE ALLOY DIAGRAM OF PERITECTIC REACTIONS. Under certain conditions of alloy behavior, some metals undergo a reaction between the solid and liquid phases during the process of solidification, which results in the disappearance of the two phases, and in their place a new solid phase is born. The new solid phase formed

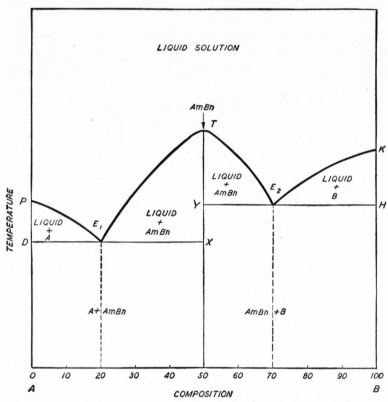

Fig. 14. Type V Alloy Behavior. Alloys that Form Two Separate Eutectics, E_1 and E_2, and a Compound AmBn

from a reaction between the liquid and solid phases may be a solid solution or an intermetallic compound. This reaction, resulting in the disappearance of two phases and the birth of a new one, has been called a **peritectic reaction.** Such an alloy behavior is illustrated by the diagram Fig. 15, where H corresponds to the formation of a compound $AmBn$. This compound $AmBn$ forms along the CHS line of the diagram from the reaction of a nearly pure solid (metal A), shown by point C, and the liquid solution of composition S. If the original melt contained just 80% metal A and 20% metal B, the result of this peritectic reaction gives birth to a pure compound $AmBn$. In the discussion of this diagram, we discover that nearly pure metal A sepa-

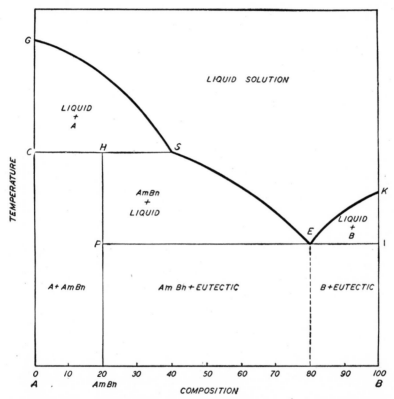

Fig. 15. Diagram of Alloy Behavior that Results in a Peritectic Reaction, which Causes the Formation of a Compound AmBn

rates from the liquid along the line GS, and upon cooling, from GS to CHS, we have a solid A and a liquid solution which may vary in composition from G to S. Upon cooling to the CHS line, the solid A reacts with the liquid solution of composition S, forming the compound $AmBn$. In case the original liquid contained less than 20% metal B, the final structural composition would contain metal A plus the constituent *AmBn*. With an original composition between 20 and 40% metal *B*, the reaction along the *CHS* line would be evidenced by the formation of the compound *AmBn* and a liquid. Cooling from the *HS* line to the *PE* line would result in more compound forming from the liquid solution and the remaining liquid becoming richer and richer in metal *B* until the temperature has dropped to the *PE* line, at which time the remaining melt would have a composition as shown by point *E*, or a eutectic composition. The remaining liquid at this time would solidify to form a eutectic structure. The final alloy would consist of crystals of *AmBn* and the eutectic.

The eutectic of this alloy solidifies along the *PEI* line, Fig. 15, with a eutectic composition which contains 20% *A* and 80% *B*, and consists of crystals of the compound *AmBn* and crystals of nearly pure metal *B*. The eutectic structure of this alloy would be similar in appearance to that of any common binary alloys solidifying with a eutectic structure.

MORE COMPLEX ALLOY SYSTEMS. Many of the most important industrial alloys contain three or more metals in their composition. Certain important effects which a third element may have on a binary alloy are listed briefly.

1. The three elements may form a **ternary** eutectic with lower melting point than the binary eutectic. Thus, the addition of bismuth to the lead-tin eutectic produces an alloy which melts in boiling water.

2. The three elements may all go into solid solution, in which case the third element has no great effect on the binary alloy.

3. The third element may combine with one of the elements of the alloy or with the impurities to produce a profound effect. Thus manganese added to iron containing sulphur renders it forgeable by combining with the sulphur to produce manganese sulphide which separates from the alloy. Such alloys are very difficult to illustrate by the alloy diagram method. However, if only three components are present, an alloy diagram may be most conveniently plotted by means of triangular coordinates. In Fig. 16, each of the components of a ternary alloy is represented by one corner of an equilateral triangle. The sides of the triangle represent the alloy systems of three binary alloy diagrams, *AB*, *AC*, and *BC*. All of the possible combinations of the three components are then formed by the length of

the perpendicular from any point Z, Fig. 16, to the opposite side of the triangle. For example, the composition of point Z will be seen to be 40% A, 40% B, and 20% C. To construct a diagram with the triangle as a base, temperatures are plotted at right angles to the plane of the triangle. The development of the diagram results in a solid model, each side of which represents one of the binary systems.

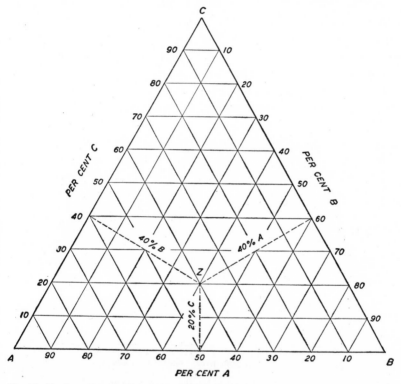

Fig. 16. The Base Triangle for a Ternary Alloy, Illustrating Method of Finding Composition. Alloy Z Contains 40% A, 40% B, and 20% C

The student should refer to a more complete text on alloy diagrams for a more detailed discussion of this type of alloy diagram.

CHANGES IN THE SOLID STATE. In dealing with the alloy diagram, we have discussed changes occurring during the process of solidification. The study of the alloy behavior is complicated by the fact that solids, during heating and cooling, undergo certain changes

in their structural makeup that may completely alter their properties. Such changes can be shown by the alloy-diagram principle.
Some of the most common changes that occur include:

    1. Changes in solid solubility upon cooling.

    2. Changes from one allotropic form to another.

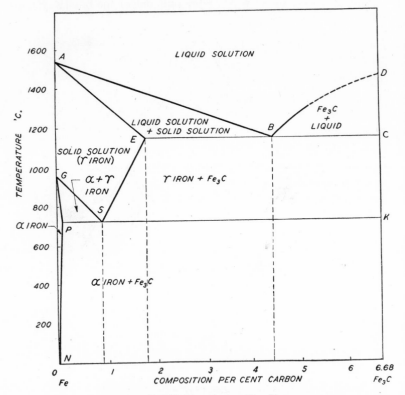

Fig. 17. Simplified Iron-Carbon Alloy Diagram

    3. Formation of eutectoid structures.

    4. Grain growth.

    5. Recrystallization.

    The first two changes, changes in solid solubility and changes
from one allotropic form to another, are common changes that may
be illustrated by the alloy-diagram method. The iron-carbon alloys,
which will be discussed in more detail later on, may be used as an

illustration of these two important changes taking place during the cooling of a solid. Fig. 17 is a simplified iron-carbon diagram showing the changes that take place within a solid solution, which exists in area $AESGA$, when the solid solution is cooled to normal temperatures. The maximum solubility of Fe_3C in gamma (γ) iron is shown by point E. As cooling of the solid solution takes place, the solubility of gamma iron for Fe_3C follows along the ES line to point S. At point S, all iron becomes alpha (α) iron, changing from the gamma form, and the solubility of the new alpha iron phase becomes practically zero, represented by point P. Point G represents the change of pure iron from one allotropic form to another, the change involving a rearrangement of a face-centered cubic atomic lattice form of iron to a body-centered cubic form of iron. The structure born along the PSK line, from a solid solution, is similar to that formed along the EBC line from the liquid solution. However, one is born from a solid, and the other from a liquid. The structure formed at B is called the **eutectic;** whereas the structure born at S is called the **eutectoid.** The student should note the similarity in appearance of the diagram in the area of solidification and the changes that follow during the cooling of the solid solution alloy. Line AB is similar to GS, BD similar to SE, PSK similar to EBC, and AES similar to GPN. The two changes, i.e., one of changing solubility and the other a change in the allotropic form of the iron, result in reactions that may be measured and account for the lines formed in the solid areas of this alloy diagram.

PROPERTIES OF ALLOYS. The properties of alloys may or may not differ markedly from their constituent metals. Much can be predicted about the properties of an alloy from a knowledge of the equilibrium diagram. The following rules will be useful:

1. If the two elements do not form solid solutions or compounds, their alloys will have properties intermediate between the two elements as would be expected of a mechanical mixture. See Fig. 18. This applies to hardness, electrical conductivity, color, and magnetic properties.

2. If the two elements form a solid solution, the alloy will be harder and stronger and have greater electrical resistance than would be obtained with a simple mixture of its constituent metals. See Fig. 19. Its color and magnetic properties cannot be predicted. In general, it may be stated that the less the solubility of one metal in another, the greater will be the hardening and the more difficult it will be to dissolve a given per cent of it in the second metal. Thus

nickel, which is soluble in all proportions in copper, does not affect the properties of copper to anywhere near the extent of phosphorus, which is only slightly soluble.

3. If the two metals form a compound, nothing can be predicted of its properties from those of its constituents.

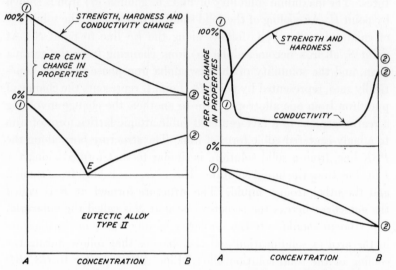

Fig. 18. Possible Effect of Behavior of Type II Alloy upon the Strength, Hardness, and Conductivity

Fig. 19. Behavior that Might Be Expected from a System of Type I Alloy

Finally, the properties of some alloys may be profoundly altered by heat treatment. These are the solid solution alloys which show a change of solid solubility with temperature, as described for lead-antimony. Such alloys may be greatly hardened by heating to the solid solution range and cooling suddenly, as by quenching in water, and subsequently aging at room or elevated temperature. The quenching preserves the solid solution, which by the aging process is broken up into very finely divided particles of one metal in the other. Such a finely divided mixture is much harder and stronger than the same mixture in coarser particles. The tensile strengths of quenched and aged lead-antimony alloys are shown in Fig. 20.

This brief review should equip the reader to tell a great deal about the properties of alloys from published equilibrium diagrams.

IRON-CARBON DIAGRAM

A careful study leading to a thorough understanding of the iron-carbon diagram in Fig. 21 is desirable because the diagram not only shows the type of alloys formed, but also indicates their proper heat-treating temperatures and helps to explain how the properties of steels and cast irons may be so radically varied by heat treatments.

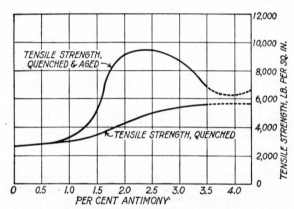

Fig. 20. Tensile Strength of Lead Antimony Alloys, after Quenching from 450° F, and after Aging at Room Temperature

IRON-CARBON ALLOYS. The alloys of iron and carbon are the most important alloys used industrially. It will be evident from an inspection of the iron-carbon diagram, Fig. 21, that they are Type III alloys because the iron will freeze with carbon in solid solution up to a limit of 1.7% carbon.

SOLIDIFICATION. Pure iron, represented by the point A, and the iron-carbon eutectic represented by the point B, melt and solidify at a constant temperature. All other alloys represented in the diagram melt and freeze over a range of temperatures.

Alloys containing 0.0 to 4.3% carbon begin to solidify on cooling to the line AB by the separation of solid solution (austenite) crystals from the liquid.

Alloys containing more than 4.3% carbon begin to solidify with the separation of Fe_3C (cementite) from the liquid, on cooling to the BD line.

In the case of alloys containing 1.7% carbon or less, solid solution (austenite) begins to freeze out on cooling from *AB* to *ALRE*. At *ALRE* all the alloy is solid, and consists of dendritic crystals. These dendritic crystals are formed, not of a single solid solution, but of

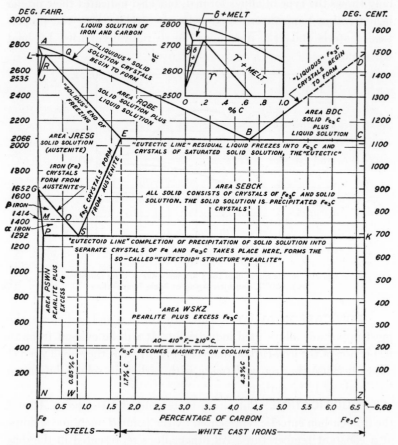

Fig. 21. Partial Equilibrium Diagram of Iron-Carbon Alloys. Inset of Delta Iron Region after Frank Adcock

an infinite number of solid solutions. The first to freeze is a solid solution relatively low in carbon content; the last to freeze is relatively rich in carbon concentration. It is to be recalled that this lack of homogeneity can be corrected by diffusion if the rate of cooling is sufficiently slow, or if the alloy is rendered homogeneous by hot working or by annealing at temperatures below the melting point. For the present it can be assumed that the area $JRESG$ of the diagram represents an alloy in one homogeneous phase, austenite.

In alloys containing from 1.7 to 4.3% carbon, solid solution (austenite) freezes out of the liquid, beginning at AB and continuing as the temperature is lowered to EB. At EB, the eutectic line, there is some residual liquid, which is of the eutectic composition. This liquid then solidifies at a constant temperature, forming the eutectic mixture. The eutectic of the iron-carbon system consists of alternating layers of Fe_3C (cementite) and saturated solid solution (austenite) in a finely divided state. The Fe_3C (cementite) and the solid solution (austenite) crystallize simultaneously at EB to form the eutectic structure. Therefore, alloys containing from 1.7 to 4.3% carbon, just below the EB line consist of mixed crystals of two constituents, austenite, and eutectic. The amounts of each vary from 100% austenite and 0.0% eutectic with 1.7% carbon alloy, to 100% eutectic and 0.0% austenite with 4.3% carbon iron alloy.

In alloys containing more than 4.3% carbon, Fe_3C (cementite) freezes out on cooling from BD to BC; the residual liquid at BC is of eutectic composition and solidifies at a constant temperature, forming the eutectic constituent. These alloys just below BC consist of mixed crystals of cementite and eutectic.

In the discussion of the other diagrams, Types I, II, and III alloys, it was considered that the structure of the solid alloy just below the solidus line and the eutectic line, remained unchanged during the cooling to room temperature, except for diffusion taking place when dealing with a heterogeneous solid solution phase. The structure at room temperature was that of the cast alloy. However, with iron-carbon alloys, very marked changes occur during the cooling from the solidus $ALRE$ and eutectic EBC to room temperature. These changes are brought about principally because iron has the ability to exist in several allotropic forms, and during the cooling the iron changes from one of these forms to another.

ALLOTROPY. In the $JRESG$ area and the $SEBCK$ area, iron exists wholly in the form known as **gamma**. This gamma iron has its atoms arranged in the face-centered cubic lattice. Gamma iron dissolves carbon; its grain size depends on temperature, time and working; and it is nonmagnetic. Gamma iron is denser than alpha iron. At normal temperatures, and in the areas *PSWN* and *WSKZ*, iron exists wholly in the form known as **alpha.** Alpha iron has a body-centered cubic lattice, is found to be magnetic, dissolves little carbon, and its grains do not change under normal conditions. Forging of the alpha iron at room temperature causes a distortion of the grains.

OTHER ALLOTROPES OF IRON. It is reported that at 2535° F. gamma iron changes to a different form called **delta** iron. This delta iron is said to have a body-centered atomic arrangement similar to alpha iron.

Pure iron undergoes certain discontinuous changes in physical properties at 1414° F. These are small changes in the internal energy, volume, electrical conductivity, etc. There is a marked change in the magnetic properties. At temperatures a little below 1414° F., iron is strongly magnetic, while at higher temperatures it is practically nonmagnetic.

Because of these changes, it has been held that at temperatures between 1414° F. and 1652° F. iron exists in the form of a distinct allotropic modification which has been called **beta** iron. As the structure of both alpha and beta iron is body-centered, this structure remains unchanged in passing from alpha to beta iron. It is stated that the marked change in the physical properties which takes place at 1414° F. is caused by a change within the atom of the iron.

FERRITE SOLUBILITY CURVE. Pure gamma iron exists on cooling from *J* to *G*, Fig. 21. At *G* all the pure gamma iron changes to beta iron. This beta iron exists during cooling to *M*, changing at *M* to alpha iron, and this alpha form remains unchanged below *M*. No change takes place at *P* with a pure iron. This alpha iron is capable of holding in solution considerable amounts of various elements such as nickel, silicon, phosphorus, etc. The solubility for carbon is very slight and is not definitely known, being perhaps less than 0.015% carbon at normal temperature. The term **ferrite** is applied to solid solutions in which alpha iron is the solvent.

The temperature at which alpha iron forms from gamma iron on cooling is lowered by the presence of carbon in solid solution in the gamma iron, that is, in austenite. This is represented in the diagram by the line *GOS*, which shows that the temperature of formation of ferrite decreases from 1652° F. with pure iron, to 1292° F. for an alloy containing 0.85% carbon. The formation of ferrite from the solid solution austenite is analogous to the precipitation of cadmium from the liquid solution of cadmium and bismuth, Fig. 6. The line *GOS* expresses the solubility of ferrite in austenite, and may be referred to as the ferrite solubility curve. The straight line *GOS* is often represented by a curved or broken line.

CEMENTITE SOLUBILITY CURVE. At the eutectic temperature 2066° F. austenite will hold 1.7% carbon in solid solution. When

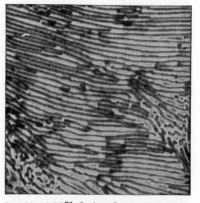

austenite of this composition is cooled, Fe_3C (cementite) precipitates from solution. The solubility of carbon in austenite at various temperatures is shown by the line *SE*, which may be called the cementite solubility curve, as cementite is the phase which is separated as the temperature drops below this line. The maximum solubility at 2066° F. is 1.7% carbon; at 1292° F. the maximum solubility becomes 0.85% carbon.

Fig. 22. 0.85% Carbon Steel, All Pearlite. Magnified 2800 Times

Reprinted from *Metallography and Heat Treatment of Iron and Steel* by Sauveur, Published by The University Press

THE EUTECTOID. It is thus seen that, no matter what carbon content is started with, austenite reaches a temperature of 1292° F. on *slow cooling* with a carbon content of 0.85% carbon. This situation will exist only so long as the metal remains at 1292° F. It cannot cool below this point without a complete separation of all the solid solution austenite into crystals of ferrite and cementite.

On cooling through this temperature, austenite containing 0.85% carbon deposits simultaneously a mixture of ferrite and cementite. This mixture is called the **eutectoid,** from analogy to the eutectic. The eutectoid structure formed from a saturated solid solution austenite at 1292° F. is often referred to as **pearlite,** because its appearance when viewed with the aid of a microscope is similar to that of mother-of-pearl, see Fig. 22.

COOLING OF A STRUCTURAL STEEL. If a structural steel containing 99.75% iron and 0.25% carbon, is cooled slowly from above the liquidus AB to normal temperature, it will solidify in the usual manner of a solid solution of its components, carbon and iron. But with a slow rate of cooling, this solid solution will not remain in the state of chemical solution below the GOS line. When it reaches the lowest temperature at which the solid solution austenite can retain all the iron in solid solution, approximately 1550° F., any further cooling will result in the separation of beta iron crystals out of the austenitic crystals. The structure of the steel will then consist of beta iron crystals formed around the solid solution austenitic crystals. As cooling continues, more beta iron crystals are precipitated from the austenite, there being a constantly increasing number of grains of beta iron among the solid solution crystals. When the temperature drops to the MO line, all the beta iron crystals change to alpha iron crystals; no other change takes place at MO. Any further cooling results in more iron crystals separating from the remaining austenite —the iron crystals now being the alpha iron form. This separation continues until the line PS is reached. At this temperature the steel consists of a mixture of solid solution (austenite) crystals containing 0.85% carbon and crystals of alpha iron (ferrite). Practically all of the carbon is now concentrated in the solid solution; the alpha iron (ferrite) grains will be almost free from it. The steel cannot be cooled below this PS line, 1292° F., without a complete separation of all the solid solution into crystals of alpha iron (ferrite) and Fe_3C (cementite). Therefore at a constant temperature of 1292° F., two changes in the austenite take place simultaneously: first, the gamma solid solution iron changes to alpha iron; second, the carbon that was dissolved in the solid solution austenite is separated from it to form separate crystals of Fe_3C (cementite). Further cooling to room temperature takes place without change of structure.

SUMMARY OF CHANGES. (1) A solid solution forms during freezing and exists down to the GOS line. (2) Precipitation of ferrite takes place from GOS to PS, 1292° F. (3) At PS, 1292° F., the remaining austenite of eutectoid proportion breaks down into separate crystals of ferrite and cementite, forming a very fine lamellar structure known as pearlite. The resultant structure of the 0.25% carbon steel consists of ferrite, usually called free ferrite, and pearlite, see Fig. 23. The amounts of each constituent are approximately 29% pearlite and 71% free ferrite. The free ferrite forms a network of crystal grains around the pearlite grains. This steel, consisting of free ferrite and pearlite is classified as a hypo-eutectoid steel.

We can estimate the relative amounts of free ferrite and pearlite in this steel at normal temperature by the same method as indicated

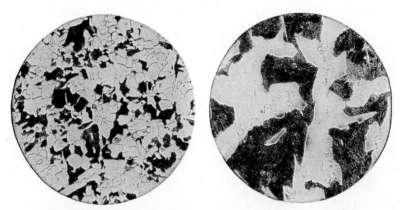

Fig. 23. Steels with Less than 0.85% Carbon; Pearlite, Dark; Free Ferrite, Light

in the case of the cadmium-bismuth alloys, i.e., the use of the lever law.

$$0.0 \ \% \text{ carbon} = N = 100\% \text{ free ferrite}$$
$$0.85\% \text{ carbon} = W = 100\% \text{ pearlite}$$

Therefore:

$$\frac{0.25}{0.85} \times 100 = 29\% \text{ pearlite}$$

Also:

$$\frac{0.60}{0.85} \times 100 = 71\% \text{ free ferrite}$$

At any temperature during the cooling of this or any carbon-iron alloy, we can use this method to estimate the relative amounts of each constituent present. Also, because the densities of cementite (Fe_3C) and ferrite are about the same, this method of estimating the amounts of each constituent is fairly accurate as to volume percentage.

COOLING OF A TOOL STEEL. When a tool steel containing 1.5% carbon is first frozen, it is composed structurally of a solid solution of gamma iron and carbon. As it cools, however, the alloy soon reaches a temperature where the gamma iron cannot hold this amount of carbon in solid solution, resulting in a separation of Fe_3C (cementite) from the solid solution austenite. This temperature corresponds to the intersection of the *SE* line, approximately 1900° F. The precipitation of Fe_3C cementite crystals continues during the cooling;

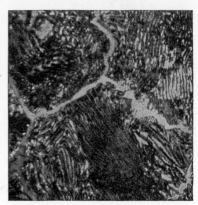

Fig. 24. 1.43% Carbon Steel; Dark, Pearlite; Light, Free Cementite. Magnified 50 Times

Fig. 25. 1.43% Carbon Steel, Same as Fig. 24. Magnified 500 Times

Reprinted from *Metallography and Heat Treatment of Iron and Steel* by Sauveur. Published by The University Press

and when 1292° F., indicated by line *SK*, is reached, the steel is composed of part solid solution austenite, containing 0.85% carbon, and part Fe_3C cementite, containing 6.67% carbon. Finally, at *SK* the remaining austenite separates into crystals of alpha iron and cementite, forming the structure pearlite. The ultimate structure consists of crystals of free cementite (approximately 10%) forming a network around the crystals of eutectoid pearlite, see Figs. 24 and 25. This steel is classified as a **hyper-eutectoid** steel.

SLOW HEATING AND SLOW COOLING OF STEEL. It should be understood that the description of changes taking place during the cooling of steel refers to cooling at a rate slow enough to allow the changes to occur in a normal manner. Each change requires some time, perhaps several minutes, and normal change is not obtained unless the proper rate of cooling is employed. It should also be understood that changes occurring on slow cooling are reversed on heating.

DECOMPOSITION OF CEMENTITE. If alloys which contain more than 1.7% carbon are slowly cooled, the cementite decomposes into iron and graphite. The graphite, in the usual form of fine soft flakes, tends to weaken and embrittle the alloy. Most iron castings are made in sand molds which allow the iron to cool comparatively slowly; this permits the formation of graphite. The graphite as it occurs in slowly cooled or grey cast iron is shown in Fig. 15, Chapter I. If the iron is cast into metal molds, it cools so rapidly that the cementite does not decompose and come out of solution in flakes of graphite. This cementite is responsible for the hardness of white or chilled cast iron.

The decomposition of the cementite into graphite and iron is influenced not only by the rate of cooling, but by the other elements present in the iron. A high silicon content tends to increase graphitization; thus when thin sections of soft iron are desired, a high silicon iron is used to insure the decomposition of the graphite. Manganese has the opposite effect; and irons having a high manganese content may have hard portions because the manganese prevents the formation of graphite.

CRYSTALLINE GRAIN. The grain size changes that occur during the heating and cooling of metals and alloys are very important. The changes can be classified as follows: (1) crystallization; (2) crystal growth; (3) recrystallization.

(1) *Crystallization* of the liquid into a solid usually results in relatively large dendritic grains. The best way to break down these large dendritic grains is by hot working.

(2) *Crystal growth* takes place in most metals and alloys at relatively high temperatures, but below the solidus. Crystal growth results from an individual grain "stealing" particles from grains surrounding it, and thus becoming larger in itself. Ultimately, the number of grains is diminished, and the average grain size is increased. This grain growth is rapid and is accelerated as the temperature is increased. The tendency of the structure is to become **single grained**. The term single grain is used to describe the structure of a piece of

metal in which grain growth has advanced to such a degree that there is only one grain in the cross section of the piece.

No grain growth will occur with the alpha form of iron, unless it has been cold worked and subjected to temperatures around 1200° F. However, gamma iron grains grow rapidly, so that heating above the *GOSK* line, Fig. 21, causes grain growth, and heating to near the solidus line results in marked grain growth.

(3) *Recrystallization* is the changing of crystalline grains into other crystalline grains without the aid of fusion. It can result from two causes: first, allotropic transformations, such as changing alpha iron grains to gamma iron grains; second, by mechanical straining, such as working of the metal. When gamma iron (austenite) changes to alpha iron (ferrite) and Fe_3C (cementite), as on cooling from *GOS* to below *PSK*, complete recrystallization takes place. Grains which crystallize out (recrystallize) above *PS* are relatively coarse; grains which crystallize out at *PS* 1292° F. are relatively fine. If a piece of steel is heated through *PS* 1292°F., to *GOS*, recrystallization completely obliterates the original grain structure, and new, and at first very small, grains of gamma iron (austenite) are formed.

GRAIN SIZE CHANGES ON HEATING. At normal temperature a 0.25% carbon steel consists of pearlite and free ferrite grains. No change of grain occurs during the heating below the *PS* line. On reaching the *PS* line, however, the grain structure of pearlite recrystallizes to form a very fine-grained austenite, the alpha iron changing to gamma iron. This change affects only the original pearlite, approximately 29% of the structure, the 71% of free ferrite remaining unchanged. During the raising of the temperature from *PS* to *GOS*, the free ferrite recrystallizes from alpha to gamma iron and is absorbed by the austenite. The recrystallized structure of gamma iron remains fine grained during this change because it is being disturbed and grain growth is being prevented by diffusion and recrystallization of the free ferrite. After the temperature has been raised to above the *GOS* line, all the iron has changed from alpha to gamma and gone into solid solution with the austenite; grain growth then sets in and continues up to the *ALRE* solidus line.

The changes taking place in grain size during the heating cycle are illustrated in Fig. 26, which shows the relative grain size changes which may be expected during the slow heating of a 0.25% carbon steel to 1800° F. and the slow cooling back to normal temperatures.

At 1800° F. the grain size of the austenite would be relatively coarse. Upon slow cooling, no marked change takes place until the

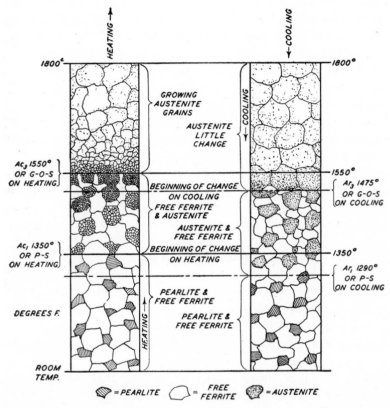

Fig. 26. Changes in Grain Structure During Heating and Cooling of 0.25% Carbon Steel

GOS line is reached, 1475° F. Here the austenite precipitates fine ferrite crystals to the boundaries of the austenite crystals. During the slow cooling from *GOS* to *PS*, this precipitation continues with gradual growth in volume and size of the newly formed ferrite grains. The grain size of the austenite is decreasing, and the grain size of the ferrite is increasing. Upon reaching the *PS* line, 1290° F., the remaining austenite recrystallizes to form the pearlite constituent.

This pearlite is a very fine mixture of crystals of ferrite and cementite (Fe_3C). From slightly below *PS* no further changes take place; however, if very slow cooling is employed, further growth of the ferrite grains may take place and a spheroidizing of the layers of cementite in the pearlite may occur.

From this it may be seen that the size and shape of the original austenitic grains influence to a marked degree the resultant grain size and distribution of free ferrite and pearlite. A very fine grain size in the original austenite will result in a very fine aggregation of free ferrite and pearlite.

If a 1.5% carbon steel containing mixed grains of pearlite and free cementite is heated, it is found that no change of grain structure occurs below the *SK* line. At the *SK* line the pearlite changes to austenite (alpha iron to gamma iron and dissolving of the Fe_3C crystals), resulting in a very fine-grained austenite. The excess cementite is unaffected at this temperature. On further heating, up to the *SE* line, this excess cementite is dissolved by the fine-grained austenite. During this heating, marked grain growth of the fine austenite is prevented by the absorption and diffusion of the excess cementite. However, some grain growth takes place which results in a coarser-grained austenite, and when the *SE* line is reached and all the excess cementite is dissolved, marked grain growth sets in and continues up to the *ALRE* line.

CRITICAL TEMPERATURE DIAGRAM. The diagram shown in Fig. 27 is seen to be part of the iron-carbon diagram and is often referred to as the critical temperature diagram. It is through this temperature range during heating and cooling that steels undergo the marked structural changes that have been described. It is apparent from Fig. 27 that the line *PS* in Fig. 21 has formed two lines *Ac1* and *Ar1*. Also, what is true of the *PS* line is true of the other lines in this section of Fig. 21. The splitting up of the temperature lines in Fig. 21 is due to a change in the temperature of transformation during cooling of iron-carbon alloys, as compared with the temperature of transformation upon heating. That is, the transformation of an 0.85% carbon steel from austenite to pearlite during cooling occurs at 1292° F. (point *S* in Fig. 21), but the change from pearlite to austenite upon heating, occurs at ·1350° F. This difference between the heating and cooling transformations, Fig. 27, is approximately 50° F., if very slow heating and cooling are employed. In reading this critical temperature diagram the *Ac* temperature lines are used if the iron-carbon alloys are being heated, and the *Ar* temperature lines are used if cooling is taking place.

The method of designating the various points, which is borrowed from the French, needs a word of explanation. The halt or **arrest** in cooling or heating is designated by the letter "A" standing for the

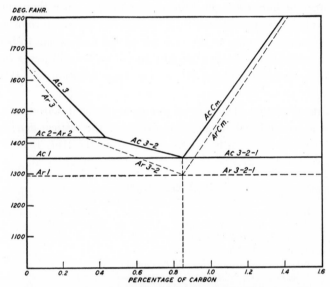

Fig. 27. Critical Temperature Diagram Showing the Lag between the Heating and Cooling Transformations

French word *arrêt*. An arrest on cooling is referred to by the letters "Ar," the "r" standing for *refroidissement*—cooling. An arrest on heating is designated by the letters "Ac," the "c" standing for *chauffage*—heating. The various arrests are distinguished from each other by numbers after the letters, being numbered in the order in which they occur as the temperature increases.

Lag. The temperatures mentioned and given in the diagram refer to conditions of equilibrium. Under practical conditions there is a delay or lag in the attainment of equilibrium, and the critical points are found at lower temperatures on heating than those given. That is, there is a difference between the *Ar* points and the *Ac* points. This difference increases with the rate of cooling or heating. For instance, the *Ac* temperatures can be raised about 300° F. from their normal occurrence by fast heating, and the *Ar* temperatures can be lowered about 1000° F., in fact, can be forced below room temperature by rapid quenching of thin sections.

The equilibrium temperatures represent very slow cooling or heating.

Effect of Impurities on Alloys. Impurities other than carbon, when added to iron, will modify or change the temperature of occurrence of critical points, or the transformation from alpha to beta to gamma iron. For instance, the addition of nickel will lower the *Ac* critical temperatures about 30° F. for each addition of 1.00% of nickel.

Critical Range. The critical points, considered collectively, are known as the critical range. For instance, the critical range of a 0.45% carbon steel, on heating, extends from the *Ac1*, 1340° F., to 1410° F. (See Fig. 27.)

QUIZ QUESTIONS

1. What is thermic analysis?
2. What information is needed to construct an alloy diagram?
3. In the study of a diagram covering the freezing of alloys, what does the liquidus line represent? The solidus line?
4. What characteristic is common to Type II eutectic alloys?
5. Define the term "solid solution" when applied to crystal structure.
6. Name the three classes of solubility relations in metals.
7. What is meant by the term "two-layer alloys"?
8. Define the term "binary alloys."
9. List some of the important effects which a third element may have on a binary alloy.
10. What are intermetallic compounds? Of what importance are they in connection with our industrial alloys?
11. What is a peritectic reaction?
12. What is a ternary alloy? What convenient method is used to plot a diagram for this type of alloy?
13. List some of the important structural changes which occur in an alloy during heating and cooling.
14. To what type do the iron-carbon alloys belong? Why?
15. On what factors does the grain size of gamma iron depend?
16. How does heat affect the magnetic properties of iron?
17. What is pearlite?

18. *When steel cools to a temperature of 1292° F., what changes take place?*
19. *Why should steel be cooled slowly?*
20. *What effect does hot working have upon grain size?*
21. *Name the two causes of recrystallization.*
22. *What effect will a fine grain size in the original austenite have upon the free ferrite and pearlite which form during cooling?*
23. *What do we learn from the critical temperature diagram?*

REMOVING INGOT HEATED TO PROPER ROLLING TEMPERATURE FROM SOAKING PIT

Photo by Bethlehem Steel Company

35-INCH BLOOMING MILL

Photo by Bethlehem Steel Company

CHAPTER VI

Shaping and Forming Metals

WITH one exception, all the available shapes and sizes obtainable in the metals have their beginning in the form of a casting. That is, the metals all start from a liquid or molten state; the molten metal is poured into a suitable mold, and allowed to solidify into a mass the approximate shape of the mold. The only exception to this practice is where the metal is in the powder state and is formed into the desired shape by pressing the powder in a metal mold. Powdered metal is welded into a solid form by means of pressure and heat, with or without the aid of fusion or the melting of the original metal powder. However, as yet only an insignificant portion of the industrial forms of metals are produced in this way. Metal shapes, in by far the largest tonnage, are produced by casting and subsequently reducing the cast form to finished or semi-finished form by some method of hot and cold plastic shaping. The metal so cast receives its shape from the sand or metal mold. A special kind of casting, made by pouring molten steel into a cast iron mold, is called an **ingot**, or **ingot casting.** This is the form in which steel is cast before plastic shaping, as in rolling or forging.

Casting. The simplest method of getting metals or alloys into the desired form is by pouring the molten metal into a mold. This pouring operation is called "casting," "teeming," or "pouring." For ordinary iron or brass casting these molds are made by shaping sand around a pattern, which is a piece of wood or metal shaped like the desired casting. The pattern is then removed without disturbing the sand and the desired metal poured into its place.

In making patterns for casting, it must be borne in mind that the casting will not be the same size as the pattern, since all metals, except bismuth, shrink somewhat in casting. Knowledge of this shrinkage is an important factor in the making of patterns.

Castings made in steel foundries by both acid and basic melting practice, in open-hearth or electric furnaces, are of more or less intricate shape and are cast in sand molds. Castings range in size from very small articles to others of great size and intricate shape within the limits of good foundry practice. Castings weighing over 150 tons have been successfully cast. The greatest single user of these castings is the railway industry in which they are used for cross heads, driving wheels, frames, etc. Factors governing the mechanical properties of the casting include composition, melting practice, design of the casting, and heat treatment.

Most of the carbon steel castings run between 0.15 to 0.35% carbon, and no heat treatment other than perhaps annealing is necessary. Other castings of higher carbon content, 0.35% and over, are usually subjected to such heat treatments as normalizing, annealing, quenching, and tempering in order to improve the mechanical properties, and assist in the finishing operations. Castings subjected to low stresses are usually given an annealing heat treatment; whereas castings requiring a high tensile strength are usually subjected to several heat treatments in order to develop the proper strength. Nearly 15% of the present production of steel castings are alloy grades, with many grades available and a resultant diversity of mechanical properties.

Finishing operations, including machining, are extremely important and the facility of such will depend largely on composition and heat treatment.

Casting gives a rough surface to the metal which for many uses must be smoothed by machining. In recent years, therefore, the practice of casting in a smooth metal mold has been increasing. This may be accomplished by ordinary gravity casting, using a refractory lining on the mold, or the process known as die casting may be used. In this process the molten alloy is forced into a special die by means of pressure exerted on the molten metal. The pressure may be obtained mechanically by a plunger action or by means of compressed air. The result of forcing this molten metal into a die under pressure is to produce a casting with a smooth surface and accurate dimensions; hence little machining is required. This process is used extensively on aluminum alloys and zinc alloys for making small parts.

CAST INGOT STEEL. The tapping of molten steel into a ladle and teeming the molten steel from the ladle into cast-iron molds for the production of the cast ingot, constitutes one of the most important operations in the manufacture of commercial steel. Ordinarily the ingots are top-poured. However, in some cases they are bottom-poured; that is, the molten steel is admitted at the bottom of the mold by means of runners. This eliminates the splashing which results from top-pouring, and gives the ingot a better surface. Instead of sand a "permanent" mold made from cast iron is used. These molds are of any convenient shape, though usually they are square or rectangular for ease in handling in the rolling mill.

The making of good ingots is one of the most difficult and important steps in the fabrication of steel, for often defects in the ingot cannot be eliminated by subsequent hot working operations, such as rolling or forging. The following are some of the major defects:

1. Pipes
2. Dendritic structure
3. Blowholes
4. Segregation
5. Slag inclusions
6. Checking, cracks, scabs
7. Internal stresses

Pipes. After the molten metal has been poured into the mold, it begins to solidify from the outside, due to the chilling effect of the cold iron mold. Because of the shrinkage that occurs when metals solidify, the solid metal occupies less space than the molten metal. This shrinkage results in a cavity or hollow in the cast ingot. This cavity which is called the **pipe** of the ingot, is usually found in the section to freeze last, the central upper portion of the ingot, as illustrated in the second, third, and fourth ingots in Fig. 1. The only way to eliminate this piped section is to cut or crop the end of the ingot. Attempts are made to design molds and regulate their cooling so that this pipe will be concentrated at the top, as it is in the fourth ingot. One method of concentrating the pipe at the top of the ingot is to have what is known as a "hot top," which is simply a smaller sand mold at the top of the iron mold. The metal in contact with the sand does not freeze as fast as that in contact with the iron, and the molten metal in this portion "feeds" down into the main portion of the ingot as it freezes and contracts, so that the pipe occurs only in the hot top. Another method is to cast the ingots large end up. This, of course, makes it more difficult to remove the ingot from the mold, especially when large ingots are made. The diagram in Fig. 2 shows comparative results of the use of two types of molds, the large-end-up and large-end-down molds in casting ingots. The

Fig. 1. Method of Testing the Steel Ingots
Courtesy of American Institute of Mining Engineers

method of solidification and the type of shrinkage cavity produced in ingots made in these two types of molds are illustrated, Fig. 2, by means of contour lines, which indicate successive skin thicknesses.

Dendritic Structure. The chilling effect of the cold iron mold also causes crystallization of the molten metal to occur in an abnormal manner; that is, the crystals form first on the surfaces of the mold and grow inwardly to form a dendritic grain structure that leaves the steel inherently weak because of the obviously weak planes so formed. Fortunately, in most cases the chilling does not extend to the center of the ingot, the central section of the ingot having a characteristic random crystal orientation and tough structure, as illustrated in Fig. 23, Chapter I.

Blowholes. Blowholes cause defective steel. These blowholes are formed by the liberation of gases during the solidification of the

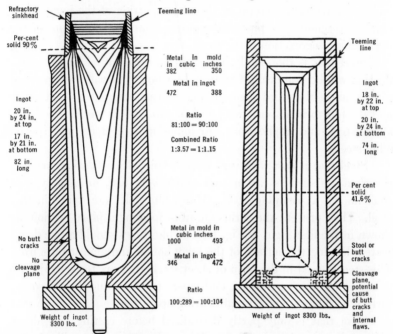

Fig. 2. Showing Freezing and Formation of Well-Deoxidized Steel Made in Big-End-Up and Big-End-Down Molds of Same Size and Cross Section

Courtesy of Gathmann Engineering Co., Baltimore, Md.

ingot. Gases from the molten steel may rise as bubbles and escape from the ingot, or may be trapped in the solidifying metal. Blowholes near the center of the ingot, known as "deep-seated," are less harmful than blowholes on or near the surface of the ingot. Surface blowholes will elongate during hot rolling, producing seams in the finished steel.

Segregation. As was seen in the study of the alloy diagram, liquid solutions segregate during solidification, the first portion to freeze being relatively pure compared to the last section to freeze. This selective freezing results in uneven concentration of the elements found in the alloy, and is called segregation. In ingot manufacture the segregation is aggravated by the chilling action of the mold. The first portions in contact with the mold freeze relatively pure, and the central portions of the ingot, which are the last to freeze, are richer in the lower freezing point constituents of the steel. This is another reason for cropping the upper portion of the ingot, since cutting to remove the pipe also removes some of the sections of the ingot where segregation is the worst.

Steel that is thoroughly degasified and deoxidized before solidification will be practically free from blowholes but will show marked piping, as in the third ingot in Fig. 1, cast without a "hot top," and the fourth ingot, cast with a "hot top." This steel is known as **killed** steel, and applications are found in tool steels and special alloy steels.

Steel that is cast with very little, if any, degasification, keeping the elements such as carbon and silicon very low, forms a type of steel known as **rimming** steel. Many blowholes are found in this steel. They prevent the shrinkage from forming a piped section, as shown in the first ingot in Fig. 1. The blowholes should all be deep-seated, leaving the surface of the ingot sound and almost pure iron. This steel is used in the form of sheet steels that are to be subjected to severe forming operations, and where the very ductile and sound surface becomes a factor in fabricating operations.

Steel that is only partly deoxidized before casting, lies about halfway between killed and rimming steel, containing, as illustrated by the second ingot in Fig. 1, some blowholes and some piping. This steel is used in the manufacture of structural steels, such as plates, rail steel and forgings.

HOT WORKING. Hot working is mechanical deformation carried out above the temperature of recrystallization. Referring to Fig. 21, Chapter V, this would be a temperature range within the lower critical temperature and the solidus of the diagram. Hot working is carried out above the annealing temperature, so that the deformed metal becomes spontaneously annealed before cooling to room temperature and therefore has a normal grain structure with normal ductility and toughness. It is not possible to include within the scope of this book any lengthy discussion of the methods used, such as rolling mills, forging hammers, furnaces, fuels, quenching methods, etc., all of which are of prime importance. The greater part of the discussion here will deal merely with the general effects of the various operations. Some of the more common methods used in the hot shaping of metals include rolling, hammering, upsetting, pressing, extrusion and spinning.

HOT ROLLING. Rolling and forging serve the following two purposes: first, they serve the purely mechanical purpose of getting the steel into the desired shape; and second, but by no means of minor importance, they improve the mechanical properties by destroying the cast structure. This breaking up of the cast structure or "refining the grain" is important because it makes the steel stronger and more ductile and gives it greater shock resistance.

Where simple shapes are to be made in large quantity, rolling is the most economical process and is used for sheets, structural shapes, rails, etc., as well as for the production of intermediate shapes for wire drawing or forging. A set of rolls in a steel mill is shown in Fig. 3.

The process of shaping steel by rolling consists essentially of passing the material between two rolls revolving in opposite directions but at the same peripheral speed. The rolls are spaced so that the distance between them is somewhat less than the height of the section entering them. The rolls grip the piece of metal and deliver it reduced in section and increased in length in proportion to the reduction. The amount of reduction and the width of the piece will govern the amount of lateral spreading.

Rolling mills, although alike as to gross features, differ greatly as to details of construction. Rolling-mill engineers are constantly endeavoring to introduce new ideas looking to greater improvements in construction, beyond which it is often necessary to alter the details of mill construction to suit the conditions, local or otherwise. The result of all these influences on mill construction has been to produce a great variation in mills so that it is unusual to find two mills exactly alike.

To describe all the details of mills and their operation is beyond the scope of this book, so the author will present only a brief descrip-

Fig. 3. Typical Blooming Mill, Showing Reducing Rolls Mounted in Position

tion of the important features of such mills. The reader may gather more detailed information from any texts on the subject.

The rolls themselves may be either steel or cast iron, consisting of a body or barrel on which the rolling is done, the neck on which the roll revolves in the bearing, and a star-shaped coupling or **wobbler** through which the roll is driven. The body of the roll may be a simple cylinder for flat rolling, or it may be grooved if the piece is to be rolled to a definite shape. The diameters of rolls vary from a few inches up to five feet. The amount of reduction depends on the size and weight of the roll. Since very large rolls are expensive, "backed-up" rolls are sometimes used; that is, rolls of small diameters do the actual work, supported by heavy idlers which prevent working rolls from being bent by the tremendous pressure.

Rolls are driven by means of a hollow cylinder which fits over the wobbler of the roll on one end and over the driving shaft on the other. This method of driving gives a certain flexibility, and, if the rolls become stuck, the coupling breaks rather than the rolls.

Roll-mill stands are built with two-high, three-high, and four-high rolls. As the names indicate, the classification is based on the manner of arranging the rolls in the housings, a two-high stand consisting of two rolls, one above the other, and a three-high having three rolls thus arranged. In all three-high mills, as in Fig. 4, each roll revolves continuously in one direction only; whereas, in two-high mills the direction of the rolls may be in one direction or in opposite directions at different intervals, in which case they are called reversing mills.

Another kind of two-high mill is the continuous mill, which consists of several stands of rolls arranged in tandem. Quantity production is best achieved through the continuous type of rolling mill. Such a mill consists of a series of rolling mill stands, one behind the other, with the rolls of each successive mill stand driven at increasing speed. The metal is fed into the first pass or mill stand and then continues to the next roll stand by means of special guides. In this way, the metal passes from one mill stand to another until it reaches the finishing pass. This practice allows much faster rolling speeds; the metal may leave the last or finishing pass at a speed of 4,000 feet or more a minute.

In such a mill, where the piece is being rolled in several different stands at the same time, it is essential that the surface speeds of the different sets of rolls be proportioned so that each set will travel at a speed as much greater than the preceding one as the lengthening of the piece requires. This relation of speed of the different stands is provided by a system of driving gears. In order to compensate for the wearing down of the rolls, the bottom roll is made adjustable. Other irregularities that cannot be overcome by adjustment are cared for by having the rolls set to run at a slightly greater speed than

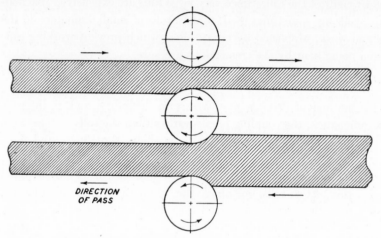

DIRECTION
OF PASS

Fig. 4. Illustrating the Principle of the Three-High Rolling Mill

that required to conform to the speed of the preceding set of rolls, thereby keeping the piece under tension at all times. Two chief advantages of this type of mill are high output and low labor costs. The necessity for a great number of rolls makes the initial cost of the mill very high. The mill is best adapted to roll large amounts of one section continuously. Complicated sections or those requiring great accuracy cannot be rolled on such a mill.

Steel is nearly always rolled hot except for finishing passes on sheet. Copper is also hot rolled to rod, for making wire. Brass and nickel silver are usually cold rolled with many intermediate annealings.

Such forms as structural parts, rails, plates, and sheets are rolled from ingots weighing from 3 to 20 tons. The ingots, with the exception of those used in making plates, are usually of a square cross section with rounded corners and are first rolled into blooms or billets. These blooms or billets are simply rectangular bars of steel which are to be reheated and rolled into the final shapes. A bloom differs from a billet only in size. It is larger and is sometimes reheated and rolled into billets. For making plates, ingots of rectangular cross section are used, in which one dimension is two or three times that of the other. Such ingots are rolled into slabs by passing through smooth rolls in such a manner that the ingot is flattened without reducing its width. Slabs are merely thick plates to be reheated and rolled into thinner plates. In the more modern rail mills, the finished rails are produced without any reheating after the rolling has begun.

In every hot rolling mill there are furnaces, known as soaking pits, which heat the steel for rolling. These pits are ordinarily heated with gas, often waste gases from the blast furnace or coke oven. The steel is heated to a temperature of from 1900° F. to 2250° F., depending upon the kind of steel being made. In making small quantities of tool steel or alloy steels, the ingots are allowed to cool before heating for rolling, but the large ingots are charged into the soaking pits as soon as possible after the mold has been removed. Inasmuch as the ingots are at a red heat when charged into the pits, it takes only one to two hours to bring them to the proper temperature for rolling. In heating for rolling, care must be taken to heat both the inside and the outside of the ingot to approximately the same temperature.

FORGING. Forging or hammering is the simplest method of reducing metal to the desired shape by deformation. The steam hammer is the principal type of hammer used for hot forging. The hammer, which may weigh from 0.5 to 30 tons, is fastened to the end of the piston rod and travels between guides. The piece to be forged rests on the anvil block, which is from 10 to 30 times as heavy as the hammer block and usually set in concrete. Hammers may be either single or double acting. That is, steam may be admitted below the piston to raise the hammer, which is allowed to fall by gravity when the lower port is opened, or steam may be admitted above the piston also, to increase the force of the blow. In any case the blow may be softened by throttling the exhaust of steam from below the piston.

The forging done by the hammer may be entirely similar to ordinary blacksmith forging, the piece being drawn, upset, shouldered, etc. Frequently, however, drop forging is employed. In drop forging, a piece of metal, roughly or approximately of the desired shape, is placed between die faces the exact form of the finished piece, and forced to take this form by drawing the die together. This method is used for automotive parts made both of steel and brass.

Large ingots are now almost always forged with hydraulic presses instead of with hammers, since the work done by a press goes deeper. Further, the press can take a cooler ingot and can work to closer dimensions.

Very large steel parts, such as naval gun barrels and oil distilling apparatus, are forged or pressed from large ingots. The forging should be done at about the same temperature as rolling; the process improves the physical properties of the steel just as rolling does. Small tool steel ingots are often forged, although rolling usually is the most economical method of reduction.

In addition to the forgings mentioned, many small articles are hand forged or drop forged from steel or wrought iron. In the final forging it is important not to have the steel too hot, for an overheated steel will have poor mechanical properties when cooled. In heating for forging, the temperature is usually judged by the eye, but where large numbers of the same pattern are being made, the pieces to be forged are heated in furnaces in which the temperature is indicated by pyrometers, and often is automatically controlled.

EXTRUSION. Some metals lend themselves to forming by pressing through an opening rather than by drawing or rolling. Lead and its alloys are best formed by extrusion. Brass rod usually is formed by this method also. It has the advantage over rolling in that it produces perfectly round rods, or rods of an intricate section, such as pinions. The metal to be extruded is placed in a closed chamber fitted with an opening at one end and a piston at the other end, and is forced out through the opening by hydraulic pressure.

The temperature and pressure required in extruding metals and alloys varies greatly. In general, the lower the melting point of the metal, the easier it will extrude at a given temperature. It should be understood, however, that extrusion is entirely a matter of solid flow and not of a plastic mass like partially molten solder. Lead can be satisfactorily extruded as pipe or cable sheath at 450° F., while brass requires around 1500° F.

MECHANICAL TREATMENT BY HOT WORKING. Although the primary object of hot working of steel or other alloys is to shape them into useful articles, the working of the metals by hot plastic deformation into different shapes also constitutes a mechanical treatment. This treatment deeply affects the structure and, therefore, the physical properties of the metals, as illustrated in Fig. 5 to Fig. 8. Some of the resulting changes of internal structure are:

1. Refinement of grain
2. Better distribution of constituents
3. Development of fiber
4. Improvement of soundness

GRAIN REFINEMENT. If we can cause the grain structure of a given metal to form a new set of crystals, and at the same time prevent any marked growth of the newly formed grains, we can materially refine the grain or crystal structure of a metal such as steel. We refer to this formation of new crystals from old as "recrystallization." The practical way in which to bring about recrystallization and refinement of grain structure is by means of plastic deformation. Plastic deformation resulting from forging, rolling, and other operations will cause spontaneous recrystallization if the temperature of the metal is above the lowest temperature of recrystallization. The temperature of recrystallization is affected by the chemistry of the metal and by the amount of plastic deformation. If hot working is carried out at relatively low temperatures, and at such a rate of deformation that little time is allowed for recrystallization, the structure resulting will be more or less like that of cold-worked metal, and the metal will become work-hardened. However, at relatively high temperatures recrystallization is very rapid, and sudden quenching of the deformed metal from the forging temperature will not prevent recrystallization and some grain growth. Large grain size produced by a high finishing temperature and very slow cooling, results in soft, weak metal. Factors which influence the grain size obtained from hot deformation are:

1. Initial grain size
2. Amount of deformation
3. Finishing temperature
4. Rate of cooling

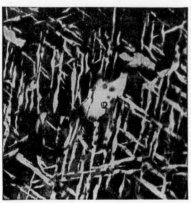

Fig. 5. Microstructure of Steel 0.30% to 0.35% Carbon. As-Cast Ingot Condition. White, Ferrite; Dark, Pearlitic Structure; Magnified 100 Times. Coarse, Weak Grain Structure

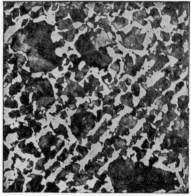

Fig. 6. Same Steel as Fig. 5; Magnified 100 Times. Section of Drop-Forged Aircraft Forging; Unsatisfactory Microstructure Due to Coarse and Banded Grain Structure

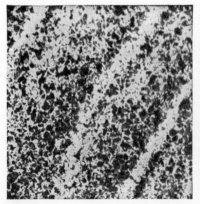

Fig. 7. Same Steel as in Fig. 5; Magnified 100 Times. Aircraft Drop Forging; Unsatisfactory Microstructure Due to Banded Grain Structure

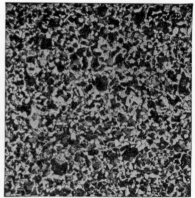

Fig. 8. Same Steel as in Fig. 5. Aircraft Drop Forging; Desirable Microstructure. Magnified 100 Times

IMPROVEMENT OF UNIFORMITY. The lack of uniformity, or segregation, found in an ingot is little altered, owing to the distance the segregated particles would have to diffuse to improve this condition. However, dendritic segregation (crystal segregation producing cored crystals) is improved by hot working. The plastic deformation breaks up the segregated shell of impurities surrounding the grains and acts as an aid to diffusion of the different elements. This diffusion never is completed, and the different segregated areas become elongated into long thin fibers, or a banded type of structure. This banded structure is called the **fiber** of the forging and produces directional properties. The slag particles and other insoluble materials are rolled out into fibers, forming weak planes where splitting may occur. This fibrous type of structure, shown in Fig. 22, Chapter I, is found in all plastically shaped steel.

Hot working, if properly carried out, will further improve metals by increasing the density, forcing the structural particles into more intimate contact, and closing up blowholes and other cavities; welding may occur if conditions are favorable.

COLD WORKING. That it is possible to shape common metals by working at ordinary temperatures was perhaps discovered about the same time as the discovery of metals. Ancients made use of cold working in shaping and in hardening their metals. The process of hammering was used first; rolling and drawing were developed later.

COLD ROLLING. Cold rolling is used largely to produce a finish for hot-rolled metals. It imparts a bright, smooth surface, insures accuracy in dimensions, and appreciably increases the tensile strength of the finished product. Cold rolling is used in the production of sheets, strip steel, bar-stock such as shaftings, flat wire, etc. Most hot-rolled material is cleaned before it enters the cold rolling mill. The cleaning operation usually involves a dip of the hot-rolled product into an acid cleaning solution. Steel is cleaned in a hot solution of sulphuric acid in water. The principal action of the cleaning operation is the removal of surface scale. The process is called pickling.

After pickling, the metal is thoroughly rinsed with water to remove the acid. After this it often is dipped into a hot solution of lime and water; when this is allowed to dry, it forms a protective film on the stock.

Cold rolling, like hot rolling, may be carried out on a two-high or a four-high rolling mill, or in a continuous rolling mill. Cold rolling is continued until the rolled section becomes too hard to continue the process, or until it reaches its final size. It may become necessary to anneal the metal after several passes through the cold-rolling mill, in order to keep it in workable condition. If annealing is carried out in open furnaces, pickling again is necessary, before re-rolling, to remove the scale and clean the metal. Today annealing of cold-rolled products usually is carried out in specially designed furnaces that complete the annealing without the formation of surface scale, or even discoloration.

PRESSED METAL. Metal in the form of cold-rolled or hot-rolled sheets or strip (narrow sheets) may be formed into many intricate shapes by forcing the sheet stock into impressions in metal dies. This process is known as stamping, or pressing, or cold forging of metals, and involves many different operations, such as bending, drawing, flanging, upsetting, punching, blanking, extruding, spinning ironing, etc. These operations are successfully carried out through proper die design, and proper operation of the press in which the dies are placed. Flat stock of steel, brass, copper, aluminum, or other metal is placed between dies, and the slow action of a power press brings the dies together, forcing the metal to assume the required shape.

The process has innumerable advantages. Many shapes may be manufactured in quantities at a rapid rate and at comparatively low cost. With the proper die design, each forging is made uniform in shape and to remarkably close size if required. Few people realize the extent of metal stamping, which produces a wealth of goods, from the insignificant collar button to the pressed steel freight car. Design engineers have made use of this process to speed up production and to insure a better quality product. The modern automobile and the airplane, most of our household appliances, tools for our home workshop, and many other articles are produced by this method of shaping metals. The only real competitors for pressed metal are the molded nonmetal plastics that are coming into favor.

DRAWING. This is the operation of reducing the cross section and increasing the length of a metal bar or wire by drawing it through a succession of conical tapering holes in a die plate, each hole a little smaller than the preceding one. Large pieces are drawn through a single die at a time on a drawbench, which is merely a device for holding the draw plate or die, with a clamp to grasp the pointed end of the rod or bar. The clamp is then drawn forward by means of a chain working on a sprocket or by means of a cable around a capstan. Die materials are: steel, chilled cast iron, tungsten carbide and diamond. Tallow is used as a lubricant. Shapes varying in size from the finest wire to those having a cross-sectional area of several square inches are commonly drawn. Due to the difficulty of making dies and the small demand for any other form, the finer sizes are drawn only to a round cross section; the larger sizes may be drawn to square, round, or irregular cross sections. The larger sections are drawn on a "drawbench." Metals can be formed to much closer dimensions by drawing than they can by rolling, and for this reason large quantities of steel and brass are cold drawn.

With wire, multiple die machines are often used. In these machines the wire passes through one die, around a capstan, through a second die and around another capstan, etc. As many as twelve dies may be used in a machine. After going through each die, the wire, of course, is greatly elongated. Thus the size of the capstans must be graduated and, even so, provision must be made for the wire to slip on the capstans, to make up for die wear and resulting change in length.

The speed of drawing in multiple die machines may reach 10,000 feet per minute on fine wire. The die or drag plate, as it is often called, may be made of a number of materials, ranging from diamond, tungsten carbide, and steel to chilled cast iron. Tungsten carbide has largely replaced other die materials because of its greater ability to retain its shape during the drawing operations.

Many shapes of tubing, bars, etc., as well as wire, may be produced by this process. Cold-drawing is used in manufacturing seamless tubing when a thin wall and very accurate finish are needed. Tubing is cold-drawn through a ring-shaped die, with a mandrel inside the tubing. This forces the metal to flow between the die and the mandrel, and in this way the wall thickness, the outside diameter, and the inside diameter may be controlled. As in any cold working operation, the metal should be free from scale and other defects before it is cold drawn.

As has already been explained, when metal is at room temperature it may be deformed permanently by the plastic flow behavior of the metal. The metallic crystals elongate by a process of shearing on weak planes called "slip" planes. If a metal is sufficiently cold worked, all the available slip planes will be used up and further deformation will produce failure by rupture. Therefore, in shaping metals cold, plastic deformation must not be carried beyond a certain point or cracking is likely to result.

Fig. 9. Photomicrograph of a .60% to .70% Carbon Steel in the Form of Hard-Drawn Wire. Magnified 100 Times

Cold-working operations may be divided into two broad classes:

1. Where the cold working is carried out for the purpose of shaping the articles only; and where the hardening effect is not desired and must be removed at various stages of plastic shaping as well as from the finished article by annealing.

2. Where the object of cold working is not only to obtain the required shape but to harden and strengthen the metal, and where the final annealing operation is omitted. High strength wire for suspension cables, Fig. 9, is obtained in this way.

In order to shape metals by cold working, they must be annealed at proper intervals. Otherwise deformation must be carried out at temperatures where annealing is simultaneous with hardening, as in hot working of metals. The method adopted will depend on the individual metal, as well as on the desired product. Metals vary greatly in the ease with which they deform. Copper, for example, may be worked readily at room temperature, whereas some steels can only be worked at a red heat. Practically all metals and alloys become brittle very near their melting point and hence must not be worked at too high temperatures. There are metals that can be worked only in certain temperature ranges without cracking. Thus zinc must be worked at 200° to 300° F.; nearly pure iron must not be worked in the blue heat range; and leaded brass must not be worked outside of certain temperature ranges which depend on the composition. Brass must not be heated too near its melting point in annealing, also, or it becomes "burnt" due to volatilization of zinc.

OVERWORKED METAL. After a metal has been subjected to severe cold-working operations, further cold deformation may cause a decrease in its strength. When this occurs, the metal is said to be overworked. This loss of strength is usually due to failure of the internal structure of the metal, such as shearing apart or splitting. Normally, the strength increases as the cold working progresses, and continues as long as the continuity of the metal is maintained.

CORROSION AND COLD WORK. The corrosion rate of metals is accelerated by cold working, particularly if such cold deformation is localized; for example, when strained metal comes in contact with unstrained, the strained metal is more subject to corrosion. The action of chemicals upon strained and unstrained metals is different.

DEFORMATION OF AGGREGATES. Steel and many other alloys are structurally composed of mixed crystals having different chemical and physical characteristics. The weak, ductile constituents deform readily. The stronger and less plastic constituents resist deformation, but ultimately, if the deformation is severe enough, the harder constituents are also deformed, either by plastic flow or by rupture, that is, by breaking up into smaller parts and flowing with the more plastic and weaker constituents. Many alloys in the cast state are rather weak and brittle, but in hot working, the brittle constituents surrounding the more ductile grains are broken up and are enveloped in a ductile phase, and the metal can be worked drastically.

Several authorities maintain that cold working breaks up brittle constituents even more effectively than hot working, and that with the plastic constituents welding the internal structure together even when working at below the annealing temperature, the structure remains sound. Cold working with annealing can be considered as a means of developing marked plasticity in metals that are structurally composed of an aggregate of plastic and brittle constituents.

WELDING. This constitutes one of the most important procedures for the assembly of metal parts. Through the process of welding, simple, easily-made metal parts are joined together to form very complicated structures like the modern automobile, ships, buildings, and machinery. Welding of metals may be defined as "crystallizing into union." The characteristic crystal formations of the metallic state are the basis for this practice. Welding together of two metal parts may be accomplished either by fusion, that is, by melting and solidification of metals, or by pressure. In pressure welding, it is recrystallization and crystal growth that account for the possibility of welding together without the aid of fusion. During the forging together of the metal parts at a high temperature, the process of recrystallization and grain growth causes the crystals to grow into one another, making possible the union of the metal parts without melting taking place. Any oxide film or dirt will interfere with the joining of the metal parts through crystal growth, so in pressure welding care must be taken to eliminate this barrier. Oxides may be removed either by chemical or mechanical methods. In making a hammered weld, the oxide, which is in a molten state during the welding operation, is forced out from between the two surfaces by the pressure of the blow. Oxides are less apt to interfere during the practice of fusion welding because they are likely to be floated out of the weld metal and to form on top of the weld as a slag covering.

Many dissimilar metals may be joined together by welding. Also many different methods may be used. Table 1 outlines many of the principal methods employed in welding.

Table 1. Principal Welding Processes

Fusion Welding (No pressure required—Metal Fused)			Pressure Welding (Pressure required—with or without fusion)		
Blowtorch Welding	Arc Welding	Thermit Welding	Forge Welding	Resistance Welding	Thermit Welding
Oxy-Acetylene	Carbon Arc	Molding and Casting Process	Blacksmith Welding	Spot Welding	Temperature of Weld Metal not to exceed beginning of fusion
Oxy-Hydrogen	Bare Metallic Arc		Power Hammer Welding	Projection Welding	
Other Gas Combinations	Coated Metallic Arc		Roll Welding	Seam Welding	
	Covered Metallic Arc			Butt Welding	
	Atomic Hydrogen Arc			Slow Upset Method Flash Method	

QUIZ QUESTIONS

1. What is an ingot casting?
2. Of what material is the pattern for a casting made?
3. Describe the process of die casting. Name the advantage of this method.
4. Of what material is the ordinary mold for a casting made?
5. Why is lead sometimes added to brass and bronze when casting?
6. What is the nature of defects called "pipes" and how may they be avoided?
7. What effect does the cold iron mold have upon the grain structure of a cast ingot?
8. What becomes of surface blowholes when the ingot is hot rolled?
9. What is the cause of segregation in an ingot?
10. What is meant by hot-working?
11. What two purposes are served by hot rolling?
12. In the rolling operation, what are "blooms" and "billets"?
13. What are slabs?
14. About how long does it take to heat an ingot for rolling?
15. Describe the process of forging.
16. Describe the process of drop forging.
17. Describe the process of extrusion.
18. Name four improvements resulting from mechanical treatment by hot working.
19. What is the purpose in cold rolling?
20. What is meant by pickling?
21. Describe the process of making pressed metal.
22. Describe the process of drawing wire.
23. What are the two classes of work given cold-working operations?
24. Metals must not be worked at temperatures which are too high. Why?
25. What means are used to develop plasticity in metals?
26. What methods of welding are related to fusion welding? What methods of welding are related to pressure welding?

This huge, newly installed press has been designed to turn out the larger-type bearings.
Courtesy of Chrysler Corporation

CHAPTER VII

Bearing Metals

WE ARE now living in the Alloy Age and we may wonder at the many kinds and varieties of metals and alloys employed by industry. We soon discover that the reasons for the great variety of metals and alloys used are not difficult to find. Each has gained its commercial status because it meets certain requirements better than some other metal, or because its use provides some special satisfaction to human needs. In many cases, availability and economy dictate the selection of the metal or alloy for some specific use. Steel is used in rails, tungsten in lamp filaments; with economy the main factor in their selection, these metals have no competition. Just because a metal is higher priced than some other is no economic reason to bar its use. Because of the large number of alloys that have been made and placed on the market, the engineer may make a selection from a great variety of alloys exhibiting combinations of properties that a few years ago were only wishful thinking. It may seem to the student of metallurgy that too many combinations are already available, but the engineer is always demanding new alloys, as yet undiscovered, that will exhibit properties now unavailable. A large number of the engineers' present inventions cannot economically be used until such time as alloys with combinations of properties needed for these new practices are made available.

BEARING METALS. Selection of a satisfactory bearing material is one of the major problems encountered in the design and construction of machinery, engines, or any part of a piece of equipment that requires motion of rotation or reciprocation. Many different materials may be chosen for use as the bearing surfaces of any moving part. The selection of any one type of metal or alloy will depend upon several factors, and the final selection may be determined by the trial and error method. In many designs, roller and ball bearings are chosen where a minimum of frictional resistance is needed and where high bearing pressures are encountered. In the solution of bearing problems, the engineer has frequently depended upon the selection of a suitable metal or alloy to be used as the bearing, with the hope that the metal selected would exhibit low frictional characteristics without any tendency to weld or seize when the bearing surfaces came into contact with each other. In most applications of metal bearing surfaces, the engineer depends upon a film of oil acting as a lubricating film to prevent welding, or seizure, and excessive wear. Theoretically, the type of metal or alloy that is chosen for the bearing surfaces should be of no consequence if a proper film of lubrication is maintained at all times between the bearing surfaces, thus preventing any metal-to-metal contact. However, there are times when there is an insufficient lubricating film present between the metal surfaces in any bearing, and a metal-to-metal contact occurs. It is then that the bearing metal should behave satisfactorily without seizure or burning out or excessive wear.

A number of metals and alloys, mostly of the white metal group, such as cadmium, lead, zinc, etc., are used as bearings of the flood-lubricated type. Bearing metals have received much attention from engineers, chemists, and metallurgists during the past few years, and as a result of diversity of viewpoints and interests, much literature covering bearing metals is available. The properties of a good bearing metal should include:

1. High compressive strength. This is essential if the bearing is not to squeeze out under high compressive loads. The compressive strength should be high enough to support the load.

2. Plasticity. It must be sufficiently plastic to allow the bearing to deform in order to take care of misalignment; it also enables bearings to withstand shocks without cracking. If a bearing is finished to a high degree of dimensional accuracy and properly installed, a harder, stronger, and less plastic metal bearing alloy may be used.

3. Low coefficient of friction. The bearing metal of lowest coefficient of friction is not necessarily the best, as other factors affect behavior and may have more obvious effects. The frictional properties of a perfectly lubricated bearing would be of no account; however, this condition is not attainable in practice. Some contact or rubbing of metal to metal takes place, and due to this a low frictional characteristic is desirable. In general, the harder the bearing metal, the lower the frictional characteristics.

4. *Long life.* Life of a bearing metal is largely a matter of resistance to wear, and this will depend upon the composition and hardness of the metal. In general, the bearing should be selected so that it will wear, rather than the shaft material. If a hard bearing metal is selected to increase the resistance to wear, it has the disadvantage that if there is any tendency to heat, it will heat more rapidly and consequently wear more rapidly.

5. *High heat conductivity.* Good thermal conductivity allows the rapid dissipation of heat generated and prevents the bearing metal from becoming overheated. Good contact between the bearing metal and the backing used to support the bearing is essential to insure good heat transfer. A good contact or adherence is often obtained by casting the bearing metal into contact with the backing. Testing the bond strength between the bearing metal and the backing is a good way to determine the efficiency of the bond.

6. *Heat resistance.* A bearing metal should maintain its compressive strength and hardness in the temperature range within which it may be expected to operate.

Besides these properties, a good bearing metal should have good casting properties and be easily workable. From this it should be clearly seen that bearing metals must meet varied requirements. They must be hard to resist wear, yet soft so that the bearing will wear rather than the shaft or spindle; tough and strong, so as to avoid failure by deformation or fracture, yet plastic and compressible so as to allow the bearing metal to conform to any slight misalignment or inaccuracy in dimensions or fit. It is apparent that no commercially pure metal, or even homogeneous alloy, can successfully meet all of these requirements. As a result, practically all bearing metals are made up of several structural crystal constituents. The more common bearing metals have a strong and plastic background or matrix in which is dispersed one or more hard constituents. It may be assumed that the strong matrix allows plastic flow for the adjustments of fitting and prevents failure under shock loading. The hard crystals dispersed throughout this background add some strength, but largely increase the resistance to wear. It has been stated that there is an advantage in having the hardest component in the bearing metal the same or at least not any harder than the shaft or journal, so that mutual polishing rather than abrasion will take place.

Lead-Base Bearing Metals. Lead has some of the properties desired in a bearing metal, but due to its low strength, alloying of the lead with some hardener metal, such as copper, tin, antimony, calcium, etc., is often practiced. Members of one group of lead-base bearing alloys contain approximately 60% lead, the other 40% being made up of tin and antimony, with a little copper in certain of the mixtures. The structure of these alloys contains a matrix of a eutectic nature with hard crystals of an intermetallic compound embedded in the eutectic matrix. Lead-base bearing metal is the cheapest of all the white bearing alloys.

Other uses for these alloys of lead, tin, and antimony include solder, type metal, sheathing for telephone cables, and storage battery grids. In fact, due to the large tonnage of lead used in batteries and paint, lead may be referred to as a chemical metal rather than a structural metal.

Tin-Base Bearing Metals. The tin-base bearing metals are called Babbitt metal. A common alloy of this class contains 85% tin, 10% antimony, and 5% copper. Copper and antimony are essential alloys in these tin-base bearing metals. A typical structure found in these alloys is seen in Fig. 1, which consists mostly of a dark eutectic matrix containing embedded needle-like crystals of $CuSn$ and cube-like crystals of $SbSn$. The hard crystals of $CuSn$ and $SbSn$ increase the hardness and wear resistance of the alloy. The physical properties of the tin-base alloys are superior to the lead-base alloys, having higher values for strength and hardness, and they are lighter. The lead-base alloys have a compressive strength of 13,000 to 15,000 lbs. per sq. in., with a Brinell hardness of 15 to 20 Brinell; while the tin-base alloys, as a class, have equal or greater strength, with an elastic limit two to three times as high and a greater Brinell hardness.

Lead-Calcium Bearing Alloys. This alloy was a World War I discovery by Francis C. Frary. When hard lead was wanted and it was found that there was a shortage of antimony as a hardener for shrapnel, Frary secured patents covering lead-base alloys, with barium and calcium as hardeners, that proved very successful. Out of this discovery a new alloy was created for bearings, containing a total of 2.5% calcium, tin, and other hardeners, and having an unusually high strength at temperatures near its melting point; consequently it is favored for high-speed gas engines. The structure of these alloys contains crystals of Pb_3Ca dispersed throughout a matrix or ground mass of tin and calcium in solid solution in the lead. This structure conforms to the usual structure of bearing metals.

Fig. 1. Babbitt Bearing Alloy. Magnified 100 Times (Dark Matrix Is Mostly Eutectic Structure; White Needle-like Crystals are CuSn Crystals; White Cube-like Crystals are SbSn Crystals)

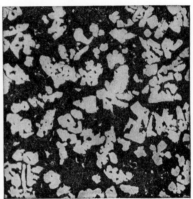

Fig. 2. Cadmium-Nickel Bearing Alloy. Magnified 100 Times (Dark Matrix Is a Eutectic Structure; White Crystals are NiCd$_7$ Crystals)

Cadmium Bearing Alloys. A very popular bearing alloy consisting of 1.25 to 1.50% nickel, the balance cadmium, has been used very successfully as a flood-lubricated bearing metal. The structure of this alloy is shown in Fig. 2 and the alloy diagram, Fig. 3. The cadmium-nickel alloy has been found to have a higher melting point than the Babbitt metals, with its properties less affected by temperature; in fact, these alloys are operative at temperatures that would melt the Babbitts. Although the alloy diagram of the cadmium-nickel system, Fig. 3, may not show accurately the complete behavior of the two metals, it will serve to illustrate the influence of nickel in forming a eutectic mixture when 0.25% nickel has been added to cadmium. It also shows the formation of an intermetallic compound with the chemical formula $NiCd_7$. The solid solubility of nickel in cadmium is practically zero. The eutectic mixture solidifies at 318° C. and consists of nearly pure cadmium and crystals of the compound $NiCd_7$. The common bearing alloy of 1.25% to 1.50% nickel and the balance cadmium, consists structurally of a matrix of the eutectic structure with an excess of free cube-like crystals of the compound

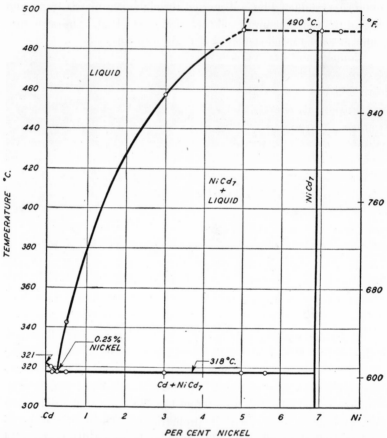

Fig. 3. Constitutional Diagram of the Cadmium-Rich End of the Cadmium-Nickel System

$NiCd_7$, shown in Fig. 2. The $NiCd_7$ compound is harder than the compound found in the tin-antimony-babbitt bearing alloys, but the eutectic matrix is slightly softer than that of the babbitt alloys.

Other cadmium bearing alloys contain silver, copper, and indium. Silver is said to improve casting characteristics and to increase strength, while indium is used to combat the corrosive action of some lubricating oils.

Bearings of the following composition have been successfully used in several makes of American automobiles: 97% cadmium, together with 2.25% silver, and 0.75% copper. The structure of cadmium-silver-copper alloy is composed of a solid solution matrix with small quantities of embedded crystals of a harder intermetallic compound formed by the copper.

Copper-Lead Bearing Alloys. Bearing alloys of copper-tin-lead or copper-lead have been successfully used when heavy compressive loads and high temperatures are encountered, such as in connecting-rod bearings in aircraft and automotive truck engines, rolling-mill bearings, and railroad service. The lead and copper form a mechanical mixture during the solidification process, inasmuch as copper has very little or no solid solubility for the lead. The cast copper-lead alloy consists of lead freezing in particles throughout the matrix of copper. The addition of the lead to the copper increases the plasticity of the bearing metal and lowers the coefficient of friction, thus improving copper as a bearing metal. The lead weakens the metal but acts as a self-lubricant. A representative structure is illustrated in Fig. 4, which shows a copper-lead alloy polished, the lead appearing dark and the copper, light. Fig. 5 shows the same alloy etched. The lead in these photomicrographs has largely eroded during the polishing operation, which accounts for the dark areas in these specimens. In the casting of bearings of copper-lead alloys, the lead is apt to segregate into large particles in certain areas of the bearing, and the alloy may form two layers, one copper, one lead. Such segregation may seriously impair the physical properties of the bearing alloy. Stirring of the molten alloy and rapid cooling during the casting operation serve to minimize this tendency to segregate. Also, the addition of nickel to the alloy seems to act as an aid in further reducing this tendency to segregate. A common binary alloy containing 25% to 36% lead and the balance copper gives satisfactory service results. Aircraft engine bearings have been made from an alloy containing 72% copper, 25% lead, and 3% tin, with or without the addition of silver.

Bearings made from copper-lead alloys have less plasticity and greater frictional properties than the tin or cadmium base alloys and therefore require more accurate sizing and assemblies. A clearance between bearing surfaces of about twice that of the Babbitt metals is required, as well as special high-grade lubricants.

Composite Bearings. Bearings to be used at high speeds and for heavy loads are often manufactured by the casting or plating of a suitable bearing metal to a hard steel or bronze supporting backing or shell. The steel or bronze backing shell is lined with the bearing metal. The thickness of this lining of bearing metal may vary from 0.060 inches to less than 0.0025 inches. The hard steel or bronze

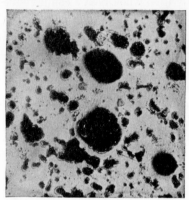

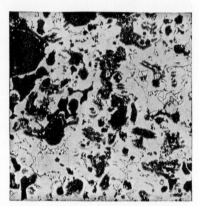

Fig. 4. Copper-Lead Alloy, Polished Section, Magnified 100 Times. Dark Areas Represent Lead

Fig. 5. Copper-Lead Alloy, Polished and Etched, Magnified 100 Times. Dark Areas Represent Lead; Light Areas Are the Copper

backing or shell serves to improve greatly the mechanical properties of the bearing. Several methods may be used to cast or attach the bearing metal to the backing, such as die casting, permanent mold casting, centrifugal casting, or electro-plating. A steel or bronze cylindrical or semicylindrical shell or strip may be used for the backing. If a cylindrical or semi-cylindrical shell is used, the bearing metal may be cast to the shell by the centrifugal casting method, whereas steel strips may have babbitt or copper-lead alloys welded to them by moving a strip of the steel horizontally through the continuous casting machine. If the bearing metal is to be added to both sides of the steel strip, a vertical casting machine method may be employed. The final bearing may be made from the lined strip by cutting off short sections and then bending or forming them to the desired shape.

One of the problems encountered in the manufacturing of a composite bearing by these methods is the problem of obtaining a good bond between the steel or bronze backing and the bearing metal. Controlling the structure of the cast bearing metal is an important factor influencing the characteristics of the bearing metal.

Zinc-Base Bearing Alloys. Zinc-base bearings of the following composition have been successfully used where the surface speeds are high and there is no shock loading or excessive vibration: 85% zinc, 10% copper, and 5% aluminum. Alloy of this composition has a hardness of approximately 130 Brinell and compares favorably with some of the copper-base bearing metals. Some zinc-alloy die castings can be made from a similar composition and require no additional bearing alloy in their finished assembly. Some applications for these bearing alloys include lathe and machine tool spindle bearings and electric motor bearings.

Porous Self-lubricating Bearings. A relatively new type of bearing material which is now available consists of a porous bronze alloy made by the pressed powdered metals method known as **powder metallurgy.** Powdered copper and tin, or powdered tin and bronze are mixed with graphite, and the cold mixture is partially welded together by means of pressure. The pressure welding is accomplished in a steel die or mold which forms the powdered metal into the shape required. The cold welded shape is then removed from the steel die or mold and placed in a furnace and heated to a temperature which further welds the pressed metal powder to form a solid. Accurate control of the density or porosity of the finished bearing is effected by controlling the pressure used in the cold welding operation and the temperature to which the pressed bearing is heated. The heating of the pressed metal powder is a sort of annealing operation which is called **sintering.** If coarse metal powders are used and little pressure and low temperatures are employed, a porous bearing metal results. Porous bearing alloys are capable of absorbing substantial amounts of oil, which is held in the pores of the bearing metal until pressure causes it to flow out to the surfaces of the bearing, thus making it a self-lubricating bearing. Oil may be added to the porous bearing alloy from any outside surface, the oil working through the spongy metal as needed. These porous bearings have many applications and fill a real need in those applications where lubrication is difficult to accomplish or where very little lubrication can be used.

Silver-Lead-Indium Bearings. A bearing alloy now widely used in aircraft engines and in other applications where a heavy-duty bearing metal is needed is the relatively new silver-lead-indium bearing alloy. This bearing alloy consists of a steel shell to which a coating of copper is electroplated. This copper layer is not a part of the bearing but merely assists in binding the steel to the silver layer which follows. This steel shell, with the thin copper surface, is then plated with about 0.02 to 0.03 inch of silver. The bearing may then be machined to size, allowing for the additional thickness of the succeeding deposits of layers of lead and indium.

The machined silver surfaces are then slightly roughened by a light sandblasting, and a thin layer of lead is deposited over the silver to a thickness of about 0.001 inch by electroplating. This plated layer can be controlled as to thickness so as to avoid any further machining operations. The indium is now plated to the lead surface with a flash plating of only a few hundred-thousandths of an inch. The indium, which alloys readily with the lead and has a melting point of 311° F., is diffused into the lead by heating the bearing to 350° F. in an oil bath. The primary role of the indium is to reduce the corrosive action that lubricants would have on the unprotected lead surface for indium is more corrosive resistant than either lead or silver.

Other Bearing Alloys. Included under the heading of bearing metals are aluminum alloys and cast iron. Some discussion of these alloys will be found in sections of this text dealing with these metals.

QUIZ QUESTIONS

1. Name some of the factors that may dictate the selection of a certain metal for a job.

2. Why is high compressive strength necessary to a bearing metal?

3. Why is plasticity important in a bearing metal?

4. Why is a low coefficient of friction desirable in a bearing metal?

5. Discuss the length of life of a bearing.

6. Why is high heat conductivity important in bearings?

7. Sum up the characteristics of a good bearing metal.

8. Why is it important to have good contact between bearing metal and its backing?

9. What is the advantage in having the hardest component in the bearing metal of the same hardness as the metal in the shaft or journal?

10. *Name several uses of the lead-base alloys.*

11. *What peculiar property of lead-calcium alloys makes them suitable for use on high-speed gas engines?*

12. *In what respect are cadmium alloys superior to Babbitt metal for bearings?*

13. *How does silver improve the cadmium bearing alloys?*

14. *What type of bearing alloys is used when heavy compressive loads and high temperatures are encountered?*

15. *Describe what steps are taken to prevent segregation of lead in the copper-lead bearing alloys.*

16. *Describe briefly composite bearings.*

17. *Name some of the applications for zinc-base bearings.*

18. *How are porous self-lubricating bearings made?*

19. *In what applications do porous bearings fill a real need?*

20. *Describe the widely used silver-lead-indium bearing.*

21. *What is the primary role of indium in the silver-lead-indium bearings?*

A variety of machine parts made up to 200 times faster than standard methods from a wide variety of metal powders. Note the intricate shape and design of many of the parts, most of which are made complete without requiring machining.

Courtesy of Chrysler Corporation

CHAPTER VIII

Light Metals and Alloys

ALUMINUM ALLOYS. Aluminum was discovered in 1825, and introduced for the first time in 1852 at a price of $545 a pound. As stated in a previous chapter, through the efforts and success of Charles M. Hall and Paul L. T. Héroult, the production of aluminum in large quantities and within a fairly reasonable price range was accomplished. Mr. Hall working in the United States, and M. Héroult working in France, made the same discovery and succeeded in developing identical processes for making aluminum cheaply. This was remarkable when we consider that the production of aluminum evaded man for hundreds of years.

Aluminum is one of our foremost industrial metals and can be manufactured nearly pure, ranging from 99.5 to 99.9% aluminum. Nearly pure aluminum may be used in the following applications: to deoxidize steel, in the Thermit mixture used in welding and in incendiary bombs, cooking and chemical apparatus, in the form of wire as an electrical conductor, as a pigment in paint, aluminum foil, welded to high-strength aluminum alloys as a covering, as fuel tanks for aircraft, etc. However, over 50% of the aluminum produced is used in the alloy form, making a series of alloys with much higher physical properties than those found in pure aluminum.

Properties of Aluminum. Aluminum is a very soft and ductile metal with a tensile strength from 9,000 lbs. per sq. in. in a single crystal form, to 24,000 lbs. per sq. in. in the fully work-hardened condition. Its excellent ductility and malleability allow the rolling of aluminum into thin sheets and foil, and the drawing of aluminum into wire. Hardness of aluminum varies from 25 Brinell in the annealed condition, to 40 Brinell in the fully work-hardened state. Good electrical conductivity is one of its most valuable properties, being 60% that of copper and 3.5 times that of iron.

Aluminum has nearly five times the thermal conductivity of cast iron, and, due to its high reflectivity and low radiating power, aluminum is useful in the field of insulation. Aluminum has very good resistance to corrosion by weathering. The aluminum ornamental spire on the Washington Monument, Washington, D. C., has successfully withstood many years of weathering. Aluminum's resistance to corrosion is largely due to the formation of a superficial film of aluminum oxide (Al_2O_3), which acts as a natural paint job in preventing any further attack by weathering.

Aluminum can be successfully welded by the blowtorch, electric resistance, and electric arc methods. The soldering of aluminum is difficult and not recommended.

Aluminum forms its own protective coating of oxide to resist corrosion, but the alloys of aluminum are less effectively protected by the natural oxide coating or film that forms on their exposed surfaces. Therefore, many of the aluminum alloys are specially treated in order to increase their corrosion resistance for many types of service.

Alclad. In order that the corrosion of aluminum alloys, particularly in the aircraft field, be reduced to a minimum, a patented product called **Alclad** has been developed. Alclad is made by coating an aluminum alloy ingot with high purity aluminum and reducing the duplex ingot by rolling and shaping to the desired dimensions. The bond of high purity aluminum has proved very efficient, and the protection offered by the coating is very good even at the edges where the coating, being electronegative, protects the exposed edges by galvanic action. Aircraft sheets, for example, made from strong wrought alloys such as 17S and 24S are coated on both sides with a thin layer of pure aluminum.

Anodic Treatment. Anodic oxidation methods are now available by which an oxide coating is artificially built up on the surfaces of aluminum alloys for increasing their resistance to corrosion. The part to be treated is made the anode of a cell whose electrolyte may contain chromic acid, sulphuric acid, a nitride, or some other oxidizing agent. The anodic coating is only somewhat resistant to abrasion but does improve the corrosion resistance. In most cases, the coating is somewhat porous, thus producing a suitable surface for paints or dyes and further protection against corrosion.

Electroplating methods are also available, and in most cases are used where an improvement in wear resistance is desired. Electrodeposits of zinc, chromium, and nickel have been successfully produced.

Machining of Light Metals. In general, the light alloys of aluminum and magnesium are easy to machine and offer no real difficulties. Factors that reduce the machinability of these alloys are greater plasticity and high thermal expansion. The softer grades of these alloys, with their greater plasticity, are more difficult to machine than the harder alloys. Magnesium alloys with their lower plasticity, as compared with the aluminum alloys, are more easily machined. In general, satisfactory machinability of the light alloys requires special cutting tools, such tools having greater rake and clearance angles than steel-cutting tools and made sharper by grinding and polishing to a smoother finish. Lubricants of kerosene and mixtures of kerosene and lard oil are used with the machining of aluminum alloys, whereas magnesium alloys may be satisfactorily machined without lubricants, using sharp tools and high machining speeds.

A free-cutting aluminum alloy has been developed containing 5.5% copper, 0.5% lead, and 0.5% bismuth, desirable because it develops a heterogeneous structure containing lead and bismuth inclusions. The free lead and bismuth aid in the machining similar to the action of lead in free-cutting brass, by acting as chip breakers and thus producing fine chips.

Aluminum alloys may be classified into two groups: (1) casting alloys and (2) forging alloys. Table 1 lists some of the more important compositions of aluminum alloys of each group.

Casting Alloys. Aluminum is alloyed for casting for two main reasons: (1) to improve strength and (2) to improve casting properties. Because most of the elements alloyed with aluminum increase the strength and hardness of the resultant alloy, the added element is called a *hardener*. These hardeners may be added to the aluminum in the melting furnace, or added to the ladle of molten aluminum. The final casting may be made by pouring or casting the molten metal into a sand mold and allowing the metal to solidify, forming the so-called casting. However, many aluminum castings are made

Table I. Alu

Compositions, Properties and Designations

Compiled by H. S. Jerabek, University of Minnesota, from Handbooks and Specifications of American Society for

WROUGHT ALLOYS

S.A.E. No.	A.S.T.M. Specification	Alcoa No.(a)	Cu	Si	Mn	Mg		Form Tested	Shear Str.,(b) 1000 Psi.	Endur. Limit,(c) 1000 Psi.
Work-Hardening Alloys[f]										
25	B25-41T	2s O				99 Al		1/16" Sheet	9.5	5
	B25-41T	2s 1/2H						1/16" Sheet	11	
	B25-41T	2s H						1/16" Sheet	13	8.5
29	B79-41T	3s O			1.2			1/16" Sheet	11	6
	B79-41T	3s 1/2H						1/16" Sheet	14	9
	B79-41T	3s H						1/16" Sheet	16	10
201	B109-41T	52s O				2.5	Cr 0.25	1/16" Sheet	18	17
	B109-41T	52s 1/2H						1/16" Sheet	21	19
	B109-41T	52s H						1/16" Sheet	24	20.5
Precipitation-Hardening Alloys[g]										
26	B78-41T	17s O	4		0.5	0.5		1/16" Sheet	18	11
	B78-41T	12s T						1/16" Sheet	36	15
	B78-41T	17s RT						1/16" Sheet	38	
		Alclad 17s T	(Coated with 99.75+Al)					1/16" Sheet	32	
		17s T						Forging	36	15
		A 17s	2.5			0.3		1/2" Rod	26	13.5
24		24s O	4.6		0.6	1.5		1/16" Sheet	18	12
		24s T						1/16" Sheet	41	18
		24s RT						1/16" Sheet	42	
		Alclad 24s T	(Coated with 99.75+Al)					1/16" Sheet	40	
		61s W	0.25	0.55		1.0	Cr 0.25	1/16" Sheet	24	12.5
		61s T						1/16" Sheet	30	12.5
		53s W		0.7		1.3	CR 0.25	1/16" Sheet	20	10
		53s T						1/16" Sheet	24	11
280		A51s T		1.0		0.6	Cr 0.25	Forging	32	10.5
27		25s T	4.5	0.8	0.8			Forging	35	15
		14s T	4.4	0.8	0.8	0.4		Forging	45	16
		70s T	1.0		0.7	0.4	Zn 10	Forging	37	19
		18s T	4			0.5	Ni 2	Forging	35	
		32s T	0.8	12		1.0	Ni 0.8	Forging	38	14
		11s T3	5.5			(Bi 0.5)	Pb 0.5	1/2" Rod	30	12.5

SAND-CASTING ALLOYS

S.A.E.	A.S.T.M. B26-41T	Alcoa	Cu	Si	Fe	Mg	Zn	Condition	Shear	Endur.(c)
33	CC	212	8	1.2	1			As Cast	20	7.5
38	C	112	7.5	1.2			1.5	As Cast	20	8
31		645	2.8	1.2			11	As Cast	22.5	7.5
35	JJ	43		5				As Cast	14	6.5
37	K	47		12.5	(Trace Na)			Modified	18	6
38	G HT1	195 T4	4					Soln. H.T.	24	6
38	G HT2	195 T6	4					H.T.	30	6.5
38	G HT3	195 T62	4					H.T.	31	7
		A334	3	4		0.3		As Cast	24	
322-1	N HT1	355 T4	1.2	5		0.5		Soln. H.T.	28	
322-2	N HT2	355 T6						H.T.	30	
322-3		355 T61						H.T.		
	N HT3	355 T51						H.T.	22	6.5
	M HT1	356 T4		7		0.3		Soln. H.T.	18	
	M HT2	356 T6						H.T.	22	8
320	L	214				3.75		As Cast	19	5.5
324		220 T4				10		Soln. H.T.	33	7
	F	122	10	1.2		0.2		As Cast		
	F	122 T2						Soln. H.T.	25.5	9.5
	F	122 T61						H.T.	29.5	
39	H	142	4			1.5	(Ni 2)	As Cast	24	8
39	H	142 T61						H.T.	32	8

(a) Aluminum Co. of America Alloy No. & Heat-Treatment Designations:
O=Annealed, W=As Quenched, T=Quenched & Aged, H=Cold Rolled to Hard Temper, 1/2H=Half Hard Temper, R=Cold Rolled After Heat Treatment, S=Wrought Alloy.
(b) In Thousands of Pounds per Square Inch. Yield Strength Taken at 0.2% Permanent Set.
(c) 500 Million Cycles in Reverse Bending. (d) Relative Forming Properties in Cold Bending; A=Best.

minum Alloys
of American Commercial Alloys
Metals, American Society for Testing Materials, Society of Automotive Engineers & Aluminum Co. of America

WROUGHT ALLOYS

Tensile(b) Strength, 1000 Psi. Av.	Min.	Yield(b) Strength, 1000 Psi. Av. Min.	Elong. % in 2 In. Av. Min.	Brinell Hardness	Cold Bend Test(d)	Corrosion Resistance in NaCl(e)	Alcoa No.	Characteristics and Uses
Work-Hardening Alloys[f]								
13 (15.5 max.)	5		35 30	23	A	B	2s O	Commercial Al; Good Forming Properties
17	16	14	9 7	32	B	B	2s ½H	Good Corrosion Resistance, Low Yield Str.
24	22	21	5 4	44	F	B	2s H	Cooking Utensils, Sheet and Tubing
16 (19 max.)	5		30 25	28	A	B	3s O	Similar to 25
21	19.5	18	8 6	40	C	B	3s ½H	Slightly Stronger and Less Ductile
29	27	25	4 4	55	G	B	3s H	Cooking Utensils, Sheet Metal Work
29 (31 max.)	14		25 20	45	A	B	52s O	Strongest Work Hardening Alloy
37	34	29	10 7	67	D	B	52s ½H	High Yield Strength and Fatigue Limit
41	39	36	7 4	85	G	B	52s H	Highly Stressed Sheet Metal Products
Precipitation-Hardening Alloys[g]								
26 (35 max.)	10		20 12	45	B	E	17s O	Duralumin. Most Common Strong Alloy
60	55	37 32	20 18	100	H	D	17s T	Hardened by Quenching and Aging
65	55	47 42	13 12	110	J		17s RT	Available in Most Wrought Forms
56	50	33 28	18 16		I	A	Alclad 17s T	Alclad Has Best Corrosion Resistance
55	50	30 30	16 16	100		D	17s T	High-Strength Heat-Treated Forgings
43		24	24	70	F	D	A 17s	Best Forming Properties. Rivets
26 (35 max.)	10		20 12	42	B	E	24s O	Strongest Alloy for Rolled Forms
68	62	44 40	19 17	105	J	D	24s T	Used Widely in Aircraft Construction
70	65	55 50	13 12	116	K	D	24s RT	More Difficult to Form Than 17s
62	56	41 37	18 16		J	A	Alclad 24s T	High-Strength Alclad; Corr. Resistance
35		21	22	65	F	C	61s W	Good Forming Properties. High Yield Str.
45		39	12	95	G	C	61s T	Will Not Age-Harden at Room Temp.
33	28	20 16	22 17	65	F	B	53s W	Good Forming Properties and Corrosion
39	35	33 28	14 10	80	G	B	53s T	Resistance
44		34	14	90		C	A51s T	For Intricate Forgings
55		30	16	100		E	25s T	Good Forgeability. Lower Cost
65		50	10	130		D	14s T	Strongest Forging Alloy
50		40	16	85		F	70s T	High Endurance Limit
55		35	10	100		E	18s T	Strong at Elevated Temp.; Forged Pistons
52		40	5	115		C	32s T	Forged Aircraft Pistons. "Low-X"
49		42	14	100		E	11s T3	Free-Cutting Screw-Machine Products

SAND-CASTING ALLOYS

T.S.(b)	Y.S.(b)	Elongation	BHN	Impact	Corr. (e)	Alcoa	
22	19	14	2 0	50 to 70	0.6	D	212	General Casting Alloy. Not Heat Treated
22	19	14	1.5 0	55 to 80	0.6	D	112	Good Casting Properties
29	25	22	4 2.5	70	1	D	645	General Casting Alloy
19	17	9	6 3	35 to 50	1	A	43	Thin, Pressure-Tight Castings. Corr. Res.
26	24	11	8 5	45 to 60	3	A	47	Alpax or Silumin. High Strength, Elong.
31	29	16	8 6	55 to 75	2.8	C	195 T4	High-Strength Heat-Treated Castings
36	32	22	4 3	70 to 90	1.8		195 T6	Aircraft, Marine, Bus, and Engine Parts
40	36	31	2 0	80 to 100	1.3		195 T62	
26	22	20	1.5 0	65	0.7	B	A334	Intricate Castings
30	26.5	20	5 3.5	50 to 65	1.3	A	355 T4	Liquid-Cooled Cylinder Heads
35	32	25	3.5 2	65 to 85	1.1		355 T6	Intricate Castings
38	35	33	1 0.5	80 to 95	0.8		355 T61	Good High-Temperature Strength
28	25	23	1.5 0	50 to 70			355 T51	Water Jackets, Exhaust Manifolds
28	26	16	6 5	50 to 70	1.7	A	356 T4	Intricate Heat-Treated Castings
32	30	22	4 3	60 to 80	1.0		356 T6	Good Corr.Resistance,PressureTightness
25	22	12	9 6	40 to 60	3.8	A	214	Good Corr. Resistance, Impact Toughness
44	42	25	14 12	70 to 85	4.5	A	220 T4	Highest Impact Toughness(h)
	18.5		0			D	122	Common Piston Alloy. Wear Resistance
25	23	21	1 0	75	0.7	D	122 T2	High-Temperature Strength
36	30	30	1 0	100	0.68	D	122 T61	Also Permanent Mold Castings
28	23	24	1 0	85	0.6	C	142	High-Temperature Strength and Stability
37	32	32	0.5 0	100		C	142 T61	Also Permanent Mold Castings

(e) Relative Resistance to Salt Water Corrosion; A = Best
(f) Can Be Hardened by Cold Work Only.
(g) Can Be Hardened by Heat Treatment.
(h) Special Foundry Practice Required.
From *Metal Progress*, by Permission of American Society for Metals, Cleveland, Ohio

by casting the molten metal into a permanent or metal mold, or by a practice of die casting in a die casting machine. The properties and characteristics may be greatly influenced by the practice used in the production of the casting. Many of the defects found in commercial castings may be attributed to the practice used in the foundry.

Many different alloys with widely different compositions are made, and Table 1 may be referred to for study of some of the more

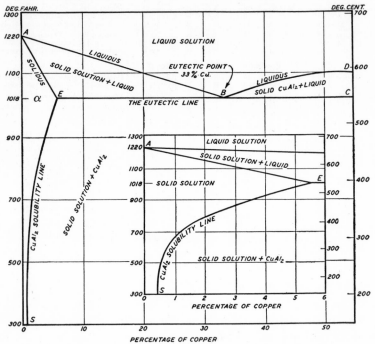

Fig. 1. Aluminum End of the Aluminum-Copper Diagram (after Stockdale, Dix and Richardson)

common aluminum alloys that are made by sand-casting technique. The two principal casting alloys are the aluminum-copper and the aluminum-silicon alloys. Perhaps the aluminum-copper may be considered the most common of all the casting alloys. These usually contain less than 15% copper alloy. A study of the aluminum-copper alloy diagram, Fig. 1, indicates that the microstructures of these alloys consist of mixtures of solid solution (α), and the eutectic, which is made up of the solid solution (α) plus the compound $CuAl_2$. The eutectic is a fine mechanical mixture of the alpha and the hard $CuAl_2$ compound. It is questionable whether or not the hard intermetallic compound $CuAl_2$ is a solid solution instead of a compound. However, although the presence of the pure compound $CuAl_2$ is questioned, the term $CuAl_2$ is widely used in referring to these alloys and will be used in the following discussion.

It will be seen in Fig. 1 that the eutectic in these alloys increases in amount with the increase in copper content until a 100% eutectic is formed which is composed of 33% copper and 67% aluminum.

The microstructure of a cast-aluminum alloy which contains 8% copper is shown in Fig. 2. The eutectic is plainly visible in the light background of the alpha solid solution. The eutectic constituent, being the last to freeze, is found between the dendritic branches of the primary crystals of the alpha solid solution.

These alloys develop exceptionally high physical properties and are readily machinable. Tensile strengths ranging from 19,000

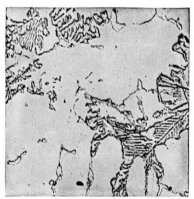

Fig. 2. Cast Aluminum-Copper Alloy. Etch ½% HF Magnified 100 Times

lbs. per sq. in. up to as high as 23,000 lbs. per sq. in. in the as-cast condition are common, with elongations from 1½ to 2% in 2 in. These alloys may be welded and heat treated, although heat treatments are more commonly applied to the forging types of aluminum alloys. Aluminum casting alloys are used extensively in the field of transportation and wherever a light structural alloy casting exhibiting the properties of these alloys is called for.

The aluminum-silicon casting alloys constitute an important series of casting alloys; the silicon in them may vary from 5 to 12.5%. These alloys are easier to cast than the aluminum-copper alloys due to greater fluidity at the casting temperature. The properties of certain compositions of these alloys may be improved by heat treatments, or by a *modified* practice in the foundry just prior to casting the molten metal in the mold. If the casting is made by the usual practice and contains about 12% silicon, the casting develops a coarse grain and is relatively brittle. By the use of a *modified* foundry practice, consisting of the addition of a small amount of metallic sodium to the ladle of molten metal, the casting freezes with a much finer and tougher grain structure. Through the *modified* practice, the foundryman can produce superior castings having distinctly higher strengths and higher elongations. The difference in grain structure of the cast metal made by the usual practice as compared with the modified practice is illustrated in Figs. 3 and 4.

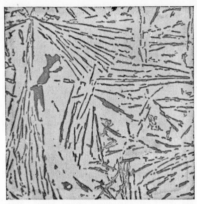 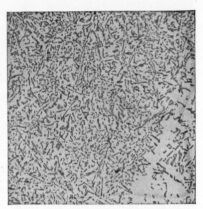

Fig. 3. Microstructure of an Unmodified 13% Silicon Casting Magnified 250 Times; ½% HF Etch

Fig. 4. Microstructure of a Modified 13% Silicon Casting, ½% HF Etch, Magnified 250 Times

The aluminum-silicon alloys exhibit excellent casting properties. This characteristic together with greater ductility and resistance to shock than exhibited by the aluminum-copper alloys, added to an even better resistance to atmospheric corrosion, make this type of casting alloy one of the most widely used in this country. Aluminum-silicon alloys are used in architectural and ornamental castings, castings for outboard motors, marine fittings, and wherever water tightness and resistance to corrosion are considered important factors in the selection of a casting.

In an addition to the aluminum-copper and aluminum-silicon casting alloys, some alloys are cast containing suitable proportions of magnesium and zinc. Alloys containing magnesium are said to be even more resistant to corrosion than the aluminum-silicon alloys and develop higher mechanical properties than the low-silicon casting alloys. Zinc may be used as an alloy in aluminum to increase its strength and hardness. It makes a cheaper alloy than copper, with approximately the same properties, but the aluminum-zinc alloys are heavier and have been reported to be less resistant to corrosion.

Wrought-Aluminum Alloys. Aluminum alloys of the forged or wrought type make up by far the greatest tonnages. The higher physical properties developed in these alloys are due to the beneficial effects obtained from the mechanical treatment of rolling, extruding, and forging. This treatment refines the grain structure and makes the alloys more homogeneous. Due to the action of breakdown of the cast structure in any forging operation, a forging may always develop properties superior to those of a casting. In general, lower percentages of alloying elements are used in the wrought alloys, as indicated in Table 5. The operations in the production of wrought aluminum alloys include: (1) casting of a blank or ingot; (2) hot and often cold working or shaping; (3) heat treatments.

Hot and Cold Working. Hot working of aluminum alloys is carried out between 600° and 900° F., and many desirable shapes of nearly pure aluminum and aluminum alloys may be produced by hot-working methods, including sheets, plates, tubes, bars, structural shapes, etc. However, it is more difficult to hot-work aluminum and its alloys than it is steel. This is perhaps due to the lower temperatures used in the hot working of aluminum compared to the temperatures used when hot-working steel.

The cold working of aluminum and its alloys results in the same work-hardening effects resulting from the cold working of any metal or alloy. Shaping by cold rolling, drawing, or by any of the methods used in our modern metalworking plants, may be used for the double purpose of getting the desired shape in the aluminum and at the same time causing improvement of physical properties through the changes brought about by the cold-working or work-hardening operation. In the production of cold-worked shapes of aluminum, the aluminum is first cast into the ingot form, the ingot form is then reduced by hot-working methods to the desired size and shape for the cold-working operations. The cold working starts where the hot working stops, although it should be recalled that annealing or other heat treatments may be given the metal before any cold reduction is started.

Aluminum finished by cold rolling may be purchased with varying amounts of cold reduction and therefore with varying degrees of hardness. The amount of cold reduction, and therefore hardness, is indicated by the designation of $\frac{1}{4}H$, $\frac{1}{2}H$, $\frac{3}{4}H$, H, to O. The annealed state is designated by the letter O, as in $2S\text{-}O$. Table 5 indicates the properties that may be expected from the temper designations used to define the tensile strength resulting from controlling the amount of cold reduction up to the maximum which it is practicable to carry out with commercial cold-working equipment.

Heat Treatment of Aluminum and its Alloys. The commercially pure aluminum 2S may be subjected to annealing after cold working. The annealing practice carried out with cold-worked 2S consists of heating the metal slightly in excess of 650° F., where complete softening is almost instantaneous, followed by cooling to room temperature. Although it is well to establish a standard practice of annealing, the exact temperature used and the time at this temperature, along with the cooling rate, is not very important provided the annealing temperature selected exceeds the recrystallization temperature of the metal. The annealing heat treatment allows the strain-hardened crystal state of the aluminum to recrystallize into new grains. These new-born grains grow to a desired size, removing, as they grow, all of the strain-hardened condition of the aluminum and restoring the original soft and plastic state of the metal.

The wrought-aluminum alloys may be subjected to annealing heat treatments similar to the pure aluminum, but with the alloyed aluminum a very slow rate of cooling from the annealing temperature is required if the maximum temperature used in the annealing operation exceeds 650° F. by much more than ten degrees. The reason for this may be obtained from a study of the aluminum-copper diagram, Fig. 1. Examination of the aluminum-copper diagram reveals that an alloy of 95% aluminum and 5% copper freezes as a solid solution alloy. Upon slow cooling of this solid solution alloy, the solubility of copper (probably as $CuAl_2$), decreases along the $E\text{-}S$ line of the diagram, so that at 300° F. the solubility of copper in aluminum is only 0.5% copper. Therefore, upon slow cooling of this alloy of aluminum-copper from around 970° F., the copper is gradually precipitated within the grains of aluminum as rather coarse particles of $CuAl_2$. This condition may be considered as the annealed or normal state of the aluminum-copper alloy; the structure is in a state that may be subjected to cold forging and consists of the relatively hard $CuAl_2$ constituent embedded in a soft aluminum matrix. This structure may be cold worked as indicated in Fig. 5, and if we wish to carry out an annealing treatment after cold working, a tem-

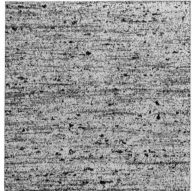

Fig. 5. Hard-Rolled Duralumin-type Alloy Sheet, with Distortion of Structure Due to Cold Working. Magnified 100 Times (after Dix and Keller)

Fig. 6. Showing Same Section as in Fig. 5, After Annealing; Many Small Particles of $CuAl_2$ Present in Structure. Magnified 100 Times (after Dix and Keller)

perature not exceeding 650°F. is sufficient to recrystallize the structure and remove the strain-hardening resulting from the cold working. A temperature of 650° F. will recrystallize the aluminum phase in the aluminum-copper alloy without markedly dissolving the $CuAl_2$ phase as indicated by the S-E line in Fig. 1. The structure developed by this treatment is illustrated in Fig. 6. The rate of cooling from the annealing temperature is not important if the copper as $CuAl_2$ is not dissolved; however, if the copper becomes dissolved, rapid cooling will keep it in solution and the alloy is not considered to be in its best annealed condition. If the alloy is to be annealed completely for severe cold-forming operations, heating to a temperature of 750° F. to 800° F. for about two hours should be used, followed by cooling at a rate not to exceed 50° F. per hour down to 500° F.

Solution Heat Treatment. Several of the aluminum alloys may have their properties greatly enhanced by suitable heat treatments. The 17S type of aluminum-copper alloy is one of the oldest and is still one of the most widely used alloys that will respond effectively to simple heat treatments. The possibility of carrying out heat treatments depends upon the changing solubility of aluminum for the constituent $CuAl_2$ during heating and cooling, within the solid state, as indicated by the curve S-E, Fig. 1. If we reheat a normal, annealed aluminum-copper alloy containing 4.5% Cu to a temperature

Fig. 7. Structure of Duralumin-Type Alloy Sheet after Heat Treatment; Practically All the Soluble $CuAl_2$ Constituent Is Dissolved. Magnified 100 Times (after Dix and Keller)

Fig. 8. Showing Same Structure as Fig. 7 Magnified 500 Times. Light Particles with Black Boundaries Are Undissolved $CuAl_2$ (after Dix and Keller)

approximately 950° F. for a period of 14 hours, most of the $CuAl_2$ phase present in the original annealed condition of this alloy is dissolved. If we cool this solid solution structure very rapidly, such as by quenching in water, most of the $CuAl_2$ phase will be retained in solution in the aluminum. The best results of this treatment are obtained if a drastic quench is used, although sometimes a slower quenching medium such as oil is employed. After this treatment, examination of the structure of the alloy will reveal very little of the $CuAl_2$ phase present. This condition is illustrated in Figs. 7 and 8. Apparently, the balance has been retained in solution by the severe rate of quenching from the solution temperature. This treatment has been referred to as a **solution heat treatment.** Improvement in corrosion resistance and increase in tensile strength are obtained by this treatment. Cold working may be carried out after the solution heat treatment, thereby increasing the strength without any effect upon the corrosion resistance of these alloys. However, properties of the solution-heat-treated alloy may spontaneously change with the passage of time at room temperature. After 30 minutes to one hour at room temperature, the solution-treated alloy may noticeably increase in strength, a phenomenon known as **precipitation hardening.**

Precipitation Hardening. The increase of strength that takes place with the passage of time at room temperature in a solution-heat-treated alloy is thought to be caused by the gradual precipitation of the $CuAl_2$ phase in very fine submicroscopic particles. This precipitation takes place at the aluminum grain boundaries and along crystallographic planes within the aluminum crystals. The very fine particles of $CuAl_2$ precipitate act as keys and build up resistance to slip, thereby greatly increasing the strength of the alloy. After the solution heat treatment, the strength of the 17S alloy is about 44,000 lbs. per sq. in., with an elongation of 20% in 2 in. Upon aging at room temperature, the strength increases rapidly within the first hour, and after 4 to 5 days the strength has increased to approximately 62,000 lbs. per sq. in. A very singular fact is that the ductility, as measured by elongation, does not change during the aging period, but remains about 20% in 2 in. This treatment produces an alloy that is almost as strong and as ductile as structural steel, with about one-third the weight.

Instead of aging the quenched alloy at room temperature in order to obtain the precipitation hardening, the alloy may be caused to precipitate the $CuAl_2$ phase more rapidly by heating somewhat above room temperature; however, rapid precipitation does not develop so high a tensile strength. Some compositions of aluminum alloys that respond to heat treatments, such as solution or precipitation treatments, do not develop any increase in tensility at room temperature after the solution treatment. However, in these alloys, heating to slightly above room temperature allows the precipitation to take place, producing an increase in strength. The precipitation hardening that takes place at room temperature in these alloys may be prevented by cooling solution-heat-treated alloys to below 0° F., and holding this low temperature. This may be accomplished through the use of dry ice (CO_2). It is assumed that the low temperature increases the rigidity of the structure enough to prevent the precipitation of the $CuAl_2$ phase; i.e., the atomic structure is so lacking in atomic mobility that any change, such as the precipitation of the $CuAl_2$ constituent, cannot take place.

The capacity for precipitation hardening, also called age hardening, to take place at room temperature depends on the presence of a small quantity of magnesium such as is found in the composition of the duraluminum type (17S) alloys. The aluminum alloys, without magnesium, age-harden much less at room temperature. The addition of silicon to aluminum-magnesium alloys produces little age hardening at room temperature but exerts pronounced precipitation hardening effects at high temperatures. The recommended heat treatment for the Al-Mg-Si type alloys consists in quenching from 960° to 980° F. in water and aging at 310° to 340° F. for as many as 18 hours in order to get the maximum precipitation hardening effects.

There are a considerable number of different types of precipitation-hardening aluminum alloys that are commercially used, some of which are indicated by the alloy combinations Al-Cu-Mn, Al-Cu-Mg-Si, Al-Cu-Mg-Ni, Al-Mg$_2$Si, and Al-Mg$_2$Zn. Recently, new alloys designated as **XA75S** and **XB75S** have been developed, having higher physical properties than the older 24S alloys and having good corrosion resistance. In general, the fabrication characteristics and heat treatments of the newer alloys are comparable to those of the older alloys.

Heat Treatment of Casting Alloys. Cast alloys of the aluminum series, as well as the forging alloys, may be subjected to heat treatments which markedly improve their physical properties. As a general rule, the casting alloys require much longer soaking periods at the temperatures used for the solution heat treatment, and the temperatures used for precipitation heat treatments, in order to bring about the desired changes in structure and in properties.

MAGNESIUM AND ITS ALLOYS. As stated previously, magnesium is the lightest of the commercial metals, having a density of 1.74 at 68° F. Its weight per cubic foot is 108.5 pounds, as compared with 175 for 99.0 per cent aluminum, and 557 pounds for copper. It has a melting point of 1202° F. and may be cast. Magnesium may also

be extruded and rolled hot or cold. Magnesium is plastic enough at
650° F. to be hot-worked by either rolling or extrusion methods. The
metal work hardens rapidly upon cold rolling and requires frequent
annealing to maintain its plastic and workable nature. Although the
mechanical properties of magnesium are relatively low, additions of
alloying elements such as aluminum, zinc, and manganese greatly
improve these properties. Some of the most common types of alloy
combinations along with their properties and designations are listed
in Table 2 of this chapter.

The magnesium alloys are second in importance to the aluminum
alloys as light structural alloys. The most prominent of the light
magnesium alloys are the series of magnesium alloys containing 4% to
12% aluminum and from 0.2% to 1.5% manganese, the balance being
magnesium. These alloys are sold in this country under the name
Dow Metal.

The most outstanding characteristic of Dow Metal is extreme
lightness, being about two-thirds as heavy as aluminum alloys. As
cast, the magnesium alloys have a tensile strength of from 18,000 to
35,000 lbs. per sq. in. After forging, the strength may be increased to
approximately 48,000 lbs. per sq. in. Although these alloys respond
to heat treatments similar to those used on the aluminum-copper
alloys, the forged and extruded shapes of Dow Metal do not require
further heat treatments for the development of satisfactory properties. This is an important advantage for these alloys. However,
casting alloys are heat treated where severe service conditions demand maximum physical properties.

Due to its high affinity for oxygen, magnesium is used as flashlight powder and, more recently, in incendiary bombs. The stability
of magnesium and its alloys has been proven by its satisfactory resistance to normal atmospheric corrosion either in the natural state
or after proper protective coatings have been applied to exposed surfaces. The problem of general corrosion is no longer an obstacle to
the use of magnesium alloys in many engineering structures. Its
lightness and easy machinability are two of the most outstanding
properties of the magnesium alloys.

Protective Coatings. When magnesium alloys are subjected to
normal atmospheric exposure, very little surface change occurs other

Table 2—Magne

Compositions, Properties, and Desig

Compiled by H. S. Jerabek, University of Minnesota, W. H. Gross of

Form	A.S.T.M. Alloy No.	A.S.T.M. Specification No.	Navy Bureau of Aeronautics Alloy No.	Navy Bureau of Aeronautics Specification No.	Navy Department Alloy No.	Navy Department Specification No.	U.S. Army Air Forces Grade	U.S. Army Air Forces Specification No.	S.A.E. No.	AMS (j)	Am. Mg. Corp. AM. No.	Dow Chem. Co.	Al	Mn	Zn
Sand Castings	4	B80-41T	A	AN-QQ-M-56	A	AN-QQ-M-56	A / A / A	AN-QQ-M-56	50	4420A / 4422A / 4424A	265-C / 265-T4 / 265-T6	H	6.0	0.2	3.0
	17	B80-41T	C	AN-QQ-M-56	C	AN-QQ-M-56	C	AN-QQ-M-56	500	4434	260-C / 260-T4 / 260-T6	C	9.0	0.1	2.0
	2	B80-41T									240-C / 240-T4 / 240-T61	G	10.0	0.1	
	3	B80-41T									246-T6	B	12.0	0.1	
	11	B80-41T	B	AN-QQ-M-56	B	AN-QQ-M-56	B	AN-QQ-M-56			403-C	M		1.5	
											244-C		4.0	0.3	
Die Castings	12	B94-41T				46M11	1	11319			230-C	K	10.0	0.1	(f)
	13	B94-41T				46M11	1	11319	501	4490	263-C	R	9.0	0.2	0.6
Extruded Bars and Rods	8	B107-41T	8	M-314c(e)			1	11335(e)		4350A	57s	J	6.5	0.2	0.7
	8	B107-41T	8	M-314c(e)			1	11335(e)	520		57s	J	6.5	0.2	0.7
	11	B107-41T	11	M-314c			2	11336			3s	M		1.5	
	9	B107-41T									58s	O	8.5	0.2	0.5
	15	B107-41T	15	M-314c(e)			1	11337(e)	521		C74s	X	3.0	0.2	3.0
	15a	B107-41T	15a	M-314c(e)			1	11337(e)	521		C74s-T5	X			
											59s	G	10.0	0.1	
	18	B107-41T									52s	Fs	2.8	0.3	1.0
Extruded Structural Shapes	8	B107-41T	8	M-314c(e)			1	11335(e)	520	4350A	57s	J	6.5	0.2	0.7
	11	B107-41T	11	M-314c			2	11336			3s	M		1.5	
	15	B107-41T	15	M-314c			1	11337(e)	521		C74s-T5	X	3.0	0.2	3.0
	15a	B107-41T	15a	M-314c(e)			1	11337(e)	521		C74s	X			
	9	B107-41T									58s	O	8.5	0.2	0.7
											59s	G	10.0	0.1	
	18	B107-41T					1	11320(e)			52s	Fs	2.8	0.3	1.0
Extruded Tubing					8	44T35(e)	1	11332(e)	520		57s	J	6.5	0.2	0.7
					11	44T35	2	11333			3s	M		1.5	
					15	44T35(e)	1	11334(e)	521 / 521		C74s / C74s / C58s-T5	X / X / O	3.0 / 8.5	0.2 / 0.2	3.0 / 0.7
							1	11318(e)			52s	Fs	2.8	0.3	1.0
Press Forgings	8	B91-41T			8 / 11	46M13(e) / 46M13		11345		4350A	C57s	J / M	6.5	0.2	0.7
														1.5	
	9	B91-41T			9	46M13(e)		11321A(e)		4360	C58s	O	8.5	0.2	0.5
	15	B91-41T			15	46M13(e)					C74s	X	3.0	0.2	3.0
	15a	B91-41T			15a	46M13(e)					C74s-T5	X			
Hammer Forgings	16	B91-41T			16	46M13		11346			65s	L	3.5 / 3.0	0.2 / 0.2	(h) / (i)
Rolled Plate, Sheet & Strip	11	B90-41T			11	47M2	1	11339	51 / 51	4370 / 4370	3s-h / 3s-o	Mh / Ma		1.5	
	8	B90-41T			8	47M2(e)	2	11338(e)		4381 / 4380	C57s-h / C57s-o	J-1h / J-1a	6.5	0.2	0.7
	18	B90-41T			18	47M2(e)		11340(e)			C52s-h / C52s-o	Fs-1h / Fs-1a	2.7	0.3	1.0

(a) In 1000 psi. Yield strength is the stress at which the stress-strain curve deviates 0.2% from the modulus line.
(b) Endurance or fatigue limit for 500 million reversals of the load, in 1000 psi.
(c) Solution heat treatment: Soaking at about 630 to 810°F. followed by air quenching.
(d) Solution treatment followed by artificial aging at about 350°F. (precipitation hardening).
(e) Applies to compositions with 0.005% Fe max. and 0.005% Ni max., for improved resistance to salt water.
    (Dow metal J-1, O-1, X-1; AM-C57s, AM-C58s, AM-C74s, AM-C52s; ASTM 8x, 9x, 15x and 18x.)

sium Alloys

nations of American Commercial Alloys

the Dow Chemical Co., and R. T. Wood of American Magnesium Corp.

Condition	Tensile Strength (A) Typical	Min.	Yield Strength (A) Typical	Min.	Elongation in 2 in., % Typical	Min.	Brinell Hardness	Shear Strength(a)	Endurance (b)	Uses and Characteristics
As Cast	27	24	11	10	5	4	51	17	10	General casting use
Cast; Soln. T. (c)	37	30	12	10	10	7	53	18	10	Sand & permanent mold castings
Cast; Soln. T.; Aged (d)	37	32	18	16	4	3	70	19	9	
As Cast	23	20	14	10	1		62	18	10	Pressure tight castings
Cast; Soln. T.(c)	39	32	14	10	10	6	61	20	10	Sand & permanent mold castings
Cast; Soln. T.; Aged (d)	38	34	20	18	3	1	77	22	10	
As Cast	21	18	12	10	2	1	53	18	8	Sand & permanent mold castings
Cast; Soln. T.; (c)	33	29	12	10	8	5	52	20	10	
Cast; Soln. T; Aged (d)	34	29	19	17	1		69	22	8	
Cast; Soln. T.; Aged (d)	32	27	20	17	0.5		85	19	7	Hard castings. Pistons
As Cast	14	12	4		5	3	33	11		Best salt-water resistance
As Cast	24	20	9	8	6	4	44	14		Aircraft tank fittings
As Cast	30		22		1		68			Thin section die castings
As Cast	33		20		3		66			General die castings
As Cast	43	40	30	26	17	12	54		17	Improved strength
As Cast; Stretched (g)	44	40	32	26	15	12	55	20	15	Screw machine rod
As Cast	42	32	27	20	6	3	42		10	Best salt-water resistance
As Cast	47	43	33	28	11	9	61		17	Bars of high strength
As Cast	42	39	30	26	19	15	51		18	Heat-treatable bar
As Cast; Aged	44	41	34	30	13	10	54		17	
As Cast; Stretched	51	45	38	33	9	6	70	23	16	Highest hardness & strength
As Cast; Stretched	40	37	30	25	17	12	50	19	12	Good ductility & impact toughness
As Extruded	42	38	27	23	15	10	58			Good strength & weldability
As Extruded	35	30	23	16	6	3	42			Best salt-water resistance
As Extruded	42	39	25	22	17	10	59			Heat-treatable shapes
As Extruded; Aged	43	40	28	25	14	8	62			
As Extruded	44	40	29	25	11	8	58			Improved strength
As Extruded	48	45	37	30	9	6				Highest hardness & strength
As Extruded	39	34	28	17	15	10				Good ductility & impact toughness
As Extruded	40	36	19	17	9	7	55			Good strength & weldability
As Extruded	35	32	17	17	5	3	40			Best salt-water resistance
As Extruded	40	36	19	17	9	7	55			Heat-treatable tubing
As Extruded; Aged	41	37	22	19	7	6	59			
As Extruded; Aged	42	39	29	25	5	4	60			Highest strength tubing
As Extruded	35	32	16		11		50			Good ductility
As Forged	41	38	25	22	9	6	56	21	17	General forging. Good ductility
As Forged	33	29	19	12	6	2	43			Weldable forgings
As Forged	45	42	30	24	7	5	69	22	18	Forgings, simple design. Strong
As Forged	41	38	24	20	16	9	59		17	Heat-treatable forgings
As Forged; Aged	42	38	28	22	14	7	62		17	
As Hammer Forged	38	35	22	20	12	6	52	16	10.5	Hammer forgings
As Hammer Forged	37	34	26	19	11	6	51		10.5	Hammer forgings
As Hard Rolled	37	32	27	24	9	4	53			Sheet with best formability &
Annealed	32	28	16		15	12	44	17	8	salt-water resistance
As Hard Rolled	45	40	35	28	8	3		20		Sheet with best combination of strength
Annealed	40	37	25		15	8		21		& salt-water resistance
As Hard Rolled	45	38	35	26	9	4				General purpose sheet alloy
Annealed	36	32	22		18	12				Good formability & strength

(f) Contains 0.5% silicon.
(g) Extruded and stretched is the condition in which bar and rod is normally furnished.
(h) Contains 5.0% tin.
(i) Contains 3.5% cadmium.
(j) Aeronautical material specification, Society of Automotive Engineers, Inc.

From *Metal Progress*, by Permission of American Society for Metals, Cleveland, **Ohio**.

than the formation of a gray discoloration, and only slight loss of strength occurs after several years of exposure. However, if these alloys are exposed to salt water and are contaminated with iron and other impurities, very rapid corrosion occurs. In order to increase the corrosion resistance of magnesium alloys, care should be exercised during their manufacture to avoid metallic impurities and flux inclusions. To further increase their corrosion resistance, magnesium alloys can be given a chemical treatment that forms a protective surface film on exposed surfaces. Much of the protection offered by chemical treatments lies in their ability to clean and remove impurities from the metal surfaces. Two commonly used chemical treatments are the chrome-pickle treatment and the dichromate treatment.

The chrome-pickle treatment consists in immersing the parts for one minute at room temperature in a bath of the following composition:

Sodium dichromate ($Na_2Cr_2O_7\cdot2H_2O$)...1.5 pounds
Concentrated nitric acid (Sp. gr. 1.42)..1.5 pints
Water..............................to make 1.0 gallon

After immersion, the part is rinsed in cold water, then dipped in hot water, and allowed to dry. The resultant coating on clean surfaces is of a matte to brassy, iridescent color. This treatment is largely used for protection of magnesium alloys during processing, storage, and shipment.

In the dichromate treatment, the parts are first cleaned and carefully degreased and immersed for 5 minutes in an aqueous solution containing 15% to 20% hydrofluoric acid (HF) by weight, the solution being at room temperature. The parts are then rinsed in cold running water. This treatment is followed by boiling the parts for 45 minutes in an aqueous solution containing 10 to 15% sodium dichromate. After boiling, the parts are rinsed in cold running water, followed by a dip in hot water to facilitate drying. The addition of calcium fluoride or magnesium fluoride to the dichromate bath will improve corrosion resistance and promote film formation and uniform coating.

Magnesium Casting Alloys. Aluminum is the principal alloying element used to improve the mechanical properties of magnesium.

Zinc and manganese are also added because they improve the mechanical properties and resistance to corrosion. Both aluminum and zinc are soluble in magnesium in the solid state to a limited extent. The magnesium end of the magnesium-aluminum alloy system is illus-

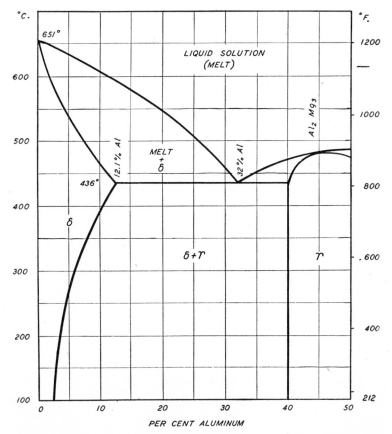

Fig. 9. Magnesium End of the Magnesium-Aluminum Diagram (after Hanson-Gayler-Schmidt & Spitaler)

trated in Fig. 9, and it will be seen from a study of this diagram that about 2% aluminum is soluble in magnesium when at room temperature. Upon heating magnesium to 436° C., the solubility increases to about 12% aluminum. This change in solid solubility with the temperature change makes it possible to subject these alloys to heat treatments comparable to those given to aluminum alloys; i.e., solution and precipitation heat treatments. The solution heat treatment usually requires heating to 760°–780° F. for 16–18 hours, followed by water quenching. The aging or precipitation treatment consists of heating the solution-heat-treated alloys to 350°–360° F. for 4–18 hours. The precipitation hardening resulting from this treatment raises the strength and hardness but lowers the ductility and toughness characteristics of these alloys.

Magnesium alloy castings require special care in foundry practice in order to produce satisfactory castings, magnesium being very sensitive to oxidation conditions and having a low specific gravity with a large shrinkage ratio. The factors of special foundry technique include: protective flux during melting and pouring, a specially treated molding sand to prevent reaction between the sand and metal, large gates and risers to compensate for the extreme lightness of the metal, and pattern design allowing for shrinkage.

Compositions of some of the most common magnesium casting alloys are listed in Table 6. The high mechanical properties of the 6% Al-3% Zn type, combined with its superior corrosion resistance, have made it the leading casting alloy. This type of magnesium alloy is heat treatable and develops its maximum properties only upon proper heat treatment.

Magnesium alloy castings are used in the manufacture of household appliances, foundry equipment, portable tools, aircraft gear and engine castings, high-speed machinery, and in the automobile industry.

Wrought Magnesium Alloys. Alloys of magnesium containing aluminum, manganese, and zinc, see Table 6, are now available in many of the standard wrought structural shapes, such as bars, rods, tubes, angles, etc. Although these alloys do not lend themselves readily to cold forming or forging methods, they may be satisfactorily shaped by hot methods such as extrusion, press forging, bending, etc. They work-harden so rapidly upon cold shaping that only small amounts of cold work can be carried out. However, at a temperature range between 550° to 600° F. most of the alloys may be successfully shaped by the usual mechanical methods. If only slight or light working is required to shape a part, temperatures as low as

400° F. may be used. An alloy with about the best cold-forming characteristics is the A.S.T.M. No. 11, containing 1.5% Mn. This is recommended for use where maximum cold-forming properties are needed, along with good resistance to salt water corrosion.

QUIZ QUESTIONS

1. *Name the uses to which nearly pure aluminum can be put.*
2. *Name the properties that make aluminum so useful.*
3. *How do you account for the resistance of aluminum to corrosion?*
4. *Describe briefly how the patented product "Alclad" is made.*
5. *What is the anodic treatment used to increase the corrosion resistance of aluminum alloys?*
6. *What factors reduce the machinability of light alloys of aluminum and magnesium, and how are these overcome?*
7. *Into what two groups are aluminum alloys classified?*
8. *Aluminum is alloyed to improve what two properties?*
9. *Why are aluminum-silicon alloys more easily cast than aluminum-copper alloys?*
10. *What effect does the addition of a small amount of metallic sodium have on an aluminum-silicon casting?*
11. *What four outstanding characteristics are exhibited by aluminum-silicon castings?*
12. *Name several uses of aluminum-silicon castings.*
13. *What is the outstanding characteristic of aluminum alloys containing magnesium?*
14. *Why is zinc alloyed with aluminum?*
15. *Why do wrought aluminum alloys have physical properties superior to those of castings?*
16. *What three operations are needed to produce wrought aluminum alloys?*
17. *Are the hot-working temperatures used on wrought aluminum lower or higher than those used on steel? Does this make such work on aluminum easier or harder than work on steel?*
18. *Describe the process of annealing commercially pure aluminum.*
19. *What precaution is observed when cooling wrought-aluminum alloys during annealing?*
20. *At what temperature does recrystallization occur during annealing?*
21. *What improvement is obtained for certain aluminum alloys by a "solution heat treatment"?*
22. *Describe the phenomenon known as "precipitation hardening."*
23. *What effect does precipitation hardening have upon elongation?*
24. *How may precipitation hardening be prevented?*
25. *Upon what does the capacity for precipitation hardening at room temperature depend?*
26. *What is Dow Metal? What is its outstanding characteristic?*
27. *Name and describe briefly the two chemical treatments given magnesium alloys to increase their corrosion resistance.*

28. *Name the principal alloying element used to improve the mechanical properties of aluminum.*

29. *Why are zinc and manganese added to magnesium?*

30. *What results are obtained from the precipitation heat treatment of magnesium alloys?*

31. *Name the factors of special founding technique for magnesium alloy castings.*

32. *List the uses for magnesium alloy castings.*

33. *Why is it that wrought magnesium alloys do not lend themselves readily to cold forming or forging methods?*

CHAPTER IX

Copper and Its Alloys

COPPER. Where copper was first produced is not known. It was known to the Romans as the metal from Cyprus, from which the name copper was derived. Many of the Ancient peoples used it. The Chaldeans had developed the art of working copper as early as 4500 B.C. The mines of Cyprus yielded copper to the early Egyptians, and from Egypt the use of copper spread into Europe. In America copper was used by the pre-Columbian peoples and the Indians long before the arrival of the Europeans. The native copper was found on the earth's surface, distributed, no doubt, by glaciers; it is doubtful if the Indians did any mining of native copper.

Copper seems to have been used first for ornaments; later it was used for tools and arms. Discovery of the hardening effects of tin combined with copper to produce bronze, gave various peoples, in succession, important advantages in war. Where, when, and how brass was discovered is not known, but the early and long-used method was by direct reduction from a mixture of copper, or some of its ores, and calamine (zinc carbonate). It was only in 1781 that Emerson invented the process of direct fusion of the metals to produce a copper-zinc alloy we call brass. In America, the first rolling of brass sheet was done in Waterbury, Conn., and Connecticut has continued to be the center of American brass manufacture.

Copper ranks next to iron and steel in commercial importance. Due to its electrical properties it is of particular interest to electrical engineers. Copper is easily rolled and drawn into wire. It exhibits great resistance to weathering, has good mechanical properties, and is of moderate cost. In ductility copper is definitely surpassed only by gold and silver. Its high ductility allows the shaping of copper without trouble from cracking, and with relatively small expenditure for power and for wear and tear of machinery. Cast copper has a tensile strength of 24,000 lbs. per sq. in., while in the cold-worked condition the tensile strength may exceed 70,000 lbs. per sq. in. Copper is a soft metal with a Brinell hardness of 35 in the *as-cast condition*. The hardness of copper may be increased to approximately 100 Brinell in cold-working operations. It has been believed by many that in ancient times copper was made approximately as hard as hardened tool steel by some method of heat treatment, a treatment that has often been referred to as *the lost art of hardening copper*. Present knowledge leads us to believe that some of the ancient tools

made from copper may have contained some impurities which contributed to its hardness and, coupled with cold forging, resulted in a harder variety of copper. We know that the only way to harden commercially pure copper is by cold work-hardening methods.

Copper is an extremely tough metal in that it has a remarkable resistance to fracture from sudden shock loads. The fact that its elastic limit upon loading is only 50% of its ultimate strength may

Fig. 1. High-Conductivity Copper, Annealed. Magnified 75 Times

Courtesy of Revere Copper and Brass, Inc.

be taken as an indication of its ability to deform without rupture when loaded beyond its elastic limit.

Commercial Grades of Copper. Some of the commercial grades of copper include:

1. Electrolytic and low resistivity lake copper, both of which run around 99.9% copper with silver and are used for electrical conductors. Structure of these types of copper is illustrated in Fig. 1.

2. Arsenical copper containing from 0.25% to 0.50% arsenic. This type of copper is used where its high recrystallization temperature is an advantage, such as in stay bolts for locomotives.

3. Fire-refined copper, other than lake copper, which has not been electrolyzed. It contains about 99.10% copper and silver with a maximum of 0.10% arsenic; used for mechanical purposes.

4. Deoxidized and oxygen-free copper with 0.000% oxygen. It possesses exceptional plasticity and good welding properties and is not subject to embrittlement resulting from exposure to a reducing atmosphere.

5. Tough-pitch copper which may contain as much as 0.070% oxygen. If this type of copper is heated in a reducing atmosphere above 750° F., the reducing gases react with the oxide particles at the grain boundaries and form cracks which cause the section to become brittle. The presence of small amounts of oxygen is essential for sound castings from the ordinary refining furnaces and results in good mechanical properties. The structure of this type of copper is illustrated in Fig. 2.

Impurities in Copper. Some of the impurities found in copper are oxygen as Cu_2O, sulphur, bismuth, antimony, arsenic, iron, lead, silver, cadmium, phosphorus, and others. Some of these impurities show a pronounced effect by lowering the electrical conductivity of the copper, whereas others have little effect.

Fig. 2. Electrolytic Tough-Pitch Copper; Copper 99.90%; Annealed. Magnified 75 Times
Courtesy of Revere Copper and Brass, Inc.

Arsenic and phosphorus have a marked detrimental effect on the conductivity of copper. Cu_2O in the concentration found in commercial copper has little effect on the mechanical properties. Silver is one of the most common impurities found in copper. It has little effect upon the properties of copper with the exception of raising the recrystallization and annealing temperatures. Lead in amounts over 0.005% reduces the hot-working properties but has little effect on the plasticity at room temperature.

Alloys of Copper. Copper is alloyed with several different metals because the resulting alloys are superior in many ways.

1. Copper alloys are stronger and harder than pure copper, and they may be further improved in their mechanical properties by cold working and, in some instances, by heat treatments.

2. Commercial grades of copper do not make satisfactory castings. Alloying of copper improves the casting characteristics, and these alloys, such as brass and bronze, are used to make castings.

3. The alloys of copper, in general, are much easier to machine than commercial copper, which is too soft and tough for easy machinability.

4. The corrosion resistance of many of the copper alloys is superior to that of commercial copper.

5. Alloys of copper-zinc (brass) are cheaper than copper due to the low cost of zinc and are superior for many uses.

6. The higher elastic nature of the copper alloys makes them superior to commercial copper, the latter being almost totally lacking in elastic properties unless it has been subjected to severe cold work hardening.

Table 1 may be used by the student as a reference table. It covers characteristics of common forms of copper and copper alloys.

Annealing of Copper. Annealing is the only method of heat treatment used on pure copper although other heat treatments are used in connection with some of the copper alloys. The purpose of annealing copper is to restore the original ductility and softness to work-hardened copper resulting from any cold-working operation.

The process of annealing cold work-hardened copper involves heating to a temperature of 1100° F., holding at this temperature for a certain period of time, and then allowing the metal to cool to room temperature. The rate of cooling from the annealing temperature of 1100° F. is without effect; therefore, fast cooling rates such as a water quench may be used. The annealing temperature of 1100° F. is above the recrystallization temperature of the cold-worked state and results in a complete change in the original grain structure without promoting undue grain growth. Annealing at temperatures higher than 1100° F. has no material effect on the strength of copper, but the ductility is reduced somewhat due to increase in size of grains.

BRASS. The alloys of copper and zinc are commonly classified as **brasses;** however, the term **commercial bronze** may be used in reference to some compositions of copper-zinc. These terms as used in the brass industry may be very misleading to the student. The copper-zinc alloys are the most important of the copper alloys due to their desirable properties and relatively low cost. Zinc readily dissolves in copper in both the liquid and solid states, forming a series of solid solutions; with less than 36% zinc, a solid solution is formed that is referred to as alpha (α) solid solution. The alpha phase is a strong and very ductile structure. If the combination contains above 36% zinc, a solid solution known as beta (β) is formed, which is rela-

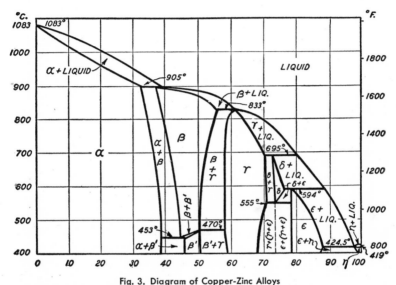

Fig. 3. Diagram of Copper-Zinc Alloys

From *Metals Handbook*, 1939, Courtesy of American Society for Metals

tively hard and much less ductile than the alpha brass. When zinc exceeds 50% in the alloy, a gamma solid solution is formed which is hard and brittle and of no value industrially except for decoration.

A study of the copper-zinc alloy diagram, Fig. 3, illustrates the areas where the alpha (α), beta (β), gamma (γ), etc., solid solutions exist. The copper-zinc diagram may be readily understood and interpreted if the student will refer back to the chapter dealing with the types of alloy systems and divide the copper-zinc alloy diagram into sections resembling the more simple diagrams described there.

Brasses containing over 62% copper consist of only one phase, the alpha solid solution, which is very ductile and has a face-centered cubic type of crystal structure. The alpha solid solution brasses are

Table 1. Copper and Its Alloys in Wrought Form

Prepared by M. G. Steele, Technical Adviser, Revere Copper and Brass, Inc.

Metal	Type Composition					Properties (Hard and Soft)			Forms	Properties and Uses	Methods of Working
	Cu	Zn	Pb	Sn	Ni	Tensile Strength	Elongation	Elastic Limit			
Copper (electrolytic)	99.9					51,000 / 32,500	4 / 47	48,000 / 12,000	Sheet; Bar; Tube; Rod; Plate	Corrosion resistance; ductility; high conductivity. Roofing; bus bar; high conductivity tubing	Stamp; Draw; Weld; Solder; Forge; Form
Copper (lake)	99.9	7 oz. silver per ton				51,000 / 32,000	4 / 47	48,000 / 12,000	Sheet; Strip; Rod	High annealing point. Auto radiator fins; lock seam tubing	Stamp; Draw; Solder; Form
Copper (phosphorized)	99.9	0.04 phosphorus max.				55,000 / 35,000	5 / 45	44,000 / 16,000	Sheet; Strip; Tube	Draws and coils better than electrolytic. Water, refrigerator and oil-burner tubing	Stamp; Draw; Forge
Copper (arsenical)	99.9	0.04 phosphorus; 0.30 arsenic				60,000 / 36,000	4 / 40	55,000 / 7,000	Sheet; Plate; Tube	High strength; resists heat and flaking. Condenser tubes	Stamp; Draw; Forge
Copper (cadmium)	99	1.00 cadmium				80,000 / 35,000	4 / 45	68,000 / 31,000	Rod	High strength. High-strength parts; trolley wire	Draw; Forge
Copper (beryllium)	98	2.00 beryllium				175,000 / 75,000	6 / 45	134,000 / 31,000	Sheet; Tube; Rod	Very high strength; hardness; high conductivity. Springs; cutting tools	Stamp; Draw; Forge; Form
BRASSES											
Gilding metal	95	5				55,000 / 35,000	5 / 38	39,000 / 11,000	Sheet; Strip; Tube	Ductility; reddish gold color. Primers; detonator fuse caps; jewelry; forgings	Stamp; Draw; Forge; Form
Commercial bronze	90	10				67,000 / 37,000	3 / 40	53,000 / 11,000	Sheet; Strip; Tube	Ductility. Used for color match; stamped hardware; bullet jackets; jewelry; caskets; screen cloth	Stamp; Draw; Forge; Form; Perforate
Rich low brass	85	15				75,000 / 42,000	4 / 43	52,000 / 15,000	Sheet; Strip; Tube	Corrosion resistance. Brass pipe; jewelry; badges; name plates; etchings; tags; dials	Stamp; Form; Draw; Blank; Etch; Weld
Low brass	80	20				85,000 / 43,000	4 / 50	65,000 / 15,000	Sheet; Strip; Tube	Corrosion resistance; yellow color. Jewelry (for gold plating); fulton bellows	Stamp; Form; Draw; Spin
Seventy-thirty or cartridge brass	70	30				86,000 / 45,000	4 / 50	65,000 / 15,000	Sheet; Strip; Tube	High ductility; deep drawing. Pins; rivets; eyelets; radiators; cartridge shells; spun articles	Stamp; Spin; Deep Drawing
High brass	66	34				90,000 / 48,000	4 / 50	70,000 / 15,000	Sheet; Strip	High ductility; deep drawing. Brass pipe; auto reflectors; stampings; radiator fins	Stamp; Spin; Deep Drawing
Leaded high brass	65	33.5	1.5			80,000 / 45,000	5 / 60	60,000 / 15,000	Sheet; Strip	Forming by bending; free machining. Engravers' brass; lighting fixtures; clock and watch backs; gears; keys	Stamp; Form; Bend; Punch
Free cutting rod	62	35	3			62,000 / 47,000	20 / 60	25,000 / 15,000	Rod	Typical brass rod; free machining. Extruded shapes; screw machine parts	Machine; Thread; Extrude

Alloy	Cu	Zn	Other			Tensile str.	Elong.		Yield / other		Forms	Typical uses	Fabricating operations
Forging rod	60	38	2			70,000 / 50,000	10 / 45		31,000 / 15,000		Rod	Hot forgings; faucet handles; shower heads	Forge; Extrude; Machine;
Muntz metal	60	40				80,000 / 57,000	9.5 / 48		60,000 / 15,000		Sheet; Plate; Tubes	Condenser tubes and heads; ship sheathing; perforated metal; brazing rod	Draw; Punch; Forge
Architectural bronze	56	41.25	2.75			70,000 / 50,000	10 / 20		55,000 / 15,000		Sheet; Strip	Strength; hardness; free cutting. Extruded shapes; forgings; interior ornamental bronze	Extrude; Forge; Machine

SPECIAL BRASSES

Alloy	Cu	Zn	Other			Tensile str.	Elong.		Yield / other		Forms	Typical uses	Fabricating operations
Silicon brass	78	20	2.0 silicon			110,000 / 55,000	4 / 61		83,000 / 12,500		Sheet; Strip	High strength; weldability. Refrigerator evaporators; fire extinguisher shells	Resistance Weld; Stamp; Draw
Aluminum brass	76	22	2.0 aluminum			83,000 / 62,000	17 / 52		75,000 / 16,000		Tube	Resistance to corrosion and erosion; self-healing skin. Condenser tubes	Draw; Extrude
Admiralty	71	28	1			95,000 / 45,000	5 / 60		92,000 / 18,000		Sheet; Strip; Tube	Resistance to corrosion, especially of sea water. Condenser tubes	Stamp; Draw; Extrude
Naval brass	60	39.25	0.75			75,000 / 54,000	15 / 45		39,000 / 15,000		Sheet; Rod; Tube	Resistance to corrosion in sea water. Tube heads; marine shafting; bolts; forged parts; window anchors	Draw; Forge

BRONZES

Alloy	Cu	Zn	Other			Tensile str.	Elong.		Yield / other		Forms	Typical uses	Fabricating operations
Phosphor bronze	98.75	0.05 phosphorus	1.2			65,000 / 40,000	4 / 48		50,000 / 15,000		Sheet; Strip	Resilience; strength; hardness; corrosion resistance. Springs; bearings; small parts	Stamp; Form; Weld
Phosphor bronze	92	0.05 phosphorus	8			110,000 / 55,000	3 / 55		85,000 / 25,000		Sheet; Strip; Rod	Similar to above. Welding rod	Stamp; Form; Weld
Silicon bronze	96.25	3.25 silicon	0.50			110,000 / 60,000	5 / 55		100,000 / 25,000		Sheet; Tube; Rod	Strength; weldability; corrosion resistance. Tanks; bolts; screws; lags; chain; locomotive hub liners; welding rod.	Stamp; Draw; Forge; Weld; Extrude; Cast
Aluminum bronze	95		5.0 aluminum			105,000 / 57,000	5 / 55		80,000 / 24,000		Sheet; Tube; Rod	Corrosion resistance; strength; golden color. Condenser tubes; gift articles	Stamp; Extrude; Draw
Manganese bronze	59	39	1.25 Fe	0.75	0.05 Mn	75,000 / 60,000	5 / 35		50,000 / 15,000		Sheet; Strip; Rod	Resistance to wear and corrosion. Welding rod; perforated coal screens; extruded wearing parts	Extrude; Perforate; Weld

NICKEL SILVERS

Alloy	Cu	Zn	Other			Tensile str.	Elong.		Yield / other		Forms	Typical uses	Fabricating operations
Nickel silver (typical)	65	20	15			93,000 / 58,000	5.5 / 45		75,000 / 15,000		Sheet; Strip; Rod	Resistance to corrosion; strength. Extruded shapes; table silver; instruments; key stock; springs	Forge; Extrude; Stamp

CUPRO-NICKELS

Alloy	Cu	Zn	Other			Tensile str.	Elong.		Yield / other		Forms	Typical uses	Fabricating operations
Cupro-nickel (eighty-twenty)	80		20			80,000 / 49,000	3 / 42		78,000 / 17,000		Tube	Resistance to corrosion, erosion, heat and chemical attack. Condenser tubes	
Cupro-nickel (seventy-thirty)	70		30			84,000 / 49,000	4 / 50		83,000 / 18,300		Tube	Same as above but more resistant to corrosion. Condenser tubes	
Cupro-nickel (zinc alloy)	75	5	20			85,000 / 50,000	5 / 35		77,000 / 23,000		Sheet; Tube; Rod	Same as 80-20 above but less resistant to corrosion. Condenser tubes	

Reprinted by Permission of American Society for Metals.

used mostly where the parts are wrought to shape. Many of the commercially important brasses are of this type. The mechanical properties of these alpha brasses depend largely upon the zinc content and the degree of cold working they receive. Fig. 4 illustrates the effect of composition upon the tensile strength and ductility of

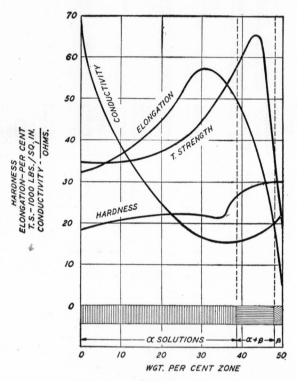

Fig. 4. Properties of the High-Copper Brasses

alloys containing up to 50% zinc. It will be seen from Fig. 4 that the tensile strength and ductility are both improved with additions of zinc up to approximately 30% zinc, above which composition the tensile strength continues to increase up to about 45% zinc, with a marked drop in the ductility when the zinc content exceeds 30%.

When the percentage of zinc exceeds approximately 38%, the structure of the alpha solid solution changes to the beta phase. This beta phase is much harder and stronger but less ductile than the alpha phase. Also, the beta phase differs from the alpha phase in that it is a body-centered cubic crystal structure, and upon cooling to approximately 880° F. the beta phase undergoes a structural transformation changing the beta (β) to a phase designated as β'. The two beta phases differ in that the β has its solute atoms haphazardly arranged in the solvent lattice, whereas the β' phase has the solute atoms orderly arranged in its atom structure of solvent atoms.

The color of brass varies as its composition from a copper red for the high copper alloys, to a yellow color at about 38% zinc. The color changes and is slightly more reddish in the β' phase.

Fig. 5. Annealed Red Brass. Copper 85%; Zinc Balance. Magnified 75 Times
Fig. 6. Annealed Cartridge Brass. Copper 70%; Zinc Balance. Magnified 75 Times

Courtesy of Revere Copper and Brass, Inc.

Red Brasses. There are four types of wrought brasses in this group: **gilding metal**—95-5, **commercial bronze**—90-10, **rich low brass**—85-15, and **low brass**—80-20. These brasses are very workable both hot and cold. The lower the zinc content, the greater the plasticity and workability. These brasses are superior to the yellow brasses or **high brasses** for corrosion resistance and show practically no bad effects from dezincification or season cracking. Due to their low zinc content, they are more expensive and are used primarily when their color or greater corrosion resistance or workability are distinct advantages. The structure of annealed red brass with its alpha phase is illustrated in Fig. 5. The applications for red brass include valves, fittings, rivets, radiator cores, detonator fuse caps, primer caps, plumbing pipe, bellows and flexible hose, stamped hardware, caskets, screen cloth, etc. These alloys may be shaped by stamping, drawing, forging, spinning, etc. They have good casting and machining characteristics and are weldable.

Yellow or Cartridge Brass. The yellow alpha brass is the most ductile of all the brasses, and its ductility allows the use of this alloy for jobs requiring the most severe cold-forging operations such as deep drawing, stamping, and spinning. Fig. 6 illustrates the structure of annealed yellow or cartridge brass, which is a copper containing from 27 to 35% zinc. This alloy is used for the manufacture of sheet metal, rods, wire, tubes, cartridge cases (from which it gets its name), and many other industrial shapes.

Unless the brass is exceptionally free from lead, it may not respond well to hot working, and all fabrication should be done cold. Lead may be used to improve the cold-working characteristics.

A rolled and annealed brass has a tensile strength of about 28,000 lbs. per sq. in. By cold rolling, however, its tensile strength may be increased to 100,000 lbs. per sq. in. Brass is obtainable in varying degrees of hardness by cold rolling, usually designated as **quarter-hard, half-hard,** and **hard.** The hard brass is brass with the maximum degree of cold rolling that may be considered practical for a given thickness of section and from a workability viewpoint.

The effect of cold working upon the mechanical properties of this alloy is illustrated in Fig. 7. The only heat treatment given to this alloy is annealing to remove any cold work hardening and to remove residual stresses as the result of cold-working operations.

Annealing of Brass. The only heat treatment applicable to alpha brass is that of annealing after cold working. Cold working, as we have seen, produces a distortion of the crystal state, which is accompanied by an increase of hardness and strength and a loss of plasticity. The cold-worked condition, with its greater strength and lower ductility, renders the metal less workable and may result in failure due to rupture of the less plastic condition of the crystal state. Restoration of the original properties may be accomplished by an annealing operation; i.e., heating of the cold-worked brass to above its recrystallization temperature. During the heating of the cold-worked brass, any internal stresses which may be present in the brass from the cold-forming operations may be removed. Three changes take place during the heating of the cold-worked brass in an annealing operation; (1) the relief of internal stresses (2) the recrystallization of the cold-worked crystal structure into new and, at first, very fine grains and (3) the growth of the fine new-formed grains into larger and fewer grains or crystals. The annealing operation completely

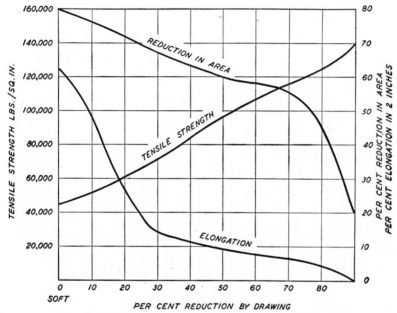

Fig. 7. Effect of Cold Drawing on the Physical Properties of High Brass

From *Metals Handbook*, 1939, American Society for Metals

removes any trace of the original cold-worked state of the brass, and restores the original ductility, with a lowering of the tensile strength and hardness to the normal values.

The effect of annealing temperatures ranging from room temperature up to 800° C. (1478° F.) on the properties of cold work-hardened brass of the yellow (high brass) composition is illustrated by Fig. 8.

Annealing may be carried out by heating the cold-worked brass to within a temperature range of 1100° F. to 1200° F., followed by cooling at any convenient rate. The rate of heating and cooling is

almost without effect on the size of the new-formed crystals. The size
of the annealed crystals is influenced largely by the amount of cold
work the brass received before the annealing operation, and the
maximum temperature used in the annealing operation. (See the dis-

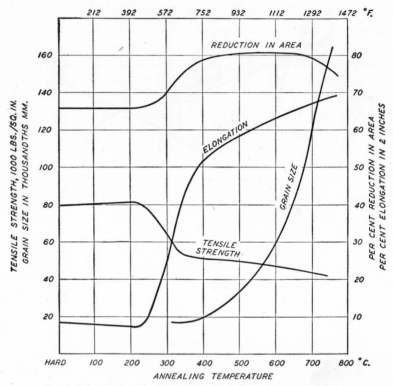

Fig. 8. Effect of Annealing Temperatures on the Properties of High Brass
From *Metals Handbook*, 1939, Courtesy of American Society for Metals

cussion of recrystallization.) The atmosphere in the annealing furnace may often be controlled to prevent excessive oxidation or even
discoloration of the surface of the brass to be annealed.

Season Cracking. Highly stressed brass and bronze may be
sensitive to failure by cracking in service under conditions of a corrosive nature. This failure is spontaneous and may occur without any
added strain from service. It constitutes one of the most serious

defects or failures in cold-worked brass. The conditions leading to
season cracking may be eliminated by careful control of the cold-
working operations, or by removal of the internal stresses before subjecting the brass to service. Annealing should remove any danger of
season cracking. Also, a low-temperature baking or annealing treatment, which may not lower the tensile strength below satisfactory
values, may be used that will prove safe as a treatment to prevent
season cracking. Low temperature annealing within temperatures of
500° F. to 800° F. may prove satisfactory as a means of removing the
internal stresses and maintaining the tensile strength within acceptable limits.

Sensitivity to season cracking may be determined by exposure
of a cold-worked brass, for approximately 10 minutes, to a mercurous
nitrate solution containing nitric acid. Satisfactory brass will show no
evidence of a crack after a period of one hour following the treatment
in this bath. See test for intergranular corrosion, page 22.

Alpha-Beta Brasses, Muntz Metal. When the content of zinc in
brass is increased from 40% to 45% zinc, the alloy is called Muntz
metal. This alloy contains both the alpha and beta constituents in its
structure. Muntz metal may be hot-worked even when it contains a
high percentage of lead. Such brass is accordingly useful for screws
and machine parts, where ease of working and particularly ease of
machining are more important than strength.

A photomicrograph of this alloy, Fig. 9, illustrates the type of
structure found in Muntz metal. As stated previously, both the alpha
and beta phases are present in this alloy. The lighter constituent is
the harder and less ductile beta phase, and the darker constituent is
the softer and more plastic alpha phase. Some of the applications for
Muntz metal include sheet form for ship sheathing, condenser heads,
perforated metal, condenser tubes, valve stems, and brazing rods.

Admiralty Metal. Admiralty metal is a copper-zinc alloy containing approximately 1.0% tin and 0.03% arsenic. Its resistance to
corrosion is superior to that of ordinary brasses that run free from
tin. The structure of this type of alloy is shown in Fig. 10. This
composition is used for tubing condensers, preheaters, evaporators,
and heat exchangers in contact with fresh and salt water, oil, steam,
and other liquids at temperatures below 500° F.

Copper-Tin Bronze. Bronze is an alloy containing both copper and tin although commercial bronzes may contain other elements besides tin; in fact, they may contain no tin at all. Bronze for "copper" coins, medals, etc. contains 4% to 8% tin, the tin being used to increase the hardness of the copper and its resistance to wear.

Tin forms compounds with copper, the compounds being dissolved in the copper up to 5% tin, forming a solid solution (α) similar to the alpha solution of the brass. However, tin increases the strength, hardness, and durability of copper to a much greater extent than zinc.

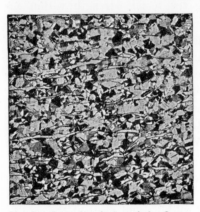 

Fig. 9. Muntz Metal, Annealed. Copper 60%; Zinc Balance. Alpha Plus Beta Structure. Magnified 75 Times

Fig. 10. Annealed Arsenical Admiralty Metal. Copper 70%; Tin 1%; Arsenic 0.03%; Zinc Balance. Magnified 75 Times

Courtesy of Revere Copper and Brass, Inc.

Over 5% tin produces a heterogeneous structure consisting of an alpha solid solution plus a compound, Cu_3Sn, that acts as a hardener in the alloy.

The alloy diagram of the copper-tin system is shown in Fig. 11. From a study of this diagram, it will be seen that the solubility of the compound Cu_3Sn decreases with a lowering of the temperature from the alpha solid solution area to room temperature. In commercial copper-tin alloys that are cast and cooled relatively fast, the solubility is about 5% tin and for slowly cooled alloys about 10% tin; i.e., the capacity to hold tin in solid solution is a function of the cooling rate. Alloys with increasing amounts of tin contain, upon cooling to room temperature, an alpha solid solution phase plus the compound

Cu_3Sn. This compound is extremely hard, brittle, and wear resistant and results in a harder alloy. The copper-tin alloys containing from 1.25% to 10.50% tin are more expensive than copper-zinc alloys but, in general, are harder, stronger, and more resistant to corrosion than the copper-zinc brasses. They are used for many parts, including high-strength springs, clips, snap switches, electric sockets and plug

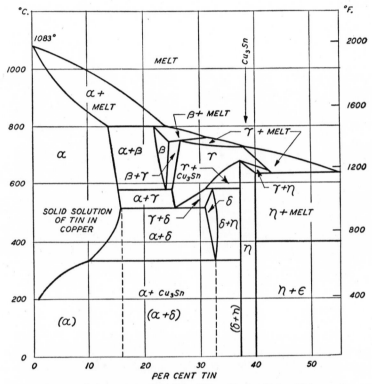

Fig. 11. Copper-Rich Portion of the Copper-Tin Constitution Diagram
From *Metals Handbook*, 1939, Courtesy of American Society for Metals

contacts, fuse clips, flexible tubing, hardware, bushings, bearings, welding rods, etc.

Phosphor Bronze. Phosphorus is added to bronze containing from 1.5% to 10% tin (see Table 1), for deoxidation purposes during melting and casting operations. The phosphorus also increases the fluidity of the molten metal, thereby increasing the ease of casting into fine castings and aiding in the production of sounder castings. Also, with the higher phosphorus content, a hard compound Cu_3P is formed which combines with the Cu_3Sn compound present in these alloys, increasing the hardness and resistance to wear. The structure of a cast phosphorus-treated bronze is shown in Fig. 12. The alpha constituent appears as dendritic crystals in a matrix consisting of a mixture of alpha phase and the hard, brittle compound Cu_3Sn. These alloys are used largely for gears and bearings.

Leaded Bronze. Lead does not alloy with copper but may be mixed with copper while the copper is in the molten state by agitation

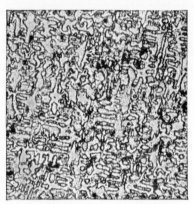 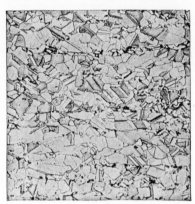

Fig. 12. Phosphor Bronze as Cast. Copper 92%; Tin 8%. Magnified 75 Times

Fig. 13. Aluminum-Silicon Bronze, Extruded. Aluminum 7%; Silicon 2%; Copper Balance. Alpha Plus Beta Structures

Courtesy of Revere Copper and Brass, Inc.

or mechanical mixing, and under suitable conditions this may be satisfactorily cast in a mold, resulting in the lead being well distributed throughout the casting in small particles. Lead may be added to both bronze and brass for the purpose of increasing the machinability and acting as a self-lubricant in parts that are subjected to sliding wear, such as a bearing. The lead particles, with their soft, greasy nature, reduce the frictional properties of the alloy. Lead is a source of weakness and is usually kept below 2% although some bearing bronzes may contain as high as 50% lead.

Aluminum Bronze. Alloys of copper containing aluminum in place of tin are known as **aluminum bronze.** They may also contain other elements such as silicon, iron, and nickel, frequently added to increase the strength of the alloy. Typical structures found in these alloys are illustrated in Figs. 13, 14, and 15. The influence of cooling rates is shown by the structures developed in these illustrations; i.e., the extruded material is practically 100% alpha phase, the forged specimen has retained some of the beta phase and shows a two-phase structure, alpha plus beta, whereas the specimen water-quenched from a temperature of 1700° F. shows a marked two-phase, alpha-plus-beta type of structure.

The structure of the slow-cooled alloys of this composition may completely change to the alpha phase upon reaching room tempera-

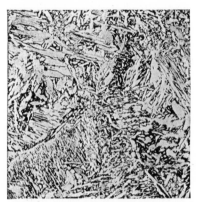
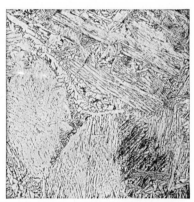

Fig. 14. Aluminum-Silicon Bronze, Forged. Aluminum 7%; Silicon 2%; Copper Balance. Alpha Plus Beta Structures

Fig. 15. Aluminum-Silicon Bronze, Heated to 1700° F. and Quenched in Water. Aluminum 7%; Silicon 2%; Copper Balance. Alpha Plus Beta Structures

Courtesy of Revere Copper and Brass, Inc.

ture; however, at elevated temperatures, the alpha phase changes to a beta phase, which may be retained, in part, at room temperature by means of rapid cooling. It is possible to improve the hardness and other properties of many of these alloys by heating to the beta phase range of temperature, approximately 1650° F., followed by rapid cooling. Upon reheating to 700–1100° F., the retained beta phase becomes unstable and undergoes a transformation with the separation of the beta phase to a fine alpha and delta crystal form. Such a change causes a marked increase in hardness and strength at the expense of ductility. Heat-treated aluminum bronzes may be used for hand tools, such as chisels, where nonsparking characteristics are essential to avoid fires and explosions. They are also widely used in the oil refineries and in other industries handling inflammable or explosive gases and liquids. Other applications include aircraft engine parts, valve seats and guides, spark plug inserts, and bushings.

With percentages below 10% aluminum, the copper dissolves the aluminum and forms solid solutions, α, β, and γ, not unlike those found in brass and bronze. The mechanical properties of aluminum bronze are superior to those developed by ordinary bronze. The tensile strength in the as-cast condition of an alloy containing 10% aluminum is about 65,000 lbs. per sq. in. It is nearly as ductile as brass and has double the ductility of tin-copper bronze. Many special aluminum bronzes are on the market, which develop very high hardness and strength; some of these are subjected to heat treatments similar to aluminum-copper alloys in order to develop their maximum properties. It is more difficult to obtain uniformity in aluminum bronzes than in the more common copper alloys.

Miscellaneous Bronzes. Other bronze alloys include **manganese bronze, bell bronzes, nickel bronze,** and **silicon bronze.** These alloys find a field of usefulness in industrial, marine, and household applications. The manganese bronze is fundamentally a brass of approximately 60% copper, 40% zinc, and manganese up to 3.5% and is well known as an alloy for ship propellers. It has excellent resistance to corrosion and good mechanical properties. The bell bronze contains 20 to 25% tin and is a hard, brittle alloy which gives a tone quality to bells that no other composition yields. Addition of nickel to bronze and brass improves their mechanical properties and is used to improve the hardness and wear resistance of gears and bearing bronzes. Silicon bronze contains, with other elements, 1 to 4% silicon, which is added to improve cold work-hardening characteristics, developing greater strength upon cold rolling or drawing. In addition to high capacity for work hardening, the silicon bronzes exhibit excellent resistance to corrosion caused by many organic acids, sugar solutions, sulphite solutions, etc. Their uses include electrical fittings, marine hardware, water wheels, boilers, pumps, shafting, and many parts that operate under corrosive conditions.

BERYLLIUM-COPPER ALLOYS. The answer to the "lost art of hardening copper" is found in some of the modern copper alloys such as the newer beryllium-copper alloys containing 1% to 2.25% beryllium. Although beryllium makes a very costly alloy, its initial cost is offset by the remarkable properties developed by this new alloy. It may be cast, worked hot and cold, welded, and given heat treatments similar to those given the aluminum-copper alloys; i.e., solution and precipitation heat treatments.

As may be seen from the alloy diagram of beryllium-copper, Fig. 16, the solubility of beryllium in copper increases with tempera-

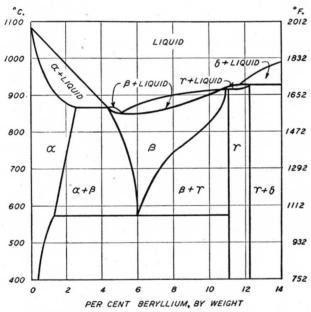

Fig. 16. Diagram of Copper-Beryllium Alloys
From *Metals Handbook*, 1939, American Society for Metals

ture from less than 1% beryllium at room temperature to more than 2% at 1500° F. Also, as the beryllium content in copper increases, the alpha solid solution, which forms first, changes to a eutectoid structure consisting of a mixture of alpha and gamma phases. Any gamma phase present in the alloy at room temperature changes to a beta phase upon heating to above 1050° F. Due to these changes in solubility and the change from one phase to another, the beryllium alloys are susceptible to heat treatments which greatly alter their mechanical properties with improvement in both strength and hardness. Heat treatments include annealing, heating, and quenching, known as solution heat treatment, and aging or precipitation treatments.

In the best annealed condition, obtained by quenching the alloy from a temperature of 1472° F., an alpha solid solution structure is developed. The tensile strength of this quenched alloy is about 60,000 lbs. per sq. in. In the quenched state, the solution alloy can be readily cold worked, and may develop a tensile strength in excess of 100,000 lbs. per sq. in. After cold working, the alloy may be subjected to a precipitation hardening treatment by heating to a temperature between 475° F. and 575° F. This treatment precipitates a hard gamma crystal phase of the alloy, rendering it much harder and less ductile. By means of these treatments the hardness may be varied from 215 Brinell to 400 Brinell, with a tensile strength, in the higher Brinell hardness range, as high as 200,000 lbs. per sq. in. These alloys exhibit good electrical properties and excellent corrosion resistance. Because they possess a combination of high Brinell hardness and tensile strength, these alloys find many applications as springs, tools, surgical and dental instruments, watch parts, firing pins, and welding electrodes. At the present time, the main objection to these alloys is high cost; and due to the difficulty in extracting beryllium from its ores it is doubtful if the price of this alloy will be reduced to that of other copper alloys.

COPPER-MANGANESE-NICKEL ALLOYS. A substitute for the beryllium alloys has been developed that contains approximately 22%–24% manganese, 22%–24% nickel, and the balance copper. This alloy exhibits age-hardening effects resulting from heat treatments and may be cast and wrought to shape. Alloys of this type may be greatly improved in strength and hardness by quenching from 1200° F. followed by tempering or aging at 660° to 840° F. for approximately 24 hours. With proper heat treatments, hardness values of Rockwell C54 and higher are obtainable with tensile strength values in excess of 200,000 lbs. per sq. in. These particular alloys may be used in applications similar to the beryllium-copper and the aluminum bronzes and are used where hardness and nonsparking characteristics are needed, such as in some applications for hand tools.

COPPER-NICKEL ALLOYS. Copper and nickel form a very simple alloy in that both metals dissolve in each other in all percentages to form a solid solution. Nickel added to brasses and bronzes has been found to improve their electrical properties and toughness. A familiar copper-nickel alloy is found in the United States five-cent piece, which is coined from alloy sheets containing 75% copper and 25% nickel. All alloys of copper and nickel with more than 20% nickel are white in color. Alloys containing 30% nickel are much used in marine service where strength and resistance to corrosion are important factors in the selection of an alloy.

MONEL METAL. Monel metal is a so-called *natural alloy* in that it is made by smelting a mixed nickel-copper ore mined in Sudbury, Ontario. It contains approximately 65% nickel, 28% copper, the balance consisting chiefly of iron, manganese, and cobalt as impurities. Monel metal is harder and stronger than either copper or nickel in the pure form; it is also cheaper than pure nickel and will serve for certain high-grade purposes to better advantage than the pure metal. Monel is a substitute for steel where resistance to corrosion is a prime requisite. Monel metal can be cast, hot and cold worked, and welded successfully. In the forged and annealed condition it has a tensile strength of 80,000 lbs. per sq. in., with an elongation of 45% in 2 inches, and is classified as a tough alloy. In the cold-worked condition it develops a tensile strength of 100,000 lbs. per sq. in., with an elongation of 25% in 2 inches. With excellent resistance to corrosion, pleasing appearance, good strength at elevated temperatures, Monel metal finds many uses in sheet, rod, wire, and cast forms. Included in the applications for monel metal are sinks and other household equipment, containers, valves, pumps, and many parts of equipment used in the food, textile, and chemical industries.

A Monel metal containing 3% to 5% aluminum, known as "K" Monel, is available. This alloy is of interest because it can be made to develop very high properties by means of heat treatment as a substitute for cold-work hardening in the other nickel-copper alloys. A Brinell hardness of 275 to 350 Brinell may be obtained by means of a precipitation heat treatment. This hardness may be further increased by cold-work hardening.

NICKEL-SILVER. Nickel-silver, also called German silver, is a brass alloy containing 10% to 30% nickel and 5% to 50% zinc, the balance copper. These alloys are very white, similar to silver, hence the name. They are resistant to atmospheric corrosion and to the acids of food stuffs. Their use depends largely upon their resistance to corrosion and pleasing appearance.

NICKEL-IRON ALLOYS. The nickel-iron alloys, aside from the nickel steels, are of considerable importance. An alloy of 36% nickel is known as "Invar," and has a very low coefficient of expansion so that it is used for standards of length. The alloy of iron and nickel which contains 46% nickel is known as "Platinite," since it has the same coefficient of expansion as glass and may be used in place of platinum to seal into glass.

The alloy of 78½% nickel and 21½% iron is known as **Permalloy** and has very high magnetic permeabilities at low fields so that it has been used in the construction of submarine telegraph cables.

The alloys of nickel and chromium, as well as the ternary alloys of iron, nickel and chromium, have the property of withstanding high temperature without scaling so that they are very useful for furnace parts, annealing boxes, etc. These alloys also have a high electrical resistance and are hence useful as windings for resistance furnaces, electric irons, and toasters. They are known by various commercial names, depending on their composition. Some of the best known are nichrome, chromel, etc.

QUIZ QUESTIONS

1. *Name the properties of copper that make it so important commercially.*
2. *Name the approximate strengths of cast copper before and after cold working.*
3. *Can copper be hardened by heat treatment?*
4. *Describe the difference in qualities of the alpha, beta, and gamma brasses. How are they formed?*
5. *With what metal is copper alloyed to form brass?*
6. *Name the uses of red brasses.*
7. *What percentage of zinc is used in cartridge brass?*
8. *Name the approximate strength of cartridge brass before and after cold rolling.*
9. *Brass is made in various degrees of hardness. How are these expressed?*
10. *What is Muntz metal and what particular uses are made of it?*
11. *What changes take place during heating of cold-worked brass in annealing?*

12.   What is meant by "season cracking" of brass and bronze, and how is danger of such failure removed?

13.   Why is tin used in bronze?

14.   What percentage of tin is used in bronze for electric sockets?

15.   Why is lead added to some brass and bronze?

16.   What can be said of the mechanical properties of aluminum bronze?

17.   What tensile strength is developed in beryllium-copper alloy? Name some of its uses.

18.   What does the addition of nickel do for copper alloys? What special uses are made of these alloys?

19.   What is Monel metal and how is it obtained?

20.   Name the percentages of nickel and iron in Permalloy. What are some of its uses?

21.   List some of the important impurities found in copper. How do they affect the properties of copper?

22.   Why are copper alloys superior to commercial copper?

23.   What is the purpose of annealing copper?

24.   Describe the process of annealing cold, work-hardened copper.

25.   Name the important red brasses.

TAKING THE TEMPERATURE OF LIQUID STEEL WITH OPTICAL PYROMETER
Courtesy of Ford Motor Co.

CHAPTER X

Steel—Man's Servant

CARBON STEELS. Although all steels contain carbon, the terms **carbon steel** or **plain carbon steel** are used to distinguish a steel to which no special alloying element, such as nickel, tungsten, or chromium has been added in appreciable amounts. In carbon steels, as well as in special or alloy steels, the constituent carbon is the principal actor in the steel. Carbon, more than any other constituent, determines the properties and uses of the steel. In fact, to make the most famous of all the metals, steel, the ancients discovered that by exposing wrought iron to the fuel of the forge fire, the fire magically changed the wrought iron into a hard iron which they called **steel**. We now know that the carbon from the fuel in the forge fire dissolved into the wrought iron and changed the iron to steel. Thus steel was born.

As we have seen in the section of this text covering the iron-carbon system, carbon dissolves readily in solid iron when iron is heated above a red heat (1360°F.), the amount of carbon thus dissolved depending upon the maximum temperature. However, upon slow cooling to below a red heat (1290°F.), iron changes from a gamma form to an alpha form, and the new alpha iron can dissolve but little carbon. Thus, any carbon dissolved in iron above a red heat is liberated or precipitated when cooled to below a red heat. The carbon, upon precipitation from iron, forms into a carbide or compound of iron, cementite (Fe_3C); it is this cementite, rather than carbon, that greatly changes the properties of iron. Cementite (Fe_3C) is relatively hard and brittle, and acts as a hardener in the iron crystal structure. The hardening and strengthening action of the cementite may be visualized as one of mechanical keying, the hard cementite particles acting as tiny mechanical keys between the weak planes within the iron crystals, thus increasing the resistance of the iron crystals to deformation. This action is much the same as that of the $CuAl_2$ compound in the strengthening and hardening of aluminum.

The total influence of carbon in steel depends upon the (1) amount of carbon, which determines the amount of hard cementite (2) size and shape of the cementite particles, and (3) the distribution of the cementite throughout the iron or ferrite crystal state.

STRUCTURE OF NORMAL STEEL. Steel that has been slowly cooled from a temperature above the critical range (see the discussion of *Critical Temperature*) develops a definite type of structure and definite mechanical properties. We know from past experience what to expect from normal steel so treated. We have seen from a discussion of the iron-carbon system, that iron-carbon alloys develop very definite structural patterns that are easily recognized. A steel containing approximately 0.85% carbon develops a pearlitic structure, one consisting of tiny plates or layers of cementite and ferrite. A steel containing less than 0.85% carbon develops the same pearlitic structure plus an excess of free ferrite. Further, a steel containing greater than 0.85% carbon develops a pearlitic structure with an excess of free cementite. As might be expected, the properties of normal steels are dependent upon the type of structure they develop upon slow cooling; and the type of structure is largely influenced by the percentage of carbon. Therefore, carbon is the principal element controlling the structure and the properties that might be expected from any steel that is slowly cooled from above its critical range. This reasoning applies to any form of carbon steel, whether it be a casting or a forging. We shall soon learn that the rate of cooling from above the critical range will greatly alter the structure and therefore the properties of any steel. Fast cooling (quenching) prevents the normal changes that might be expected, and this constitutes one of the most important factors influencing the properties of steel. The treatment of steel by process of controlled heating and cooling is known as the **heat treatment of steel.**

CARBON IN STEEL. The carbon content of steel may vary from a few hundredths of 1 per cent to 1.40 per cent carbon. The lower percentages are nearly in the range of pure iron, and the properties that very low carbon steel exhibits are those of nearly pure iron. The upper limit of carbon (1.40%C) has been determined by practice, and this limit is controlled by two very obvious effects: (1) the decrease in plasticity and resultant brittleness in the higher percentages of carbon (2) the danger of breakdown of cementite (Fe_3C) into graphitic carbon and ferrite. With the carbon content beyond 1.40% carbon, a weak and brittle steel results, developing properties similar to cast iron. The object of increasing the carbon is to increase the hardness of the steel. Under these circumstances if the carbon were to change from cementite to graphite, the objective of increasing the carbon content would be unattained. Graphitic carbon is a soft and friable form of carbon, and acts as a softener, decreasing the hardness and strength of iron. The tendency of cementite to graphitize, increases with the increase in amount of carbon or cementite; therefore, steels containing the upper limits of carbon are more liable to graphitization than the lower carbon percentages. However, under normal conditions of heating and cooling, steels containing less than 1.40% carbon may be safely handled without the formation of any graphitic carbon. With the carbon all in the combined form as cementite (Fe_3C), the properties that might be expected from hot-worked steels of varying carbon content are illustrated in Fig. 1.

INFLUENCE OF MINOR CONSTITUENTS. We are now familiar with the marked change that carbon makes on the structure of iron, changing iron from a simple metal to a very complex alloy, producing an increase in the hardness and strength, and reducing the plasticity. Along with carbon, all steels contain varying amounts of manganese, silicon, sulphur, phosphorus and other impurities. These other constituents may influence the behavior of the steel, adding therefore to the variables that should be considered when steels are selected for some specific use. We will consider briefly some of the effects produced by these minor constituents.

Manganese. The steel maker cannot make good steel without the use of manganese. Manganese promotes soundness of steel ingot castings through its deoxidizing effect, and by preventing the formation of harmful iron sulphide, promotes forgeability of the steel. Manganese content in regular steels varies from about 0.30 to 0.80%, but in special steels it may run as high as 25.0%. It combines readily with any sulphur in the steel, forming manganese sulphide (MnS), thus preventing the sulphur from combining with the iron. If sulphur is allowed to combine with iron to form sulphide of iron, the effect would be to produce a steel that would be brittle when hot, known as **hot short** steel, resulting in difficulty and perhaps failure during

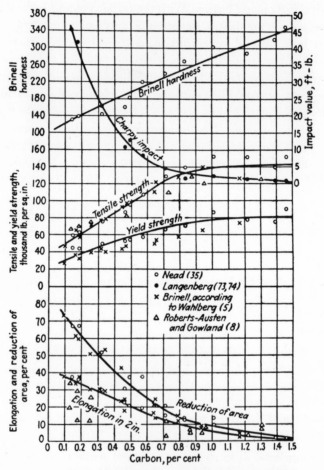

Fig. 1. Effects of Carbon on the Properties of Hot-worked Steel
From *The Alloys of Iron and Carbon*, Vol. II, by Sisco. Reproduced by Permission of The Engineering Foundation

the forging operations. Any excess manganese (over the amount necessary to satisfy all the sulphur) combines with what carbon is present, forming a carbide of manganese (Mn_3C), this carbide associating with the Fe_3C in cementite. Mn_3C has properties similar to

Fe_3C, increasing the hardness and strength, and lowering the plasticity of steel. Manganese is a very important alloying element in many of our special steels.

Silicon. The silicon content of carbon steels varies from 0.05% to 0.30%. Special alloy steels may contain over 2.25% silicon. Silicon dissolves in iron in both the liquid and solid state, forming a solid solution with the iron at room temperature. With a silicon content of 0.30% present in carbon steels, the silicon has very little influence on either the structural characteristics or the mechanical properties of the steel. However, the presence of silicon in the steel during the steel melting operations increases the soundness of the steel ingots by opposing the formation of blowholes, and acts as an aid during the deoxidizing process.

Sulphur. Sulphur content in steel may vary from a trace to 0.30%. In the usual types of steel, the sulphur content is held below 0.06%. Sulphur should always be combined with manganese, for which it has a great affinity, to form manganese sulphide, MnS. This manganese sulphide occurs as pale elongated particles, bands, or strings in steel forgings or rolled stock. Manganese sulphide weakens steel by breaking up the continuity of the steel; and in the shape of elongated particles, it develops directional properties. However, manganese sulphide has a greasy, lubricating effect, and breaks up the chips during the machine cutting of steel, thereby increasing the ease of machining. Steels that are very free cutting usually contain a higher content of sulphur than ordinary steels.

Phosphorus. The phosphorus content of satisfactory steels varies from a trace to about 0.05%. As in the case of silicon, phosphorus remains dissolved in the solid iron and forms a solid solution at room temperature. It is believed that phosphorus increases the tendency toward a coarse-grained steel and therefore may weaken the steel. Also, phosphorus has a marked tendency to segregate in the last sections of a casting to solidify, producing a heterogeneous, dendritic structure. This effect of phosphorus (producing a segregated structure) may result in marked banding of the steel during subsequent hot-working operations, consequently developing marked directional properties in a forging.

Oxides in Steel. Oxides of iron (FeO), manganese (MnO),

silicon (SiO_2), aluminum (Al_2O_3), and other oxides may become trapped in the freezing steel. These impurities are often referred to as dirt in steel. In general these impurities are considered harmful, in that they are associated with the iron in a mechanical manner, being entangled throughout the structure of the steel. These oxide particles break up the continuity of the structure and impart directional properties to the forged steel. Also, as might be expected, they form points of weakness in the steel and may be the cause of the beginning of a fracture and failure. Many failures of steel parts have been traced to particles of dirt in the steel.

Gaseous Impurities. Nitrogen, hydrogen, carbon monoxide and oxygen are always present in varying amounts in steel. These gases may occur as bubbles in the steel or may be dissolved or combined. The effects of these gases have not been accurately determined. However, from the results of all investigations it is thought that all these gases are harmful in that they decrease the plasticity and embrittle the steel. No doubt, the freer the steel is from any of these gaseous impurities, the higher the quality and the more apt it is to be satisfactory.

SELECTION OF CARBON STEELS. Although the quality of steel is not determined by carbon content solely, the carbon content of the steel largely dictates the use to which the steel is to be placed. The quality of any carbon steel is largely determined by the exacting control used by the steel maker; i.e., the metallurgical control used during the steel-making operations and the testing and inspection given the semifinished or finished steel. Close control of the amount of carbon and control of the impurities, oxides and slag, all constitute factors that contribute to good steel. In the selection of a carbon steel for any specific use, both the carbon content and the amount of minor constituents will influence the choice of the steel. In order that the reader may have some suggestions to follow in the selection of a steel, Table 1 should be studied. It will serve as an indicator of the influence of percentage of carbon in the choice of a steel.

To further indicate how selection of a steel may be influenced, the following discussion of certain types of steels should be studied.

COMMERCIALLY PURE IRON. There is now marketed a very low-carbon iron alloy, or steel, known as ingot iron, having a carbon

Table 1. Carbon Content of Carbon Steels for Different Uses

Carbon Range Per Cent	Uses of Carbon Steel
0.05–0.12	Chain, stampings, rivets, nails, wire, pipe, welding stock, where very soft, plastic steel is needed
0.10–0.20	Very soft, tough steel. Structural steels, machine parts. For case-hardened machine parts, screws
0.20–0.30	Better grade of machine and structural steel. Gears, shafting, bars, bases, levers, etc.
0.30–0.40	Responds to heat treatment. Connecting rods, shafting, crane hooks, machine parts, axles
0.40–0.50	Crankshafts, gears, axles, shafts, and heat-treated machine parts
0.60–0.70	Low carbon tool steel, used where a keen edge is not necessary, but where shock strength is wanted. Drop hammer dies, set screws, locomotive tires, screw drivers
0.70–0.80	Tough and hard steel. Anvil faces, band saws, hammers, wrenches, cable wire, etc.
0.80–0.90	Punches for metal, rock drills, shear blades, cold chisels, rivet sets, and many hand tools
0.90–1.00	Used for hardness and high tensile strength, springs, high tensile wire, knives, axes, dies for all purposes
1.00–1.10	Drills, taps, milling cutters, knives, etc.
1.10–1.20	Used for all tools where hardness is a prime consideration; for example, ball bearings, cold-cutting dies, drills, wood-working tools, lathe tools, etc.
1.20–1.30	Files, reamers, knives, tools for cutting brass and wood
1.25–1.40	Used where a keen cutting edge is necessary; razors, saws, instruments and machine parts where maximum resistance to wear is needed. Boring and finishing tools

content below 0.05% carbon. This low-carbon iron or steel is made by the basic open-hearth process. This alloy differs from wrought iron in that it does not contain an appreciable amount of slag, and in that it is cast into ingots similar to steel. It is supplied in the form of rods, bars, wire, sheets and plates. Such iron or steel, due to its low carbon content, cannot be hardened by heat treatment, and any increase in hardness over the annealed or hot-rolled condition is brought about by cold-working operations.

Ingot iron has two distinct advantages over iron alloys containing more carbon. It is very ductile and has a high resistance to corrosion. Due to its high ductility, it can be formed cold by drawing or bending into intricate shapes.

TIN PLATE. The ordinary "tin cans" are not made of tin but of sheet steel which has been coated with a very thin layer of tin and thus is known as tin plate. Tin plate steel is ordinarily made in the basic open hearth and rolled into billets which are sold to the sheet mills for subsequent manufacture into sheets suitable for tin plating. The steel contains from 0.10% to 0.20% carbon and more phosphorus than results from the basic open-hearth process of manufacture. The phosphorus content of the steel is usually increased by the addition of ferro-phosphorus to the molten steel, as it is believed that a high phosphorus content prevents the sticking together of the sheets upon annealing. The billets are first hot-rolled into sheets and finally cold-rolled to sheets of the final thickness, after which they are annealed to facilitate forming into cans, etc. Tin plate for food containers remains one of the stable, high-tonnage products utilizing very low-carbon steel sheets. The use of sheet metal containers for other purposes is increasing.

WIRE, RIVETS, AND NAILS. Such articles are made from either open-hearth or Bessemer steel containing 0.10% or less carbon. The chief requirements of such materials are that they shall be soft enough to form easily and sufficiently ductile to withstand much deformation without cracking. In their manufacture, ingots weighing several tons are hot-rolled to rods of small dimensions and then rolled, drawn, or forged to the required shape.

STRUCTURAL STEEL. Steel for ordinary structural uses, such as beams and angle iron, is a common steel made by the basic open-hearth process, and contains from 0.05% to 0.10% carbon. This steel is usually used in the hot-rolled condition and has a rather low strength when compared with the heat-treated steels of higher carbon content or alloy steels which are usually heat treated. In general, the requirements for this type of steel are strength, ductility, and ease of machining. Under this class of steel may be included the plate steel, which is rolled into plate of varying thicknesses and widths.

FORGING STEEL. Steel for hot forging may contain from 0.25% to 0.65% carbon. Such material is usually rolled into billets or rods of convenient size and then cut and forged into the desired shapes. The forging may consist of several operations, and in machine forging, such as drop forging, several different sets of dies may be used in bringing the pieces to their final shapes.

SCREW MACHINE STEEL. The material from which some parts are made, such as screws, may have very poor mechanical properties, providing it can be machined very easily. Many screws are made in an automatic machine on which the operator does nothing but adjust the machine, start feeding the stock, and remove the finished parts. These parts are made of a steel which can be easily machined, due to its low carbon content and high manganese sulphide content. Such steel contains less than 0.20% carbon, about 0.60% manganese, and about 0.15% sulphur. The manganese combines with the sulphur to form the compound MnS, which is distributed as small inclusions through the bar. These inclusions make the steel brittle but easily machined, as the chips formed from machining break into small particles rather than come off as long ribbons. Such steel is usually made by the Bessemer process.

AXLES. Common railroad axles are made from a basic open-hearth steel containing approximately 0.50% carbon. In making these axles, the ingot is first rolled into billets which are cut into the desired length and forged into axles. These axles are finally machined to the exact dimensions.

WHEELS. Railway car wheels are made from a basic open-hearth steel, the ingots of which are rolled into blooms, the blooms cut into pieces, and these pieces, through several pressings, formed into wheels. The rims of wheels intended for passenger car service are usually machined to their final shape; while for freight cars they are rolled to their final shapes. The composition of wheel steel is very similar to that of rail steel.

STEEL CASTINGS. Many steel parts used in machines and structures are made from steel castings. These castings are made by steel foundry practice, and the castings are usually made to the specifications of the customer. Chemical composition and tensile strength are the usual specifications included in the purchase of steel castings. Carbon content of steel castings may vary from 0.25% to 0.65% carbon. The tensile strength may vary from 75,000 to 150,000 lbs. per sq. in., depending upon the chemical composition and any heat treatment given the casting. To a great extent, the properties and classification of the steel casting depend upon the type of heat treatment it has received. Castings used on low-stressed applications are usually given an annealing heat treatment, whereas castings requiring a high tensile strength are usually subjected to several heat treatments in order to develop the proper strength.

RAILS. The greatest tonnage of rails is now produced by the basic open-hearth process. The steel contains about 0.75% carbon and is deoxidized with silicon and manganese by additions to the furnace or ladles to such an extent that no aluminum need be added

Fig. 2. Microstructure of Properly Annealed Tool Steel, Magnified 500 Times

to the molds. As mentioned before, rails are usually rolled without intermediate reheating. The modern rail rolling mill has reached a high state of mechanical perfection.

SPRINGS. Steel with a high elastic limit is desirable for springs; i.e., a steel which will not permanently deform after being subjected to a high stress. In cheaper steels, desirable springs are made from a rather high-carbon steel which in some instances contains a considerable percentage of manganese and silicon. Such steels are usually used in the heat-treated condition, as the elastic limit can be materially increased by proper heat treatment.

TOOL STEELS. Practically all carbon tool steel is made either by the crucible or electric furnace process, and great care is exercised in order to keep the impurities, such as phosphorus and sulphur, and the nonmetallic inclusions, or dirt, at a minimum. These steels may contain 0.65%–1.40% carbon, depending upon use to which they are put. Such tools as hammers and stamping dies are made from steels of the lower carbon content, because they cannot be brittle and need not be exceptionally hard; while such tools as razors, lathe tools, and drills are made from steels of higher carbon content.

Tool steels, even in the annealed condition, are rather difficult to machine in certain types of machining operations; however, it has been found that by a special annealing treatment, the cementite of these steels may be spheroidized, thus greatly improving the machinability. A photomicrograph of a well-spheroidized material is shown in Fig. 2. The small balls seen in this picture are cementite, while the balance of the material is soft ferrite.

Most tool steels, both carbon and alloy materials, are sold under various trade names. Steel manufacturers issue literature describing the particular uses to which each type of steel is suited, and recommend brands for definite services.

QUIZ QUESTIONS

1. *What is the special significance of the terms "carbon steel" and "plain carbon steel"?*
2. *What is cementite and how is it formed?*
3. *Name the three factors that represent the influence of carbon in steel.*
4. *What element has the greatest influence on the properties of normal steels?*
5. *What is the maximum amount of carbon to be used in steel? Why?*
6. *What is meant by "hot short" steel?*
7. *What function does silicon perform in steel?*
8. *What is the effect of manganese sulphide in steel?*
9. *What harmful effects do impurities cause in steel?*
10. *Name the harmful effects of gases in steel.*
11. *Name the factors in steel-making operations that contribute to good steel.*
12. *What percentage of carbon is used in steel?*
13. *In general, what uses are made of steels having high carbon content?*
14. *What is ingot iron? What are its two distinct advantages?*
15. *Of what are ordinary tin cans made?*
16. *What is the chief requirement of steel used in rivets, nails, etc.?*
17. *What is the carbon content of structural steel?*
18. *What special property is required of steel from which screws are made?*
19. *How is tensile strength developed in steel castings?*
20. *What method is used to deoxidize steel for rails?*
21. *What special property is demanded of steel for springs?*

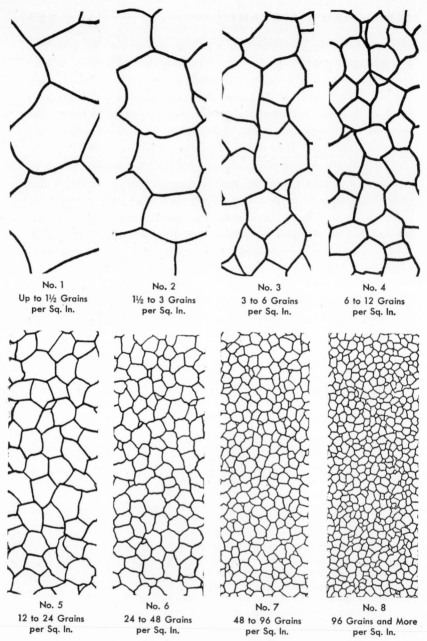

No. 1 Up to 1½ Grains per Sq. In.	No. 2 1½ to 3 Grains per Sq. In.	No. 3 3 to 6 Grains per Sq. In.	No. 4 6 to 12 Grains per Sq. In.
No. 5 12 to 24 Grains per Sq. In.	No. 6 24 to 48 Grains per Sq. In.	No. 7 48 to 96 Grains per Sq. In.	No. 8 96 Grains and More per Sq. In.

A.S.T.M. GRAIN SIZE CHART. GRAIN SIZE MEASURED AT 100 MAGNIFICATIONS

Courtesy of American Society for Testing Materials. Tentative Standard E 19-33T

CHAPTER XI

Heat Treatments for Steel

HARDENING OF CARBON STEEL

THE properties of all steels may be changed very decidedly by heating and cooling under definite conditions. The object of heat treatment is to make the steel better suited, structurally and physically, for some specific application. For thousands of years people did not, scientifically, know what steel was or why it hardened, and it is only within the last few years that the principles involved in the heat treatment of steel and other alloys have been understood. As late as 1540 A.D. metallurgical literature described steel like this:

> Steel is nothing else but iron worked up with much art and much soaking in the fire until it is brought to a perfect mixture and given properties that it did not before possess.
>
> Likewise, it may have taken up suitable material of a fatty tendency, also a certain moisture and thereby become white and denser. The long firing also opens up and softens its pores, which are drawn together again tightly by the power of the cold of quenching water. The iron is thus given hardness and the hardness makes it brittle. As iron can be made from any iron ore, likewise steel can be made from any pure iron.

The most important heat treatment is that of hardening, although, as has been seen, annealing of cold-worked metals is very important to the cold-working industry.

PRINCIPLES INVOLVED IN HARDENING. Hot-rolled or forged steel that has been slowly cooled from above a red heat consists structurally of pearlite with either free ferrite or free cementite, depending upon the carbon content. Also, this slow cooled state of steel results in a relatively soft and plastic condition. If we want to increase the hardness of steel, we carry out two operations: (1) The first operation in the hardening of steel consists of heating the steel to a temperature in excess of the critical temperature or

Ac 1-2-3 line of Fig. 1; (2) The second operation is the rapid cooling
or quenching of the heated steel back to room temperature.

The object of the heating operation is to change the steel from
the normal and soft pearlitic type of structure, to a solid solution
structure called "austenite." This can be accomplished by the heating of any carbon steel to within the temperature range suggested

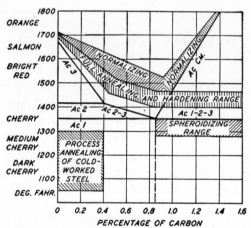

NOTES: 1. HEATING SHOULD BE SLOW AND UNIFORM
2. FOR BEST RESULTS NEVER HEAT HIGHER THAN NECESSARY
3. NORMALIZING = AIR COOLING
4. ANNEALING = FURNACE OR PACK COOLING
5. HARDENING = QUICK COOLING

Fig. 1.   Critical Temperature Diagram Showing Visual Normalizing,
Annealing, and Hardening Ranges

for the hardening of steel as shown in Fig. 1. Steels with less than
1.0% carbon, upon heating to within this range, will become 100%
austenitic; whereas, steels with greater than 1.0% carbon will contain an excess of free cementite in the austenite. The amount of
free cementite, in the higher carbon steels, will depend upon the
total amount of carbon contained in the steel, and on the maximum
temperatures to which the steel is heated. It will be recalled, the
AcCm line of Fig. 1 indicates the solubility of carbon in austenite,
and can be used to determine the amount of free cementite present
in the steel at any selected temperature. When any carbon steel is
heated through the temperature zone, *Ac 1-2-3* of Fig. 1, the alpha
iron in the steel changes to gamma iron. The newborn gamma iron

dissolves the cementite, and greatly refines the grain structure of the steel. When we have refined the grain structure and dissolved the cementite, forming an austenitic structure, the first operation in the hardening of steel has been accomplished. It is with the austenitic type of structure that we can now carry out the second and equally important operation in the hardening of steel, that of rapid cooling or quenching of the austenite.

The object of the second operation in the hardening of steel is to undercool or prevent any change in the austenite other than that of cooling, until a temperature of approximately 200°F. is reached. If we successfully undercool the austenite to 200°F., it changes rapidly to a hard and relatively brittle structure known as "martensite." Martensite is the structure of fully hardened steel; it is born from austenite at approximately 200°F. by the rapid change of gamma iron of austenite to the alpha iron found in pearlite. However, this is the only resemblance of martensite to pearlite, as martensite is hard and pearlite is soft; and pearlite contains cementite in rather coarse particles; whereas martensite apparently retains the carbon or cementite in a dissolved or nearly dissolved state. At least the microscope does not reveal the form of the carbon in martensite.

The second operation in the hardening of steel, that of quenching or rapid cooling of austenite, produces martensite, a structure that is relatively hard and, in the higher carbon steels, brittle. The magic of this simple operation changes a soft, plastic steel to a hard, brittle steel.

MARTENSITE. The true structure of martensite and the reasons for its high hardness and strength are still among the mysteries of modern science. We recognize martensite from its hardness and its structural appearance, which is that of a needle-like structure, Fig. 2. It is thought that martensite consists of a freshly formed alpha iron of a tetragonal atomic orientation born at approximately 200° F. from austenite, with the carbon or cementite in a supersaturated solid solution, or partly precipitated state. The hardness of martensite is in all probability due to several causes. We know that metals are soft and weak due to the easy manner in which the crystals deform by the slipping or sliding of the layers of atoms within any grain. We also know that anything we do, such as reducing the grain size or precipitating hard particles to the slip planes of the crystals, will result in a harder and stronger metal.

There is more resistance to slip along grain boundaries than along the planes formed by the pattern of atoms within the grains; therefore, a fine-grained metal with numerous grain boundaries offers more resistance to slip or deformation by slip than a coarse-grained metal. Also, hard particles such as iron carbide (cementite) interfere with sliding since these particles are precipitated in a very fine submicroscopic size along the slip planes, analogous to the precipitation

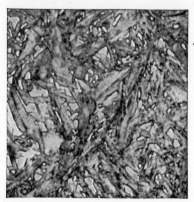

Fig. 2. Martensitic Structure of Hardened Tool Steel; Very Coarse Needle-like Structure Is Due to Quenching from a Coarse-grained Austenitic Condition. Magnified 1500 Times

hardening occurring with aluminum alloys. Thus, some understanding of why metals become hard may be advanced to explain the hardening of martensite. Other theories suggest a condition of distortion of the atomic lattice or disturbed atomic orientation due to a condition of strain as accounting, in part, for the extreme hardness of martensite. Thus, the hardness of martensite may be accounted for by the presence of a fine precipitation of iron carbide, very fine grain size, and possibly a condition of strain.

In any event, the martensitic state of steel is one of the most famous and common structures found in steels. Man for thousands of years has produced steel with a hardness suitable for tools, by the simple operation of quenching austenite and automatically forming martensite at approximately 200° F.

WHY QUENCHING IS NECESSARY. There is only one way to fully harden a piece of steel, and that consists of undercooling austenite to approximately 200° F.; thus martensite and hardened steel result. For thousands of years man has known that it required rapid cooling from the hardening temperature to produce fully hardened steel. Only recently has a complete understanding of this operation been known. Knowledge of this change has been largely developed by Bain and Davenport, whose investigations revealed the rate or time it takes for austenite to transform at different temperatures during the cooling cycle. Fig. 3 illustrates the rate of quenching of austenite necessary in order to produce martensite with 0.85% carbon steel. It is apparent from Fig. 3 that only two types of structures can be obtained from the usual method used in quenching

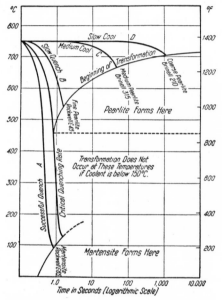

Fig. 3. Chart Showing Schematically the Time and Temperature of Initial Transformation of a Eutectoid Steel as Cooled at Various Uniform Rates. Logarithmic Abscissa

Reproduced by Permission, from *Transactions of the American Society for Steel Treating, Volume 20*, Published by American Society for Metals, Cleveland, Ohio

of steel in any hardening operation—that is, pearlite and martensite. A slow quench as in *B*, Fig. 3, results in the transformation of austenite to pearlite. However, the pearlite formed by this slow quench is a very fine pearlite with a Rockwell hardness of C45. During the slow quench, the transformation of austenite to pearlite, or the change from gamma iron to alpha iron with a precipitation of cementite into very fine plates, takes place at approximately 1000° F., in about two seconds. Slower cooling, as in *C* and *D*, Fig. 3, cools austenite to a lesser degree, and allows a more complete transformation to a coarse pearlite. However, if faster cooling is employed, faster than *B*, no change of the austenite takes place until 200° F. is reached; this causes the birth of martensite. The rate of quenching necessary to undercool austenite to 200° F. is referred to as the "critical rate" of quenching. From a study of Fig. 3, it will be seen that the rate necessary to undercool austenite to below 1000° F., and thereby prevent the birth of softer pearlite, is approximately one second cooling time. Any faster cooling, faster than the critical rate, will only result in a better opportunity to form martensite. However, any slower cooling than the critical rate will result in the formation of soft spots or all soft steel. Such soft spots are due to the formation of a type of pearlite from austenite at about 1000° F. The pearlite that forms at 1000° F. upon quenching has also been called **primary troostite.** Fig. 4 illustrates the structure of a hardened tool steel that was cooled slightly slower than the critical rate, developing a spot of primary troostite or pearlite. Although very little austenite can be undercooled below 200° F. without changing to martensite regardless of the cooling rate, it has been recently discovered that austenite does not change completely to martensite at a fixed temperature such as 200° F. The temperature at which austenite starts to change to martensite, and the temperature at which the change becomes complete, depend on a number of factors, principal among which is the composition of the steel. As a result of this discovery, that martensite forms from austenite over a range of temperatures, it has been found that some austenite may be retained at room temperature. The amount of austenite so retained at room temperature may vary from 1% to 30%. The retained austenite may be transformed to martensite by

Fig. 4. Primary Troostite or Fine Pearlite in Martensite as a Result of Quenching Slower than the Critical Rate. Magnified 1500 Times

the tempering operation or by a method of cold treating, i.e., cooling the hardened steel to sub-room temperature (70° to minus 110° F.). The cold treating causes the retained austenite to transform to martensite without any loss of the maximum hardness the steel is capable of attaining. The temperature at which austenite begins

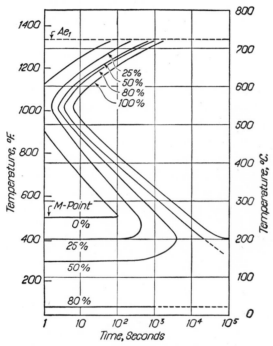

Fig. 5. Schematic Diagram Illustrating the M-point for an 0.80% Carbon Steel

Reproduced by Permission, from *Tool Steels* by Rose, Roberts, Johnston, and George, Published by American Society for Metals, Cleveland, Ohio

to transform to martensite has been designated by the letter M and referred to as the **M-point.** A schematic diagram illustrating the M-point for an 0.80% carbon steel is shown in Fig. 5. In this illustration, it will be noted that the M-point, or the temperature of the beginning of the austenite to martensite transformation, occurs at approximately 500° F., and the transformation to martensite is 80% complete at room temperature; i.e., at room temperature the structure of the quenched steel consists of 80% martensite and

20% retained austenite. The retained austenite may be transformed to martensite by a method of cold treating or by tempering or by a combination of tempering and cold treating. Cold treating, or the cooling of hardened steels to subnormal temperatures, has become a common practice with many of the low alloy and special high alloy steels. Such steels have a tendency to retain more austenite at room temperature than the common carbon steels and respond noticeably to cold-treating methods.

Quenching Media. We have seen that to harden steel fully, i.e., to form martensite, requires rapid cooling from the austenitic temperature range. As we shall also see, all steels do not require the same speed of cooling to transform them to martensite or to prevent the formation of any softer structure. However, they all require a rate of quenching that will undercool the austenite to somewhere near room temperature regardless of whether it is fast or slow. Carbon steels, in general, require a fast rate of cooling such as obtained by a water quench and may be classified as **water-hardening** steels. Many of the low alloy steels may be fully hardened with a slower rate of cooling than obtained in a water quench and are often quenched in oil. Such steels may be classified as **oil-hardening** steels. Some of the high alloy steels have a very slow rate of transformation from austenite and upon cooling in still air from the austenitic temperature will develop, when cold, a fully martensitic structure. Such steels are referred to as **air-hardening** steels. Therefore, the common quenching media used in the hardening process are water, oil, and air.

The action of any liquid quenching medium may be described as having three stages:

1. The first stage occurs when a piece of hot steel is immersed in the liquid bath and the liquid coming in contact with the hot metal is converted into a vapor which may completely envelop the hot metal, forming a blanket around it and preventing any further contact with the cooling liquid. Unless this vapor film is broken, cooling of the hot metal takes place by radiation and conduction through this film, resulting in a relatively slow cooling rate. If this film is maintained, failure to harden or form martensite will result.

2. The second stage occurs when the film formed by the vapor

surrounding the hot metal collapses and breaks away from the surfaces of the hot metal and allows the hot steel to come into contact with the cooling liquid. During this stage, the cooling liquid wets the hot metal surfaces, bursts into vapor, and creates a boil of the quench bath. This greatly activates the cooling liquid and creates the fastest stage of cooling. The old timer said of this stage, "The water bites the steel."

3. The third stage of cooling occurs when the hot metal approaches the boiling point of the liquid quenching medium and cooling continues by liquid conduction and convection, resulting in a relatively slow cooling rate. However, during this stage of cooling, a fast rate of quenching is not as necessary as during the earlier stages, particularly during the second stage when the steel is passing the temperature range where the transformation of austenite is at a maximum.

The vapor film formed during the first stage of quenching may prevent the successful hardening of the steel. Soft steel, soft spots, warping, and cracking may be a result of the vapor stage. A great majority of the common hardening difficulties occur during this stage.

Water is the most commonly used quenching medium and is used in the hardening of many of the common carbon and low alloy steels. Steels that have a very rapid transformation rate from austenite and are shallow hardening require water or some aqueous solution as a quenching medium.

In order that the quenching rate may be great enough to consistently harden carbon steel, water should be kept at a temperature below 80° F. and be continuously agitated during the quenching operation. Agitation of the cooling medium allows a more uniform and faster cooling action. A 5% sodium-chloride brine solution usually results in a more satisfactory quenching medium for carbon steels. The brine gives a faster and more uniform quenching action and is less affected by increase in temperature. A 3% to 5% sodium hydroxide quenching bath also is recommended as a good quenching medium for carbon steels. This bath cools even faster than the sodium chloride bath.

Oil is frequently used as a quenching medium and may be used when the operation involves the hardening of carbon steels of such a thin section that quenching in oil results in the formation of martensite. Thin sections such as knives, razor blades, and wire may be successfully hardened in an oil-quenching medium. Oil is recommended as a quenching medium in preference to water whenever it can be used because of less danger of cracking with less distortion and quenching stresses. The action of oil is quite different from that of water as it has a more rapid quenching rate during the first or vapor stage but a much slower rate during the second stage when the oil is wetting the hot metal surfaces. Oil can be used only with light sections of shallow hardening steels and for heavy sections when the hardening operation is carried out with steels that have a slow transformation rate from austenite and are deep hardening, as in many of the alloy steels.

Oil cools steel much more slowly during the last cooling stage. This is desirable because it results in much less danger of severe internal stresses, warping, and cracking. Also, as this last stage is usually below the M-point for most steels (500° F.), no undesirable results occur. Oils differ in quenching characteristics and should be carefully selected. Such properties as flash point, boiling point, density, and specific heat should be considered. Also, care used in the selection of the proper volume and design of the quenching system is essential in order to control the temperature of the quenching oil. In general, it requires approximately one gallon of oil for every pound of steel quenched per hour; therefore, if 100 pounds of steel are to be hardened every hour, a tank of 100 gallons capacity is required, and some method used whereby the temperature of the oil in the tank is maintained between 80° and 150° F. Keeping the oil hot (120°–130° F.) is advantageous and will give a good quenching rate and reduce the danger of cracking and warping of the steel by lowering the residual quenching stresses.

Air cooling is employed with some high alloy steels of the air-hardening type. Steels to be hardened are removed from the heating furnace and exposed to still air. The rate of cooling in air may be modified by the use of an air blast, but no quantitative results have been established when the velocity of air striking the hot steel is varied.

Hot-quenching treatments are used in an attempt to combine

the principles of hardening and tempering in the same operation and consist of quenching the hot steel in a molten salt bath held at a constant temperature, usually between 350° and 800° F. The steel is quenched in the hot bath and held long enough to equalize at the temperature of the quenching bath, or long enough to transform from austenite isothermally into martensite or some softer type of structure. The hot-quenching methods will be discussed under the austempering and martempering methods of heat treating.

BAIN "S" CURVE. To further illustrate the transformation of austenite undercooled to below the critical temperature, Fig. 6, referred to as the "S" curve, may be studied. The "S" curve indicates the time it takes for austenite to transform at any temperature to which it has been undercooled from 1300° F. to 100° F. From Fig. 6 we learn that, as austenite is undercooled, the rate of transformation from austenite to pearlite increases until we undercool to 1000° F. Below 1000° F. to 450° F. the rate of transformation slows up and it takes longer to complete the transformation. From 450° F. the rate of change increases with lower temperatures to approximately room temperature. From Fig. 6, it will be seen that it takes approximately one hour at 1300° F. to transform from austenite to soft pearlite. If we undercool austenite to 1000° F., it takes only about eight seconds to complete the transformation to pearlite. However, the pearlite formed at 1000° F. is a much finer and harder pearlite than that formed at 1300° F. If we successfully undercool austenite to 550° F., it requires about two minutes for the transformation of austenite to begin and about one hour for the completed change to a very fine and relatively hard Rockwell C56, pearlitic type of structure. Finally martensite is formed at approximately 200° F.

EFFECT OF CARBON. The hardening capacity of steel clearly increases with the increase of carbon up to about 0.60% carbon. The carbon plays two parts in the hardening of steel: (1) Up to about 0.60% carbon, it makes easier undercooling austenite to 200° F. therefore making it easier to harden the steel. Apparently carbon acts as a retardant, slowing up the rate of transformation. (2) The carbon present in the fresh-born martensite increases the hardness; in fact, the carbon, dissolved or partly precipitated in the form of cementite, probably is the greatest single factor in causing the martensite to

Transformation of Austenite in 0.78% Carbon Steel
at Constant Sub-Critical Temperature

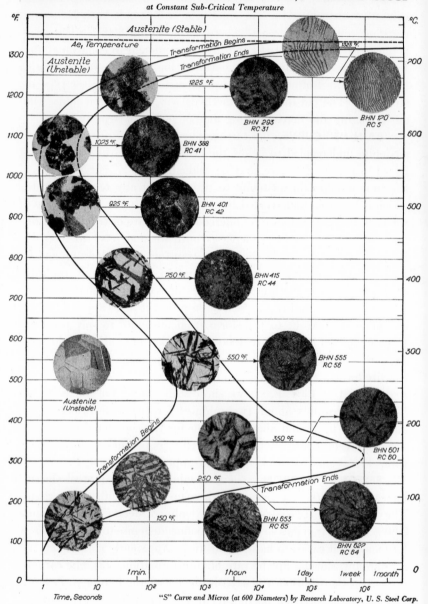

Fig. 6. Transformation of Austenite in 0.78% Carbon Steel
Reproduced by Permission, from *Metal Progress*, *1941*, Published by American Society for Metals

be hard. The carbon, as cementite Fe_3C, probably acts in much the same way as the $CuAl_2$ in the hardening of aluminum. Fig. 7 illustrates the effect of carbon upon the hardness of carbon steels in both the hardened and normal pearlitic condition. An interesting fact is that the maximum hardness obtained in steel by making it martensitic never exceeds a Rockwell hardness of C67 or a Brinell hardness of 745, regardless of the carbon content and special alloys.

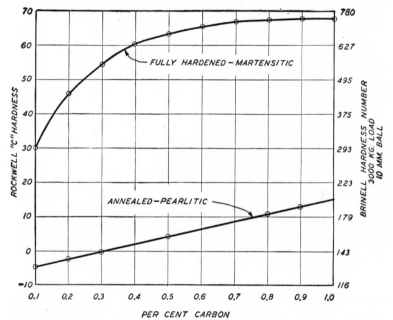

Fig. 7. Effect of Carbon Content upon Hardness of Carbon Steel in Martensitic and Pearlitic Conditions (Approximate)

Increasing the carbon content beyond 0.85% increases the hardness of the steel in both the pearlitic and martensitic condition, but also, the high carbon content increases the rate of transformation of austenite to pearlite, and therefore makes it more difficult to successfully harden this steel to a full martensitic condition.

Although the curve for fully hardened steel, Fig. 7, shows that it is possible to obtain an appreciable increase in hardness in low carbon steels by heating and quenching, it becomes increasingly difficult to trap 100% alpha martensite in the lower carbon steels.

Steels with less than 0.30% carbon are commonly not hardened because of this difficulty. The curve, Fig. 7, shows a possible hardness of Rockwell C55 with a 0.30% carbon steel. This hardness cannot be obtained unless the section is very thin and is drastically quenched in a water spray of severely agitated brine or caustic solutions. With a carbon content of 0.20%, it is not practical to expect maximum hardness of Rockwell C45 from the ordinary quench-hardening operation. However, in the event the shape and size of the steel part is such as to lend itself to drastic quenching and a

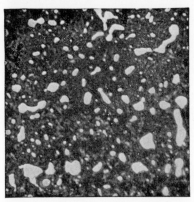

Fig. 8. Undissolved Cementite in a Tempered Martensitic Background. High Carbon Tool Steel. Magnified 1500 Times

quenching method designed to give maximum cooling speeds is employed, marked increase in hardness and other mechanical properties may be had by the simple process of hardening. Recently, this practice has been applied, with satisfactory results, to the manufacture of strong and tough cartridge cases made from 0.27% carbon steel. The major problem in their successful hardening was one of obtaining a severe enough quench to undercool the austenite of this low carbon steel to about 200° F. However, when the carbon content of steel exceeds 0.30% carbon, it becomes increasingly easier to harden the steel to a fully martensitic condition and obtain the maximum hardness indicated by Fig. 7. In the hardened condition, steel containing over 1.00% carbon consists of martensite with some free cementite particles, illustrated by Fig. 8. The greater hardness of this type of steel is due to the presence of cementite, and not to a greater ability to harden.

SHALLOW HARDENING OF CARBON STEELS. It has been pointed out that in order to harden a piece of steel, make it martensitic, it must be rapidly cooled from the proper hardening temperature. It is to be expected that the action of the liquid quenching media in the rapid cooling of the steel acts only on the surface of the steel object. The interior of any steel object must of necessity cool at a slower rate than the surface. It is natural to expect from this behavior of the cooling medium that the interior of the steel object may cool slower than the rate required to produce martensite, and thus remain relatively soft and tough. Due to the fast cooling rate needed in the hardening of carbon steels, the center of any steel object may remain soft and tough, only the surface attaining maximum hardness and becoming martensitic. This leaves the steel object with a hard surface and a tough core; this characteristic of carbon steel has made it a favorite where a combination of hardness and toughness is needed. The very property that makes carbon steels difficult to harden, rapid transformation rate, allows us to produce a hardened tool or steel object with a hard wear resistant surface and a tough core to guard against breakage.

The shallow hardening effect of carbon steels makes it difficult to harden a piece of carbon steel with a heavy section. The tremendous amount of heat energy stored up in a heavy section may even prevent the surface of the steel from cooling fast enough to produce a fully hard surface. In any event, the penetration of hardness in a heavy section would be very slight, and perhaps not great enough to prove satisfactory. To avoid this mass effect, heavy sections may be cored or hollow bored, thereby cutting down the maximum section. If the section cannot be reduced, a special or alloy steel may be employed with a deeper hardening effect, thus overcoming the effect of the heavy section. Also, in recent years, the steelmaker has discovered that grain size plays an important part in controlling the hardening ability of steel. A coarse-grained steel will harden with a deeper penetration of martensite than will a fine-grained steel of the same chemical composition.

EFFECT OF GRAIN SIZE. For many years plants in the consuming industry have endured continued variation in the quench-hardening results of carbon steels. Steels with the same chemical composition, given identical heat treatments, yield variations during hardening; some steels harden satisfactorily, others harden with a very deep penetration of hardness, and still other steel objects harden to a very shallow depth, and in some cases with soft spots. This condition resulted in every up-to-date and well-controlled plant keeping the different steel heats separate. (If each heat of steel was kept separate, it soon became evident that individual heats varied in such important properties as hardening ability and distortion during hardening.) It has been determined that one of the most important factors contributing to this condition was the inherent grain size with which a steel was born. The inherent grain size refers to the grain size that a given steel develops when heated to the proper hardening temperature. The steelmaker, during the steelmaking operations, can control the inherent grain size of a steel and therefore control, within certain limits, the grain size the steel will develop upon heating to above the critical temperature, as in hardening of the steel.

It has been determined that fine-grained steels have a fast rate of transformation from the austenitic condition and are therefore shallow hardening; whereas the coarse-grained steels are deep hardening and more easily hardened, with a slower rate of transformation. The standard grain-size chart as determined by the American Society for Testing Materials is shown on p. 228. With this added control of grain size, carbon steels are treated with much greater uniformity and receive much favor, as they are inherently better suited for many applications than special or alloy steels. Fig. 9 illustrates the effect of inherent grain size upon the depth of hardness of one inch rounds of 1.0% carbon tool steels.

EFFECT OF VARYING HARDENING TEMPERATURE. The penetration of hardness in any standard carbon tool steel may be affected to a large degree by control of the maximum temperature selected by the hardener. It will be recalled that the grain size of austenite is a minimum at a temperature close to the *Ac 1-2-3* line of Fig. 1. Heating beyond the *Ac 1-2-3* temperature results in grain growth of the newborn austenite. By heating to just above the *Ac 1-2-3* critical temperature a very fine grain results in a shallow hardening effect; whereas, heating beyond the critical temperature and developing a coarser-grained austenite will produce a deeper hardening effect. Larger pieces to be hardened, forging dies, etc., which require a deep penetration of martensite are usually heated to a much higher temperature in the hardening operation to insure uniform surface hardness and rather deep penetration of hardness; small dies and thin sections may be hardened from a temperature close to the critical temperature with satisfactory results.

WARPING AND CRACKING. Warping and particularly cracking are serious menaces in nearly every hardening operation. In fact, one of the most severe tests a piece of steel receives is that of quenching in water or brine from the hardening temperature. The quenching operation may ruin the steel object by causing severe distortion or even breakage of the piece. Warping or cracking is

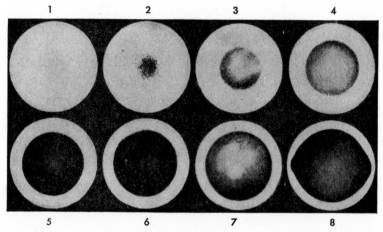

Fig. 9. No. 1 Coarse to No. 8 Fine-Grained Steels, Illustrating Effect of Penetration of Hardness. Hardened Steels, Cut or Sectioned and Etched to Bring Out Depth of Hardening (White Is Hard; Dark Core Is Soft)

Reproduced by Permission, from *Transactions of the American Society for Steel Treating, Volume 20*, Published by American Society for Metals

caused by severe stresses or load, set up by uneven contraction and expansion that takes place during the hardening operation. Some of the sections of the steel object being hardened may be expanding while other parts of the same steel may be contracting. At least the contraction that takes place during the severe cooling as in quenching will never be an even contraction; therefore, some distortion always occurs. Distortion or warping will always take place, and if the stresses become severe enough and the steel is made martensitic and brittle, danger of breakage by cracking is always present. The distortion that takes place as a result of the hardening operation leads to the costly operations involved in straightening and grinding the hardened steel in an attempt to remove the distortions and make the steel parts true to shape. A study of the part to be hardened may often save a great deal of future trouble and cost. The heat treater may exhibit real skill and craftsmanship in the manner he selects to treat a given steel object to be hardened. Some of the many factors influencing warping and cracking may include: (1) Un-

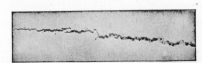

Fig. 10. Slag Stringer in Steel as a Source of Trouble in Hardening Operations

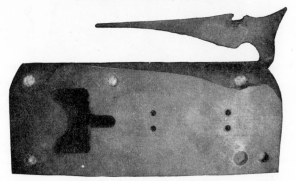

Fig. 11. Hardened Die of Carbon Steel with Corners and Edges Spalled Off; Shallow Hardening Steel

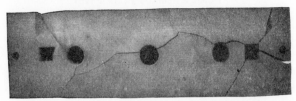

Fig. 12. Die Split in Hardening; Deep-hardening Steel

balanced and abrupt changes in section; (2) Sharp corners and deep tool marks, which act as crack formers; (3) Intricate shapes, with many cut out sections; (4) Defects in the steel, such as seams, dirty steel, segregation, and coarse grains, which may weaken the steel and cause trouble. Fig. 10 illustrates a slag stringer in steel that caused failure in the hardening operation. Fig. 11 illustrates a common type of failure in shallow hardening carbon tool steel, that of spalling failure. Corners or surfaces of the steel spall from the body of the object. Fig. 12 illustrates the bursting or splitting type of failure occurring in deep hardening type of steels, steels that harden nearly all the way through the object. Fortunately, these failures may be avoided in the majority of the hardening operations.

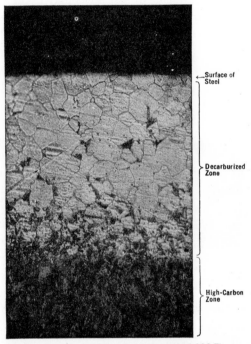

Surface of Steel

Decarburized Zone

High-Carbon Zone

Fig. 13. Decarburized Tool Steel; Magnified 200 Times

SOFT SKIN OR SURFACE. Soft skin or surface on hardened steel is the result of burning off the surface carbon or decarburization of the steel. Decarburization of steel causes a low carbon or nearly pure iron layer to form on the surface of steel, leaving this decarburized surface soft after the hardening operation. Fig. 13 illustrates a badly decarburized carbon tool steel. Decarburization may be prevented by proper control of the atmosphere surrounding the steel during the heating operation. The proper use of lead or salt baths, or the control of the gaseous atmosphere in an oven type of hardening furnace, may prevent any decarburization from taking place. However, all steels as received from the steel mill retain a decarburized skin which will cause trouble unless it is removed prior to the hardening operation. All steel should be bought oversize so that it may be ground or machined, removing the decarburized surface, before the hardening operation.

SOFT SPOTS. Soft spots or soft areas may occur on the surface of hardened tools and dies. These soft spots are caused by the transformation of austenite to pearlite at 1000° F. in the quenching

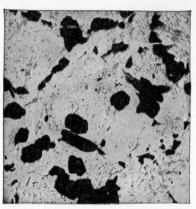

operation. Allowing the quenching medium to get too hot or dirty, poor agitation of the quenching medium, scale or dirt on the steel surface, interference to the quenching action by the tongs or holders used in handling the steel, or anything else that will retard the quenching action may contribute to soft spots. Deep recesses in the steel surfaces where pockets of vapor may collect will prevent proper quenching action and cause soft areas.

Fig. 14. Soft Spots in Hardened Steel. Soft Spots, Black in Light Martensite; Magnified 500 Times

To avoid soft spots, a spray quenching practice, which allows the cooling medium to flow rapidly past the parts to be hardened may be necessary. Fig. 14 illustrates soft areas in martensite.

EFFECT OF ALLOYS. In general, alloy steels, steels containing special alloying elements, are easier to harden than plain carbon steels. Alloy steels are less sensitive, and allow more latitude in the selection of a hardening temperature and in the manner of quenching. This makes it easier for the heat treater to carry out the hardening operation and obtain the desired results. In general, alloy steels may be quenched in oil to produce the hardened state. Oil, being a slower cooling medium than water or brine, causes less distortion and danger of cracking.

TEMPERING OF HARDENED STEEL. The heat-treating operation known as "tempering of steel" is carried out following the hardening operation. Tempering of steel consists of heating quenched, hardened steel, steel in the martensitic condition, to some predetermined temperature between room temperature and the critical temperature of the steel for a certain length of time, followed by air cooling. The rate of cooling from the tempering temperature in most cases is without effect. There are very few applications where a fully hardened martensitic condition of steel may be successfully used, because of its brittle condition. The heat treater, by means of the tempering operation, conditions the hardened steel for successful performance.

The hardening operation, if properly carried out, imparts to the steel the following characteristics:

1. The smallest grain
2. Maximum hardness
3. Minimum ductility
4. Produces internal stresses and strains

In this condition, steel is sometimes harder than necessary, although the most obvious deficiency is the lack of toughness in fully hardened steel. This lack of toughness, with the internally stressed condition present, makes hardened steel unsuitable for use. The hardness is needed in most applications, but the extremely brittle condition makes it necessary to subject the steel to further heat treatment, i.e., tempering. In order to relieve this stressed state and decrease the brittleness, while preserving sufficient hardness and strength, the steel is generally tempered. Reasons for tempering are:

1. To increase toughness
2. To decrease hardness
3. To relieve stresses
4. To stabilize structure
5. To change volume

EXPLANATION OF TEMPERING. Quench-hardened steel is considered to be in an unstable condition, that is, the structure of the hardened steel (martensite) was obtained by severe quenching of the steel from the austenitic state, thereby undercooling the austenite to nearly room temperature before it transformed to the martensitic structure. Perhaps in most quenching operations some austenite is retained at room temperature.

The martensitic structure of the hardened steel is much different from the structure of normal pearlite formed in steels that have been slow-cooled from the austenitic state. The fresh-born martensite is known as alpha martensite and has a tetragonal atomic arrangement. Martensite in this condition is eager to change to a more stable structure more nearly pearlitic and actually undergoes this change when given an opportunity, such as when the temperature is raised during the tempering operation. Upon heating the alpha martensite formed in plain carbon steels to approximately 200° F., the tetragonal atomic arrangement is said to change to a body-centered cubic lattice similar to the pattern found in alpha ferrite. The martensite tempered to 200° F. with the body-centered cubic structure is known as beta martensite. Microscopic examination of the tempered beta martensite reveals a darkening of the needle-like martensite structure. This change is accompanied by a decrease in volume causing a shrinkage in the dimensions of the hardened steel. Further heating causes the beta martensite to precipitate carbon in the form of cementite (Fe_3C) which has been held in supersaturated solution in the martensite. The precipitated cementite particles are of minute size when this action starts, so tempering to low temperatures around 400° F. will not reveal their size by microscopic examination. However, if the tempering temperature is raised beyond 400° F., the minute cementite particles continue to grow in size, finally becoming microscopic.

The grains of iron also grow in size. The hotter the hardened steel is heated, the faster this change, the atomic structure becoming less rigid and more free to change and, finally, the martensite may be changed to a soft coarse structure similar to pearlite. The microscope may be used to follow the structural changes taking place during the tempering of a martensitic structure, but the structural details, such as the action of precipitation, cannot be resolved as a result of the lower temperatures used in tempering. Apparently the cementite particles do not reach a size that becomes microscopic until a temperature of 600° F. is reached. Figs. 15 and 16 illustrate the change from martensite that might be expected upon tempering to 600° F. and 1200° F., as seen with the aid of a microscope. Actually, the cementite has grown to a size that is easily seen with the microscope.

Any retained austenite found in hardened carbon or low alloy steels may be transformed to martensite or a tempered form of martensite upon reheating to 500° F. The changing of austenite to martensite upon tempering is accompanied by an expansion which may be very marked. Such a change results in added internal stresses and should be taken into consideration by increasing the tempering time so as to at least partially remove them. Transforming the retained austenite to martensite by reheating to 500° F. will effect a change in the original martensite resulting in a loss of maximum

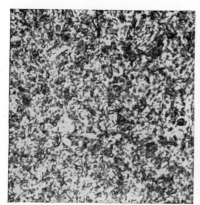

Fig. 15. Martensite Tempered to 600° F. Cementite Particles May Be Seen in This Specimen. Magnified 1500 Times

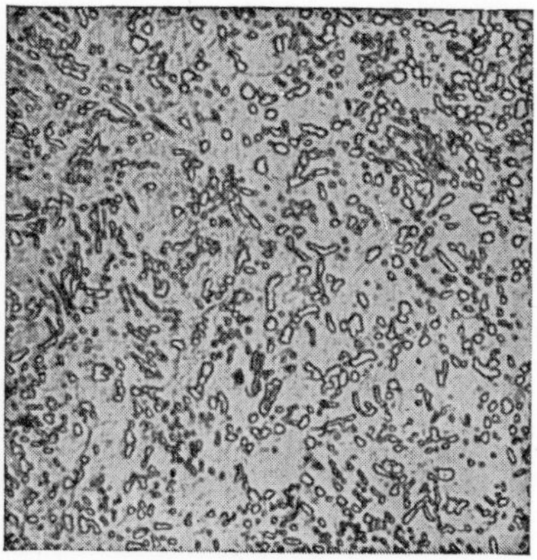

Fig. 16. Martensite Tempered to 1200° F. White Cementite Particles Have Grown to an Obvious Size in This Treatment, Which Is a Spheroidizing Treatment

hardness. It has been discovered that any austenite retained at room temperature may be transformed to martensite by cold treating, i.e., cooling the hardened steel to subnormal temperatures (70° to minus 110° F.). Cold treating to transform the austenite will not result in any loss of hardness of the original martensite as that which occurs during tempering and will result in maximum hardness being obtained. The cold treating of hardened steel may be followed by the usual tempering treatment and is sometimes used after a tempering treatment. There is some danger of cracking due to residual stress and added stresses during a cold treating operation; however, this may be avoided by first tempering the hardened steel and then subjecting it to the cold treatment followed by another tempering treatment.

EFFECT OF TEMPERING UPON HARDNESS AND TOUGHNESS.

Too little is known about the exact influence of tempering upon the
hardness and toughness of hardened steels. It is assumed that softening of the martensite is progressive throughout the whole of the
tempering range. Fig. 17 illustrates the change that might be expected when a hardened 1.10% carbon steel is tempered. It is certain that tempering of hardened plain carbon tool steel, at tem-

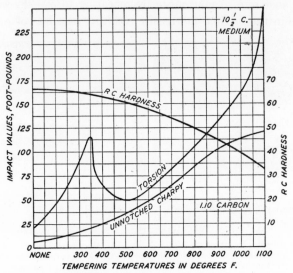

Fig. 17. Influence of Tempering Temperatures on Fully Hardened
1.10% Carbon Steel as Indicated by Rockwell Hardness, Torsional
Impact, and Unnotched Charpy Impact Testing (after Palmer)

peratures above 390° F., reduces its cutting hardness and its hardness
as measured by the Rockwell and Brinell hardness testing methods.
Tempering of carbon tool steel at temperatures near room temperature has been reported as increasing the hardness of some quenched,
hardened steels. It has been noted that quenched, hardened steels
increase in hardness with time when aged or tempered at room
temperature. This increase in hardness may be due to some retained
austenite in the quenched steel slowly changing to martensite at
room temperature.

It should be understood clearly that the purpose of tempering
is not to lessen the hardness of quenched steel, but to increase the

toughness so as to avoid breakage and failure of the heat-treated steel. Fully hardened steel with a carbon content greater than 0.60% carbon is brittle and therefore dangerous as a tool or structural part of a machine. Any slight overload or sudden shock load may cause failure. The heat treater by means of tempering may reduce the brittleness and increase the plasticity of martensite, thereby imparting a greater degree of toughness to the steel. Measuring hardened steel for toughness and resistance to failure has been a difficult task and is yet a debatable undertaking, particularly in fully martensitic steels. Tests have been made by impact testing and torsional impact testing methods, and some very interesting results have been obtained. Fig. 17 illustrates the effect of tempering on a fully hardened carbon tool steel as measured by the Charpy impact testing methods, and the torsional impact method. If we assume that these methods of testing are measures of toughness, then it becomes apparent that the gain of toughness upon tempering is not progressive over the entire tempering range. In fact, tempering to within a temperature range of 500 to 600° F. may show a loss of toughness. Because of this effect, the region of 500–600° F. has been referred to as the **brittle tempering range.** Also some steels, particularly in the chromium-nickel steels of relatively high carbon content, develop a seemingly brittle condition if tempered around 1150° F. The cause of this condition has not been clearly explained. Such steels may be cured of this brittle condition by quenching from the tempering temperature when the steel will have its expected toughness.

EFFECT OF TIME IN TEMPERING. In general, the longer the time of treatment at a given tempering temperature the better the results from tempering. Longer time seems to release, to a greater extent, the locked-up stresses of the quenched steel, and to increase the plasticity and toughness without marked decrease in the hardness. Apparently, increasing the temperature during tempering increases the rate of any transformation, such as precipitation and growth of the cementite, but changes in the structure seemingly continue with time and allow a more complete change to take place. It is recommended that at least one hour be allowed at any tempering temperature for satisfactory results. Some tempering operations being carried out consume many hours.

VOLUME CHANGES. It is known that when austenite changes to martensite during the hardening operation, a marked expansion takes place. Martensite has the greatest volume of all the structures in steel. Aging of freshly formed martensite at room temperature results in a contraction in volume, and, upon tempering, the contraction continues. This volume change, and other changes taking place during tempering, are accompanied by an evolution of heat. This change in volume adds to the problem in controlling the size and shape of steel during heat-treating operations. Tempering usually will bring the steel back to more nearly the original volume; in some steels, the tempering temperature selected for the steel is somewhat determined by the amount of contraction that takes place, or at what temperature it returns to more nearly its original volume.

TEMPERING METHODS. Tempering of steel may be accomplished in liquid baths such as oil, salt, or lead. These baths are heated to the correct temperature, and the steel is immersed in the bath for the determined length of time, after which the steel is removed and allowed to cool to room temperature. Tempering is very successfully carried out in air tempering furnaces. In these furnaces, air is heated by gas or electric means, and the hot air is circulated around parts to be tempered. These furnaces are fully automatic.

COLOR OXIDES. If a piece of carbon steel is polished and then heated, the brightened surface will take on what are known as **temper colors.** These temper colors form because the bright surface of the steel oxidizes and forms films of varying thickness of oxide of iron. For many years, man has used these color oxides to indicate the temperature of steel heated to low temperatures. They are not any indication of the physical condition of the steel, and at best are only a rough estimate of the actual temperature. Table 1 gives some idea as to the color that might be expected at different temperatures on heating, and a few suggested uses for the different tempering temperatures. In using this method for tempering, steel is hardened and polished, then slowly heated over a fire or any hot medium until the color corresponding to the desired tempering temperature is seen on the polished surface. Care should be taken to prevent heating beyond the temperature desired. Cooling may be carried out by oil quenching or cooling in air.

Table 1. Temper Color Chart

Degrees Fahrenheit	Oxide Color	Suggested Uses for Carbon Steels
430	Faint Straw	Twist drills, taps, lathe tools, paper cutters
460	Dark Straw	Punches and dies, flat drills, wood-cutting tools
500	Bronze	Rock drills, hammer faces, shear blades
540	Purple	Axes, wood-carving tools
570	Dark Blue	Iron and steel chisels, knives
610	Light Blue	Springs, screw drivers, saws for wood
630	Steel Gray	Springs; cannot be used for cutting tools

AUSTEMPERING. From a study of Bain's "S" curve, Fig. 6, it becomes apparent that it is possible to obtain only two structures of uniform hardness in a carbon tool steel by the usual methods of quench hardening, i.e., a structure with a Rockwell hardness of 40–42C, or a structure (martensite) with a Rockwell hardness of 64–65C. To obtain a hardness of Rockwell 56C, the heat treater makes his steel fully hard, Rockwell 65C, then by means of reheating or tempering he reduces this hardness to the specified one, Rockwell 56C, and thereby obtains an increase in plasticity and toughness. This method of heat treatment is used in the greater tonnage of heat-treated steels. However, a microscopic amount of steel parts is now being treated by a relatively new and novel method, that of **austempering.**

A study of Bain's "S" curve will reveal that if we can successfully undercool austenite to 550° F., austenite at this temperature will transform to a structure that is supposedly a very fine pearlite that may exhibit a uniform Rockwell hardness of 56C. It requires the holding of austenite at 550° F. for about one hour to complete this change. Now we have obtained a structure with a uniform hardness without first the birth of martensite. This method of tempering has been called austempering, or the direct tempering of austenite.

It is accepted that a steel with a Rockwell hardness of 56C obtained by austempering is much tougher than the same steel treated to the same Rockwell hardness by the usual method of hardening and tempering. Also, never producing martensite, this method eliminates much of the danger of cracking, and reduces the amount of distortion or warping resulting from the rapid quench to nearly room temperature that is required in the formation of martensite. It is true that in austempering an equally fast rate of cooling is required, but the quench is stopped at the austempering temperature, which is well above room temperature, before any martensite can be formed.

The quenching media for austempering is usually a molten salt bath held at the required temperature. Steel is heated to the hardening temperature and quenched into the molten salt and held there until the transformation has been completed, then allowed to cool to room temperature. The difficulty encountered in austempering is in preventing the austenite from transforming around 1000° F. by obtaining a quenching rate fast enough in a hot quenching medium. At the present time, only objects of relatively thin section may be successfully treated by this method. Some of the applications include springs, light tools, screws, pins, needles, etc.

MARTEMPERING. Martempering is the name given to the process of hardening whereby steel is heated in the usual way to the austenitic range, but, instead of water or oil quenching, the steel is quenched in a hot salt bath. The steel is held long enough in the hot quenching bath to allow the temperature to equalize throughout the steel and then is removed from the quenching bath and cooled to room temperature in air, followed by the conventional tempering operation.

Martempering differs from austempering in that isothermal changes occur during the austempering operation with a complete change from austenite to a tempered form of martensite before the temperature is lowered to normal. In the martempering operation, little or no change from austenite occurs until the steel is lower in temperature than the quenching medium. A study of the S-curve, Fig. 18, indicates what might be expected from the martempering process. The steel in an austenitic condition is quenched at a rate equal to or faster than the critical rate, to a temperature above 400° F. If the quenching rate is fast enough, the austenite is undercooled to this low range, 400° to 500° F. (approximate). The quenched steel is held at the temperature of the hot bath just long enough to cool uniformly to approximately the temperature of the bath, a matter of a few seconds to a few minutes. The time spent in the hot quenching

bath should be long enough to equalize the temperature of the
quenched steel section, after which the steel is removed from the
quenching bath and allowed to cool to room temperature. During
the cooling cycle from approximately 500° F. to room temperature,
the austenite will transform to martensite. (See Fig. 18.) The temperature of the quenching bath is usually maintained slightly above
the M-point, or the beginning of the austenite to martensite change;

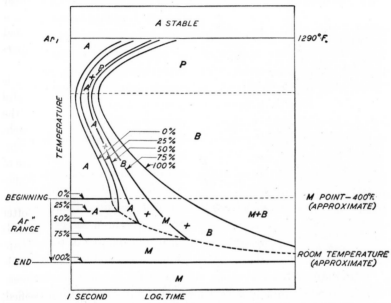

Full lines represent per cent of austenite transformed. A = austenite, P = pearlite, B = bainite, M = martensite or tempered martensite

Fig. 18. Modified S-Curve diagram. The S-Curve for a Plain Carbon Tool Steel (0.80% C)
Showing the Time Required for Transformation at Each Temperature. Schematic

Reproduced by Permission, from *Tool Steels* by Rose, Roberts, Johnston and George, Published by American Society for Metals, Cleveland, Ohio

otherwise an appreciable quantity of martensite will form during the
quenching cycle and defeat the purpose of the process. The M-points
for the different steels vary, but, in general, satisfactory results from
martempering have resulted by holding the temperature of the
quenching bath at 400° F.

The principal advantage of martempering is that less internal
stresses result from a lower temperature differential between the

outside and center of the steel during the transformation stage from austenite to martensite. Both austempering and martempering have this advantage, but martempering would be selected when maximum hardness is required. Both methods eliminate failures from cracking, which is always a threat from the usual quenching methods. Fig. 19 illustrates a slight crack in martensite resulting from water quenching of the specimen used for this photomicrograph. Such a crack has been referred to as a martensitic crack and may be avoided by austempering or martempering.

Fig. 19. Crack in Martensite Due to Severe Stresses Resulting from the Hardening Operation. Magnified 1500 Times

Successful martempering is dependent upon the successful undercooling of austenite to the temperature of the hot quenching bath. The difficulty encountered is largely due to the use of a steel mass that cannot be successfully undercooled, so that the austenite transforms to a softer form of pearlite. However, this process has been successfully applied to a number of parts made from carbon and low alloy steels.

NORMALIZING. If a normalizing heat treatment is specified, it usually refers to a heat treatment that involves heating steel to above its critical range, Fig. 1, followed by cooling in air. The maximum temperature, the time at that temperature, and the cooling conditions are very influential, and in any application should be carefully worked out. The normalizing heat treatment is applied to steels that are known to have poor structures, structures that are uneven in grain size and segregated. Normalizing is used for forgings that have a banded and laminated type of structure, see Fig. 7, Chapter VI, and Fig. 20 of this chapter. Fig. 21 illustrates the improvement of structure obtained from a normalizing heat treatment applied to a forging of low alloy steel, carbon 0.30 to 0.40%. Normalizing also is used as a treatment to improve the uniformity and refine the structure of castings as well as forgings. It improves steel from the viewpoint of better results obtained in other treatments, including annealing and hardening. Also, some steels develop satisfactory physical properties from a single normalizing heat treatment, so that they are put into service without additional heat treatments. Steel forgings may vary in physical characteristics even when made out of the same lot of steel. This is due to the different handling each may receive while being forged and while cooling from the forging heat. The temperature of the forging at the finishing operation and the cooling rate from the finishing temperature play an important part and influence the structure of the finished forging.

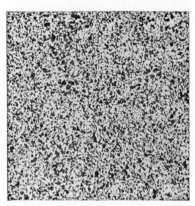

Fig. 20. Structure of Hot-forging, Showing Badly Banded Structure and Mixed Grain Size. Undesirable Structure. Magnified 75 Times

Fig. 21. Same Steel Shown in Fig. 20 after Correcting the Undesirable Structure by a Normalizing Treatment. Magnified 75 Times

Any variations in these factors account, in a large measure, for the variations found in forgings and constitute one of the main reasons for specifying a normalizing heat treatment. Occasionally, in high-carbon steels, hot-worked steel may be treated so as to develop a structure as illustrated in Figs. 22 and 23. This cementite surrounding pearlite is a network structure which may be described as an eggshell-like structure, causing a very poor physical condition if subjected to a hardening heat treatment. To break up this type of eggshell structure of cementite and distribute the cementite more uniformly throughout the entire structure, we might specify a normalizing heat treatment. Heating to within the normalizing temperature range, Fig. 1, followed by air cooling would cure this condition.

Occasionally very much higher temperatures than those recommended in Fig. 1 are used in normalizing. This is true when the structures are difficult to break up. Using higher temperatures increases the solubility and diffusion rate, thus aiding in the operation.

Cooling in air means removing the steel from the heating furnace and exposing it to the cooling action of air in a room. The best practice consists in suspending the steel objects in air, or placing them on a special cooling bed so that they become surrounded by the cooling action of the air. Careless practice, such as dumping the

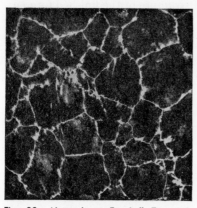

Fig. 22.   Network or Eggshell Type of Structure in Hypereutectoid Steel; Magnified 100 Times

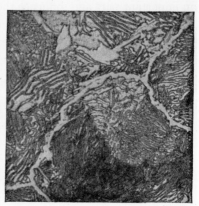

Fig. 23.   Same as Fig. 22, but Magnified 500 Times

steel objects into a pile on the floor of the shop, may result in very poor treatment and very non-uniform structure.

ANNEALING. The usual annealing heat treatment requires heating steel to above the *Ac 1-2-3* critical temperatures, Fig. 1, followed by suitable cooling. The heating is carried out slowly and uniformly, usually in regular oven-type furnaces. The time at heat should be long enough to ensure heating to the selected temperature and to allow the structure to become completely refined. The rate of cooling from the annealing temperature varies with the analyses of the different steels and with the properties most desired in the annealed steel; however, in general, the steel is cooled very slowly either with the furnace (furnace annealed), or cooled in a container surrounded by heat-insulating material (box or pot annealed).

The principal reason for specifying annealing is to soften the metal so as to make the steel easier to cold form, machine, etc. Annealing may be carried out to develop mechanical properties that are required and obtained only by this treatment; for example, high ductility.

ANNEALING FOR FREE MACHINING. Metal machining problems are very complex, and to put any steel into the best structural condition for easy machining operations may require special considerations based on the type of steel, type of cutting operations, and the degree of surface finish desired. Annealing of the steel to a specified Brinell hardness, while a guide to the machinability of a steel, may not indicate the presence of a structure that will produce the easiest machining characteristics with the best surface finish. Annealing for free machining should be carried out to a specified type of structure and Brinell hardness.

There are two basic types of structures from annealing heat treatments: (1) the laminated pearlite type and (2) the spheroidized cementite type of structure. To obtain the laminated type of structure, the steel is heated to within the annealing range, Fig. 1, and slowly cooled, at a rate of approximately 100° F. per hour, down to about 1000° F. or below. The spheroidized type of structure is obtained by heating to the critical temperature, *Ac 1-2-3*, or slightly below this temperature for several hours, followed by cooling slowly to about 1000° F. The degree of spheroidizing depends largely upon the time of soaking at the spheroidizing temperature. Cementite that is out of solution and red hot will ball up or form into spheres, and, upon slow cooling, the cementite that is precipitated will add to this spheroidized condition of the cementite. Fig. 24 illustrates the degree of spheroidization desired in an S.A.E. 3250 type of steel that is to be machined in automatic screw machines.

Many of the carbon tool steels and low alloy steels are annealed to a completely spheroidized structure usually requiring a long annealing time cycle. The steel to be annealed is heated to the austenitic temperature range and held or soaked at this temperature generally from 1 to 4 hours. The cooling cycle is controlled from the annealing temperature so as to cool at a maximum rate of 50° F. per hour to a temperature of 1000° F. or below. The cooling rate is largely controlled by the furnace characteristics and the size of the load in the furnace. A large well-insulated furnace with a large tonnage charge will cool very slowly and result in a well-spheroidized structure. A small furnace with a light load will cool relatively fast and may cool too fast to obtain the desired degree of spheroidization.

Recently, it has been discovered that spheroidization may be effected during a shorter cycle than the usual time required by the

S. A. E.-3250 Steel
Spheroidized Heat Treatment

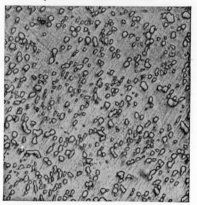

Desired Microstructure

C.....0.45—0.50	Ni......1.50—2.00
Mn....0.30—0.60	P......0.025 max.
Cr.....0.90—1.25	S......0.025 max.

Fig. 24. Results of Spheroidized Heat Treatment of S.A.E.-3250 Steel; 3% Nital Etch; Magnified 750 Times

slow-cool method. This new process requires accurate control of temperatures and relatively fast cooling from a high to a low spheroidizing temperature. In this process, the steel is first heated to slightly above the lower critical AC1 of the steel and held there for about two hours. The heat is then lowered relatively fast to a temperature of 1200° to 1300° F., the cooling rate being as rapid as is possible to obtain. The steel is then held at the lower spheroidizing temperature, 1200° to 1300° F., for a period of from 4 to 15 hours, depending upon the degree of spheroidization and softness required. After the soaking period at 1200° to 1300° F., the steel may be removed from the furnace or furnace cooled if softer and stress-free steel is required. The hardness or softness resulting from a spheroidization cycle depends largely upon the degree of spheroidization and upon the size of the spheroidized cementite particles.

In general, continuous cutting, as in lathe and screw machines, requires a spheroidized structure in the high-carbon steels, but a laminated structure in steels of lower carbon steel below 0.40% carbon. Laminated pearlitic types of structures are best for cutting operations, including gear cutting, milling, facing, broaching and splining, regardless of the carbon content of the steel being treated.

ANNEALING OF COLD-WORKED STEEL. Cold-worked steels may have their original structure and ductility restored by a simple annealing operation consisting of heating to within the process annealing range shown in Fig. 1, followed by slow cooling; however, the rate of cooling may not affect the structure or properties greatly. This operation may be carried out in regular oven-type furnaces, although frequently it becomes necessary to anneal the cold-worked steel without scaling or ruining the surface finish, i.e., **bright annealing.** Bright annealing may be carried out in specially designed muffle furnaces containing reducing gases, or through the use of containers or boxes. The steel to be annealed is placed in a box and sealed. Gases that will prevent oxidation are forced into the box to displace any air present, and the box with the charge of steel and gas is heated to the annealing temperature.

Control of grain size in steels having lower carbon content, and control of the size and shape of cementite particles in steels of higher carbon content constitute the most important factors governing the results of any annealing operation following cold working.

STRESS-RELIEF TREATMENT. Forgings, castings, and welded structures may retain a high residual internal stress or load due to uneven cooling and shrinkage effects. These internal stresses may be the cause of serious warping and even failure by rupture. Due to internal stresses, castings that have been accurately machined and assembled into a complicated machine tool may warp (after going into service) and cause the finished machine to become inaccurate or prevent its proper operation. These internal stresses may be removed in any annealing operation. However, if the parts to be stress-relieved do not need an annealing operation, they may be treated by

heating to a much lower temperature than recommended for annealing. In fact, internal stresses may be partly removed at room temperature, but this may require months; whereas heating to above room
temperature but below the critical temperature of steel or cast iron
will remove the internal stresses in a few minutes. Frequently a
temperature of 1200° F. is recommended for the stress relief of cast
steel, cast iron, and welded structures. Cooling from the stress-relieving temperature should be carried out so as to prevent any uneven
cooling. This usually requires furnace cooling to at least 800° F.

HEAT-TREATING FURNACES. Heating steel for the purpose of
annealing, hardening, tempering, etc., may be carried out in a number of different types of furnaces. The choice of any furnace depends
largely upon the type of heat-treating operation and upon the size
and tonnage of the steel involved. Large-scale heat-treating operations are carried out in batch type or continuous type furnaces which
are equipped with means of automatic temperature control and mechanical devices for the handling of the steel in and out of the furnace
and into the quenching baths. A great many of the furnaces are
designed and constructed to carry out some specific heat-treating
operation, and accordingly, a great diversity of types and designs of
furnaces are in use.

Furnaces are of the oil-fired, gas-fired, or electric type. Oil-fired
or gas-fired furnaces may be designed as direct-fired, semi-muffle, or
muffle. The direct-fired furnaces allow the steel to come into direct
contact with the hot gases of combustion and are mainly used for
heating steel for forging operations. The semi-muffle type is so designed that the gases of combustion are deflected and do not impinge
directly upon the steel being heated, although they circulate around
it. This affords better control of the heat, which results in a more
uniform product.

In order to protect steel from oxidation during any heat-treating
operation, furnaces of the full-muffle type are commonly used. These
full-muffle furnaces are so constructed that they provide a chamber,
known as the **muffle,** separate from the combustion chamber, into
which the steel to be heated is placed. The gases of combustion circulate around the chamber or muffle and cannot come in contact
with the steel being heated.

In the electric-type furnace, the resistors are usually placed around the outside of the muffle. The muffle is made of a special heat-resisting alloy or special refractory material. The hot gases of combustion, or, in the case of an electric furnace, electric resistors, heat the muffle and the steel within the muffle. A neutral or reducing gas may be supplied to the interior of the muffle so as to greatly increase the degree of protection afforded the steel during the heat-treating cycle. The full-muffle type furnace is commonly employed with the so-called **atmosphere-type furnace** and is used when maximum protection from oxidation is required.

Recent improvements in heat-treating furnaces have been made possible because of improved heat-resisting alloys for muffles and other parts, improved refractories, more efficient burner equipment, improvement in temperature control apparatus, and better electric resistor alloys.

Furnace Atmospheres. Heating steel in an electric furnace or in a muffle furnace in the presence of air results in the oxidation of the steel surfaces with the formation of scale and loss of surface carbon (decarburization). The ideal atmosphere is one which will not scale or burn out carbon (decarburize) or add carbon to the steel (carburize) during the heating operation. In order to obtain this ideal atmosphere, artificial gas atmospheres are added to the heating chamber in a muffle or electric furnace. The selection of the ideal gas atmosphere for the heating chamber depends upon many factors, such as the type of steel being treated, the temperature of the operation, etc., and requires a careful study of the problem involved and an understanding of the reactions occurring at the temperature of operation. In general, this problem is solved by trying several gaseous mixtures and analyzing their effect upon the steel being treated. The most common gas mixtures contain a relatively high percentage of CO or H_2, both of which are reducing gases, and may be used to prevent the formation of surface scale or decarburization. The presence of CO_2, H_2O, or O_2 in the gaseous atmosphere may result in harmful and excessive scale or surface decarburization. However, this will depend upon the type of gas used, the type of steel, and the temperature of operation. In general, the atmospheres used in any heat-treating operation are such as to produce a light scale, thus preventing decarburization to a depth of more than 0.001 inch, all of which could normally be removed in any finishing operation.

LIQUID HEATING BATHS. Both molten lead and molten salt baths are used for the heating of steel in operations involving hardening, annealing, tempering, etc. Molten lead is a fast-heating medium and gives complete protection to the surfaces of the steel. With a melting point of 621° F., lead may be used successfully from 700° F. to about 1600° F. Lead oxidizes readily with the formation of a dross, making a dirty bath, and gives trouble because of the sticking of lead and dross to the surfaces of the steel being heated. This can be overcome by suitable lead coverings such as wood charcoal, coke, carburizing compounds, salts, etc. The steel can be further protected from lead sticking to its surfaces by the use of a coating of a thin film of salt or some other material which is applied to the steel before it is placed in the lead bath. Dipping of warm steel into a saturated brine solution and allowing it to dry leaves a protective salt film on the steel. The use of a water emulsion containing bone charcoal, rye flour, potassium ferrocyanide, and soda has proved successful. The steel is dipped into the emulsion and allowed to dry before placing in the lead bath.

Molten salt baths have been found to be satisfactory for the heating of many steel parts that are to be given heat treatments. They transmit heat quickly and uniformly and afford a protection to the steel during the heating cycle. Upon removal of the steel from such a salt bath, a thin film of salt adheres to it, giving further protection from air prior to the quenching, etc. Although the ideal salt bath has not been discovered, if care is used in the selection of a salt and precautions are exerted in its use and maintenance, good results may be expected. Salts may be used for low-temperature tempering. They usually consist of nitrates and may be used in a range of temperatures from 300° F. to 1000° F. Salt baths used in temperature ranges of 1000° F. to 1650° F. consist mainly of sodium carbonate, sodium chloride, sodium cyanide, and barium or calcium chloride. In a temperature range of 1800° F. to 2400° F., salt baths are made from mixtures of barium chloride, borax, sodium fluoride, and silicates. Precautions should be observed in the use of salt baths in order to prevent violent reactions from the mixing of certain salts. One should also be careful to prevent moisture from coming into contact with the fused salts. With the cyanide salts, precautions should be observed because of their poisonous nature.

QUIZ QUESTIONS

1. Name the two operations necessary to the hardening of steel.
2. What is "austenite" and how is it formed?
3. What is "martensite" and how is it formed?
4. What is the structural appearance of martensite?
5. With careful cooling, at what temperature does martensite form?
6. Describe the "critical rate" of quenching.
7. Below what temperature should water be kept during quenching?
8. Why should water be agitated during quenching?
9. In what respects is brine superior to water for quenching?
10. What type of work is successfully hardened in oil quenching medium?
11. What effect does the carbon in steel have upon the rate of transformation?
12. State effect of carbon upon newly formed martensite during hardening.
13. Why does a carbon content beyond 0.85% make steel difficult to harden?
14. What effect does a fast cooling rate needed in the hardening of carbon steels have upon the center of objects hardened?
15. What means is used to aid the cooling of work having heavy sections?
16. Name an important cause of unsatisfactory variations in the results of quench hardening.
17. What may be said about the rate of transformation of fine-grained steels? Coarse-grained steels?
18. If deep penetration of hardness is desired in large pieces, how does this affect the temperature in the hardening operation?
19. What causes warping and cracking during hardening operations?
20. How is distortion that takes place during hardening operations corrected?
21. Name a type of failure occurring in deep-hardening steels.
22. What effect has the rate of cooling from the tempering temperature?
23. How may decarburization during the heating operation be prevented?
24. How may soft spots on the surface of hardened tools be avoided?
25. What advantage has oil as a cooling medium in alloy steels?
26. What four characteristics are furnished to steel by hardening?
27. Name five results of tempering hardened steel.
28. What happens to the atomic structure of hardened steel when it is tempered?
29. What is the purpose of tempering?
30. For satisfactory results on a tempering operation, how much time should be allowed at tempering temperature?
31. What effect does tempering of steel have upon volume?
32. What are temper colors and how are they used?
33. Describe the process of austempering.
34. Name several examples of austempered work.
35. What is accomplished by normalizing?
36. Describe an annealing heat treatment.
37. What two basic types of structure are obtained by annealing?
38. What is meant by "bright annealing"?
39. What temperature is frequently recommended for stress relief of cast steel, cast iron, and welded structures?

IRON ORE BEING MINED BY OPEN PIT OR STRIPPING OPERATION

Photo by Bethlehem Steel Company

ORE STORAGE YARD SHOWING ORE BRIDGES OR CRANES

The Different Grades of Ore Are Stored Here and Used as Needed by the Blast Furnace

Photo by Bethlehem Steel Company

CHAPTER XII

Surface Treatments

MANY metal objects made from either ferrous or nonferrous metals may be subjected to some form of surface treatment that affects only a thin layer of the outer surfaces of the metal. Such treatment may be carried out for the purpose of developing greater resistance to corrosion, for greater sales appeal from an appearance viewpoint, to increase the surface hardness, or to obtain a combination of hardness and toughness in the same object that would be difficult or impossible by any other method. Surface treatments include plating, oxidation, flame hardening, induction or Tocco hardening, case carburizing and hardening, and nitriding.

PLATING. Plating of metal surfaces with another metal is one of the most common methods employed for obtaining satisfactory resistance to corrosion or for bettering appearances. Many different metals may be used in plating including nickel, silver, chromium, copper, zinc, gold, cadmium, tin, iron, lead, cobalt, platinum, rhodium, and tungsten. Also, many alloys of these metals may be used.

Surfaces of metal objects may be plated by several methods, such as (1) electroplating, which is the depositing of a metal onto the surface of a metal object by electrolysis, (2) by means of dipping the metal object into a molten bath of the metal to form the coating (this method used extensively for tin plating known as **tin plate,** and for plating of zinc, **zinc galvanizing**), (3) depositing of metal onto a surface by action of a vapor, such as in the **sherardizing process,** where the objects to be coated are placed in a tight drum with zinc powder and heated to 575°–850° F. A surface coating of zinc is formed by the action of the zinc vapor which penetrates and forms a zinc surface coating, (4) by means of a spray of atomized molten metal directed onto the surfaces of heated metal objects, known as the **Schoop metallizing process,** (5) a surface plating called **Parkerizing** in which an iron phosphate coating is applied to iron or steel parts by immersing them in a hot solution of manganese dihydrogen phosphate for 30 to 60 minutes, and (6) a process known as **hard facing** for hardening surfaces of iron and steel, in which a hard metallic layer is welded to a softer metal by the fusion welding process.

PHOSPHATE COATINGS. Phosphate coatings, produced by immersion of metal parts in a hot solution of manganese dihydrogen phosphate for 30 to 60 minutes, result in a surface that is gray in color but after oiling or waxing becomes black. Thinner coatings, modifications of this process, are applied in a much shorter time by spraying or dipping in hot phosphate solutions containing catalyzers. In the **Bonderizing** process, which is a modification of the Parkerizing process, a thin coating of protection is obtained by immersion in a hot phosphate solution for a period of 30 seconds or longer. Such a coating is primarily intended as a base for paint and in itself offers only a temporary protection to the surfaces so treated.

A phosphate coating has proved advantageous in resisting excessive wear and seizure of machine parts and to minimize scuffing during the wearing-in period. It has been successfully used on parts such as pistons, piston rings, camshafts, and other engine and machine parts.

SURFACE OXIDATION. Oxide films formed on metal surfaces will build up resistance to corrosion and change the appearance of metal objects. Aluminum may be treated to develop a very thick adhering film of surface oxide which enhances its resistance to corrosion by means of electrolytic oxidation. Steel objects with a bright, clean surface may be treated by heating in contact with air to 500°–600° F., and thus a color oxide film is formed (temper color) which adds to sales appeal in some instances and increases the resistance to corrosion. A heavy blue or black oxide film may be formed on steel by heating the steel in a bath of salts of low melting point. These salts are sold under various trade names, and the operation is referred to as **bluing** or **blacking** of steel, being used on gun parts, small tools, spark plug parts, etc.

METAL SPRAY PROCESS. Through the use of a gas-fired pistol, metal in the form of wire or powdered metal is fused and then sprayed from the gun and deposited upon the surface that is to be coated. The action is similar to that of a paint gun. The sprayed metal adheres to the surfaces of the part due to the impact of the tiny particles. This adherence is aided by the proper preparation of the surfaces to receive the metallic coating. Usually a rough surface, such as prepared by sand blasting, is required for good adherence. The coating is not very strong as it is somewhat porous in nature, but it has proved satisfactory for the building up of worn parts of machines, such as shafts, cylinders, rolls, etc., and may be used to build up resistance to corrosion and wear. A number of different metals, including aluminum, zinc, tin, copper, lead, brass, and bronze, may be sprayed onto surfaces by this process. However, the process is limited commercially to the metals having a relatively low melting point. The coating is somewhat thicker than those produced by hot dipping and electroplating methods, usually ranging from .004 inch to 0.025 inch.

HARD FACING. In the hard-facing process, air-hardening steels such as high-speed steels, natural hard alloys such as stellite, tungsten carbide, and boron carbide, and special stainless steels may be fused to metals requiring a harder or tougher wear- and shock-resistant surface. The hard-facing alloy may be fused to almost any metal part by either the oxyacetylene torch or the electric-arc method of welding. In applying hard-facing alloys, it is important to prepare the surfaces to be hard faced by grinding, machining, or chipping, so as to clean and remove rust, scale, or other foreign substances. The work to be hard faced is often preheated before applying the hard-facing alloy. This preheating may be carried out in a furnace or by use of an oxyacetylene flame. If arc-welding methods are used, the atomic hydrogen process is recommended; however, good results can be obtained with straight arc-welding equipment when a short arc and low current are used. If the oxyacetylene blowtorch is used, it is recommended that the flame be adjusted to a reducing or excess of acetylene flame. The technique employed when using the oxyacetylene blowtorch is to heat the surface to be hard faced to a sweating temperature, heating only a small section at a time. The hard-facing rod is then brought into the flame and allowed to melt and spread over the sweating area. If the operation is properly carried out, the hard-facing rod spreads and flows like solder. Additional hard-facing alloy may be added and the required built-up thickness accomplished. With ideal welding conditions, the bond between the hard-facing alloy and the parent metal is very strong, in most cases being stronger than the hard-facing alloy alone. Fig. 1 illustrates the type of structure found in a hard-faced steel surface using Haynes Stellite. Though there is practically no penetration between Haynes Stellite and steel, the bond is actually stronger than the deposited metal. The deposited metal is pure Haynes Stellite, undiluted with iron from

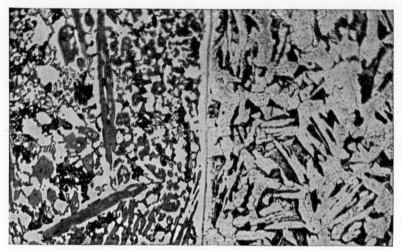

Fig. 1. Photomicrograph of Straight-Line Nature of Bond Obtained when Haynes Stellite (Left) Is Properly Applied to Steel (Right) with the Oxyacetylene Blowpipe.

the base metal, and hence possesses maximum wear resistance. This hard-facing process may be applied to nearly all steels and many alloys. Many of the uses include hard-facing tractor shoes, dies, cutting tools, plowshares, exhaust valve seats, airplane tail skids, pulverizer hammers, dipper bucket teeth, etc.

FLAME HARDENING. Flame-hardening methods may be used when a hard surface and a soft interior are needed, a combination of properties that may be more difficult and costly to obtain by any other method. Flame hardening is used to surface harden large and small gray cast-iron machine parts, parts that would not permit heating in a furnace and water or oil quenching for hardening due to danger of warping and cracking. Any large steel or cast-iron section requiring a high surface hardness that would be difficult to obtain by the usual methods might be successfully hardened by the flame-hardening method. In this process of surface hardening, heat is applied to the surface of the steel or cast-iron part by an oxyacetylene flame. Only a thin layer of the surface metal is brought up to the hardening temperature, and as the torch moves slowly forward heating the metal, a stream of water follows the torch, quenching and hardening the surface as it becomes heated. The speed of the torch is adjusted so

Fig. 2. Flame-hardening Machine. Hardening of a Gear by Rotating It between a Number of Gas Burners. After the Gear Teeth Reach the Correct Hardening Temperature, the Gear and Rotating Table Are Lowered into the Quenching Tank, Which Is a Part of the Unit

Courtesy of Massachusetts Steel Treating Corporation

that the heat penetrates only to the desired depth, thereby controlling the depth of hardness. The technique of flame hardening may be carried out in several different ways. Small parts may be individually heated and then quenched. In the case of cylindrical shapes such as shafts, gears, etc., the surface may be heated by slowly rotating the part and exposing the surface to the flame of a torch or a series of gas burners as illustrated in Fig. 2. Upon reaching the hardening temperature and when the heat has penetrated to the desired depth, the part may be quenched for hardening. Both steel and grey cast iron may be treated by the flame-hardening process. In general, a steel to be hardened by this method should have a carbon content of at least 0.40%. The best range of carbon is between 0.40 and 0.70%

carbon. Higher carbon steels can be treated, but care must be exercised to prevent surface cracking. If special alloy steels are used, the low alloy type seems to respond satisfactorily and works the best. Applications of the flame-hardening process include rail ends, gears, lathe beds, track wheels for conveyors, cams and cam shafts, etc.

INDUCTION HEATING FOR HARDENING. In the induction heating or Tocco process as applied to the surface hardening of steel, heat-

Fig. 3. Setup for Induction Hardening of a Gear

Courtesy of Massachusetts Steel Treating Corporation

ing is accomplished through the use of inductor heating coils placed around the surface to be hardened. A high-frequency current at high voltage is transformed into low-voltage current with high amperage and passed through the inductor coils or blocks surrounding but not actually in contact with the surfaces to be hardened. The inductor coils induce a current in the surface of the steel. This induced current rapidly heats the metal to the proper hardening temperature. When the area to be hardened has been subjected to an accurately controlled current of high frequency for the correct length of time, the electric circuit is opened, and, simultaneously, the heated surface is quenched by a spray of water from a water jacket built into or around the inductor blocks or heating coil. Figs. 3 and 4 illustrate two setups used. In Fig. 3, the work is rotated between the heating coils and quenched by a water jacket surrounding the heating coils and part.

The time cycle for the complete operation is only a few seconds. With split-second heating control and instantaneous pressure quench-

Fig. 4. Surface Hardening of a Grinding Machine Spindle. Upon Reaching the Correct Hardening Temperature, the Spindle Is Removed and Quench-hardened

Courtesy of Massachusetts Steel Treating Corporation

ing, a good surface hardness is obtained with a gradual blending of the hardness into a soft core that is unaffected by heat. This process may be applied to many different carbon and alloy steels, provided the carbon content is high enough to permit quench hardening.

Because special inductors or coils are required for each job and automatic timing has to be worked out for each particular case, the equipment for induction surface hardening is costly. However, because of the short time cycle involved, production from the equipment is high. Maximum returns come from quantity production of the same piece. Close control of the heated zone together with greatly reduced distortion during heat treatment are two distinct advantages of this method over general hardening methods. Figs. 5

and 6 illustrate the results that may be expected through the use of this process. Fig. 6 shows the hardness penetration or case-hardness values that may be expected.

CASE CARBURIZING AND HARDENING. Probably the oldest of heat treatments is that of carburizing, and it is believed the early metalworker made his steel by adding carbon or carburizing wrought

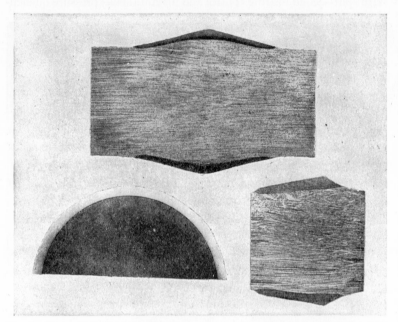

Fig. 5. Etched Sections of Shafting, Illustrating the Characteristic Casehardening Effect Obtained by the Tocco Induction Heating Method

Courtesy of Ohio Crankshaft Company

iron. Carbonaceous gases from charcoal in the ancient's forge fire added carbon to the wrought iron, thus increasing the hardness, at least the surface hardness, and making the wrought iron hardenable by quenching. One of the most important of heat treatments in modern metalworking plants consists of heating low carbon steel in contact with a carbonaceous fuel, thus generating a rich carbon gas and allowing the low carbon steel to dissolve the carbon from the gas, producing a surface layer that is harder and one that can be made very hard by quenching. The low carbon steel absorbs carbon from the fuel and diffuses the carbon into the interior slowly. The outer layer, high in carbon, is called the **case;** the balance of the unaffected steel interior, low in carbon, is called the **core.** The process of carburizing is used when (1) a combination of hard, wear-resisting surface and tough core is wanted, and (2) when it is cheaper to obtain a metal object with a hard surface by this method. Applications for this process include gears, cams, crankshafts for machines and air-

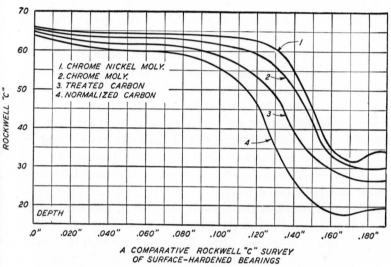

A COMPARATIVE ROCKWELL "C" SURVEY
OF SURFACE-HARDENED BEARINGS

Fig. 6. Hardness Depth Characteristics of Four Types of Steel Induction-hardened by the Tocco Process

Courtesy of Ohio Crankshaft Company

craft, firearm parts, roller bearings, ball bearings, conveyor chain, chain links, cheap tools, screws, bolts, etc.

Carburizing. Factors governing the carburizing and hardening process include:

1. Chemical composition of the steel
2. The carburizing operation
3. The hardening operation

The Steel. Care should be used in the selection of the steel, and the selection should be based on the requirements demanded by the service in which the finished steel is to be placed. In general, a good grade of plain carbon steel with a carbon content, preferably below

0.20%, will prove satisfactory. A low carbon steel is required so that in the subsequent hardening operations, the core of the steel will remain tough. Many low alloy steels are used for casehardening by this method due to superior strength and wearing qualities. The alloying elements commonly used in the steels subjected to carburizing include the following: nickel, chromium, vanadium, and molybdenum.

Nickel lowers the hardening temperature, thereby reducing the possibility of distortion in heat treatment and also surface decarburization. It toughens and strengthens the steel. High-nickel steels quenched from high temperatures tend to retain austenite in the case, with a resultant reduction in surface hardness.

Whereas nickel tends to reduce the rate of carburization, chromium increases it. Chromium enhances the wear resistance of the case as well as the strength and hardness of the core. Many fine-grained chromium steels are used because of their low cost, hardenability, and wear resistance. Combinations of nickel and chromium in proper proportions result in excellent physical properties.

Chrome-molybdenum steels and steels with molybdenum and nickel have been used extensively with good results. Like chromium, molybdenum increases the strength, toughness, and hardenability.

Chrome-vanadium steels used in carburizing result in harder, tougher, and finer-grained parts. Because of the high heat-treating temperatures required for these steels, with the possibility of greater scaling, decarburization, and distortion, such steels are usually hardened in cyanide liquid baths.

Carburizing Operation. The three types of carburizing agents used are solid carburizers of the charcoal class, gas carburizers, and liquid carburizers. The solid carburizers usually contain charcoal as a base to which are added varying amounts of barium carbonate, calcium carbonate, sodium carbonate, oil, etc. The gas carburizers are usually gases such as carbon monoxide, illuminating gas, and propane; in fact, any gas that is rich in carbon may be used. The liquid carburizers contain sodium or potassium cyanide to which is added sodium chloride, sodium carbonate, and other mineral salts, of which there are many mixtures on the market. *It should be remembered that cyanogen compounds are deadly poisonous, and every precaution should be adopted when using them.*

The carburizing operation with solid carburizers is carried out by packing the steel with the carburizing agent into suitable boxes or pots, or using a furnace designed with a retort into which the steel and carburizer are charged. The steel and carburizer together are heated to above the critical range of the steel, $Ac3$, or between 1500°

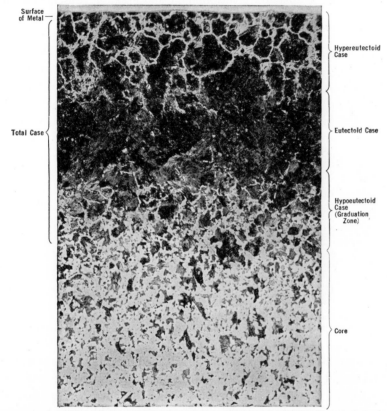

Fig. 7. Machine Steel, 0.10% to 0.20% Carbon, Carburized So That an Unsatisfactory Case Was Produced with a Network or Eggshell Cementite in Hypereutectoid Layer. Etched with Picral. Magnified 75 Times

and 1750° F. For general practice a temperature of 1650° F. will give good results. Inasmuch as ferrite will dissolve but little carbon, whereas austenite has the ability to dissolve large amounts, carburizing is carried out above the $Ac3$, with the steel austenitic, not ferritic. At the carburizing temperature, the steel picks up carbon

from the gas generated by the carburizer. The amount of carbon
pickup depends upon the temperature and the nature of the carburizer. In general, a carbon pickup of 1.15% carbon or below is considered good practice, although a carbon content of 0.90% carbon is
the best for maximum hardness and toughness of the case. However,
if the carbon runs above this amount and grinding is used to finish

Area of Free
Cementite
(White
Constituent)

Fig. 8. Carburized and Hardened Surface of Ball Race Illustrating Defective Case Due to
Excessive Percentage of Free Cementite in the Martensitic Structure. Magnified 1000 Times

the parts after hardening, the high carbon surface may all be removed
and any ill effects from the higher carbon eliminated.

Fig. 7 illustrates the results of carburizing so as to get a pickup
of carbon in excess of 0.90%, the outer layer of the case having a
hypereutectoid structure containing pearlite (dark) with a network
of excess cementite (white). This condition of network cementite is
considered undesirable and should be removed in subsequent machining operations before hardening, or removed by grinding after
hardening. Free cementite in a massive or network form may lead
to cracking during the hardening operation or cause failure of the
part in service due to the brittle nature resulting from this condition.

Fig. 8 illustrates a condition of massive free cementite developed from a casehardening operation which caused failure of a ball race. A satisfactory case obtained from a carburizing operation is illustrated

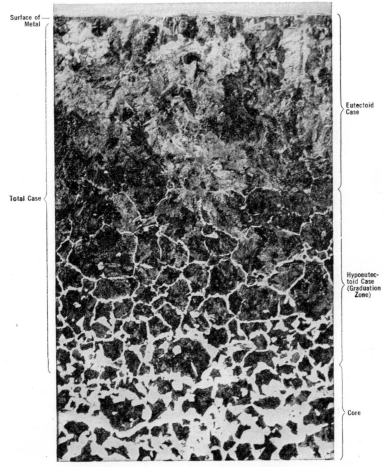

Fig. 9. S.A.E. 1020 Steel, Carburized to Produce a Satisfactory Eutectoid Case. Etched with Picral. Magnified 75 Times

in Fig. 9. The maximum carbon content of the case in this sample is approximately 0.90% carbon, which results in no excess or network cementite. This type of case is recommended and may be obtained by proper control of the carburizing operation.

Carbon will gradually diffuse into the steel, and by controlling the time at the carburizing temperature the penetration may be controlled. The rate of penetration may vary a great deal with different steels and carburizing practice; however, a penetration of approximately 0.006 in. per hr. for shorter carburizing time should be expected. If a very deep or thick case is needed, over 0.100 in., an average hourly penetration of only 0.002 in. might be expected so as to require some 48 hours carburizing time. The case depth may be measured by several different methods. In Fig. 10 the case thickness obtained from a carburizing cycle is revealed by deep etching a section of the carburized part. Cooling slowly in the box or pot after carburizing will result in a high-carbon case on a low-carbon core, but both case and core will be in a soft and pearlitic condition. Figs. 11 and 12 illustrate the condition of low-grade, low-carbon, screw-stock steel after carburizing and slow cooling. The banded and segregated condition of the original steel results in the uneven penetration of the carbon seen in this steel.

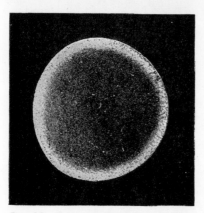

Fig. 10. Deep-etched Section of Case-hardened Steel. Light Outer Layer Illustrates Case Depth. Not Magnified. Etchant 5% Nital

The carburized case is not machinable after hardening; therefore any parts to be machined or drilled after carburizing must be kept soft. The work may be cooled from the box or pot and any machine work done before hardening; however, this is not possible if the work is pulled out at the carburizing heat and quenched for hardening. To overcome such difficulties, inert materials are packed around places to be kept soft, and holes and other places are packed with fire clay and other suitable materials to keep them unaffected by the carburizing compounds.

Selective Carburizing. Another method employed to isolate the work from the action of the carburizers is to copperplate them. The whole piece can be plated with copper and the copper machined off the particular portions to be hardened, or selective plating of portions to be kept soft may be employed.

Case carburizing seeks to attain a certain level of surface hardness and wear resistance coupled with good adherence of this surface or case to the inner portion or core of the work. Carburizing media, carburizing temperatures and times, and alloying elements control the rate of absorption of carbon at the surface and the rate of diffu-

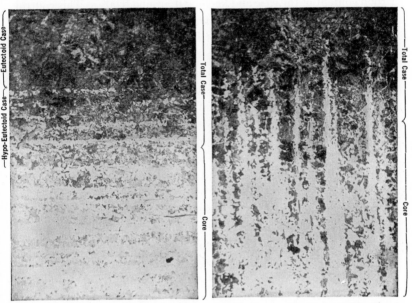

Fig. 11. Carburized Screw Stock, Longitudinal Section. Magnified 100 Times

Fig. 12. Same as Fig. 11, but End Section of Rolled Stock

sion of this carbon. Carburizing conditions and heat treatment are based on the depth of the case needed, the structure and hardness desired in the case, and the desired structure and properties of the core. A hypereutectoid case with the cementite in a network or in spines is brittle like an eggshell, see Fig. 7, and is likely to spall off either on quenching in heat treatment, during grinding, or in service. Slow cooling of high-carbon austenite results in a tendency of the excess carbides to separate in embrittling forms. It is therefore desirable to have the carbide in a more or less spheroidized form, thus eliminating embrittlement of the case and adding to its wear resistance. This is obtained by controlling and using a relatively fast rate of cooling from the carburizing temperature to below the critical range—roughly below 1200° F. In industry this may be done by using separate cooling chambers either water jacketed or cooled by passing a cooled gas through this chamber.

Another method that may be selected in order to avoid a brittle eggshell case of free cementite is that of controlling the maximum carbon content of the case and keeping it around 0.90%. This control of the carbon content of the case may be had by either the liquid or gaseous carburizing process, but it is almost impossible to obtain by the pack-carburizing process using the solid carburizers.

Gas Carburizing. Both continuous and noncontinuous, or batch-type, furnaces are used in the gas carburizing process. Carburizing may be accomplished by means of city gas, natural gas, propane, butane, and special gas mixtures produced from compounded oils that are fed into the retort containing the work to be cased. A popular gas carburizing machine of the batch type consists of a cylindrical drum or retort of special noncarburizing alloy steel within an outer heat-insulated cylinder. Heat is applied to the annular space between the inner and outer cylinders. The work is charged into the furnace on suitable fixtures, and the furnace is sealed. The carburizing gas or oil is introduced into the retort and circulated by means of a fan. This process has the advantage of being fast and offers the possibility of close control of the total case depth and the total carbon of the case.

In controlling the total carbon of the case by this process, one method that has proved successful employs the use of a neutral gas during the heating-up cycle. After the carburizing retort has been purged of any oxygen in the form of CO_2, a natural or propane carburizing gas is introduced into the retort. A supply of about 30 cu. ft. per hr. of carburizing gas will then yield an efficient carburizing atmosphere. The time and temperature are closely controlled with the carburizing temperature running between 1650° to 1700° F. After a predetermined time at the carburizing temperature, the carburizing gas is shut off, and the steel is allowed to cool in the neutral atmosphere. Cooling in the neutral atmosphere increases the case depth or penetration of the carbon and reduces the carbon concentration at the surface of the steel by diffusion of carbon from the outside toward the lower carbon core.

Treatment after Carburizing. The lowest-cost treatment after carburizing is to pull the steel out of the carburizing boxes while at the carburizing heat and quench in water or brine for plain carbon steels. Special alloy carburizing steels may be quenched in oil from the carburizing temperature. This treatment will result in a fully hardened case with a Rockwell hardness of over 60C. The core of the steel will also be hardened to its maximum, which may run less than Rockwell 20C. The disadvantages of this treatment are due to the amount of warping and distortion resulting from the high quenching temperature, and perhaps a rather brittle condition of the steel due to excessive large grains in both case and core. It will be recalled that heating steel above its critical temperature results in grain growth, and due to the length of time the steel is held at the carburizing temperature, rather large grains may develop. A practice that might be selected to avoid excessive distortion would involve cooling the carburized steel to a lower temperature before quenching. A quenching temperature of 1400° to 1500° F. may be selected; this will result in less distortion but will not improve the grain size. To refine the case and fully harden it requires cooling from the carburizing heat to below the critical temperature *Ac 1-2-3* and reheating to slightly above this temperature and quenching. This will result in a very fine and hard case. If the core is to be refined, cooling to below the critical temperature *Ac1* is required and then reheating to above the *Ac3* critical temperature followed by quenching, preferably in oil, to avoid excess distortion. Following this treatment, often referred to as the regenerative quench, the steel may be reheated to the proper temperature of the case (1400°–1450° F.) followed by quenching to produce a martensitic case with its maximum hardness of Rockwell 67C. This double heat treatment following carburizing will result in the maximum combination of physical properties that can be developed by carburizing and hardening. Fig. 13 illustrates the fracture appearance of a steel treated by the double quench, resulting in a hard brittle case and a tough core.

Carburizing that produces a case with a carbon content in excess of 0.90% is one of the major causes of trouble and may be greatly aggravated by the method used in the hardening operation following the carburizing cycle. Fig. 8 illustrates an undesirable condition found in a case hardened ball race treated by slow cooling from the carburizing temperature of 1700° to 1500° F., followed by a direct quench in brine. The slow cool from 1700° to 1500° F. in a rich carburizing atmosphere served to segregate the excess cementite into a massive condition near the surface of the steel. This condition of massive cementite in the hard martensitic matrix of the fully hardened steel resulted in a brittle and cracked ball race.

Fig. 13.   Fracture of Casehardened Steel Given Double Quench

Newer grain-controlled carbon and special alloy steels are available for carburizing, and due to a fine grain even at the higher carburizing temperatures, such steels may be quenched direct from the carburizing treatment without excessive distortion and brittleness. Even if these steels are slow cooled to room temperature, they usually require only a reheating to the hardening temperature of the case, and upon quenching, the core properties are satisfactory and no regenerative quenching is required.

Tempering of the quench-hardened carburized steels may be done at a low temperature for the relief of stresses; and tempering at high temperatures may be carried out to increase the toughness of the hard and otherwise brittle case. Most casehardened steel is finished in the machine shop by grinding. If tempering has been carried out, there will be less danger of further warping and less danger of grinding cracks developing.

Liquid-Bath Carburizing and Hardening. Many small parts, made from low carbon steel, that require a high surface hardness with only a light or thin case, may be successfully carburized and hardened in the cyanide liquid baths. Steel to be casehardened is immersed in a molten bath containing more than 25% sodium cyanide held at a temperature usually around 1550° F. At this temperature, the steel will pick up both carbon and nitrogen from the bath, and in 15 minutes a penetration of approximately 0.005 in. is obtained. The nitrogen in cyanide-hardened cases is present as finely dispersed iron nitrides which impart high hardness and brittleness. If deeper penetration is required, a longer time is necessary. A treatment of one hour results in about 0.010 in. depth of case. To harden the case, quenching direct from the carburizing temperature into water or brine is practiced. If less distortion is needed than from the usual practice, lower carburizing temperatures may be employed, or it may be cooled to lower temperatures before quenching.

To keep the liquid carburizer active as a carburizing agent, the concentration of the sodium cyanide must be maintained preferably above 25% concentration. This may be accomplished by frequent additions of new carburizer or by additions of a salt mixture rich in sodium cyanide. The pots used in this process may be made from pressed steel although special pots containing nickel and chromium are frequently used because of their much longer life and lower ultimate cost. Steel parts may be wired and suspended in the molten baths, and in many instances small parts are placed in wire baskets while in the carburizing bath. If a wire basket is used, care must be exercised in the quenching operation to insure even and fast cooling of all the parts treated to obtain uniform surface hardness. All parts placed in the molten bath must be free from moisture, or danger from an explosive spattering of the bath may occur. The operator should be well protected by gloves and goggles or helmet. The fumes given off by the bath, because of their obnoxious nature, should be removed by means of a hood over the bath and suitable exhaust system.

Liquid-bath carburizing and hardening result in distinct advantages over pot or pack carburizing. Lower temperatures are used, which reduce the depth of penetration because of the lower diffusion rate but also reduce distortion. The process allows for rapid heat transfer to the parts and also results in the elimination of oxidation during heating. The hardening action of the nitrogen is added to that of the carbon. When parts are removed from the cyanide bath, a film of cyanide adheres to the surfaces and acts as excellent protection from oxidation or decarburization during transfer to the quenching medium. These are a few advantages of cyanide hardening over pack hardening. It might be added that the clean, superficial hardness of surfaces resulting from cyanide hardening, done speedily and at low cost, makes this process more adaptable than pack hardening of small parts where service requirements permit the use of a thin case.

CHAPMANIZING. In developing thin cases harder than those from cyaniding and faster than those from nitriding, a process called **Chapmanizing** is used in which dissociated ammonia gas is bubbled through the molten cyanide bath thereby increasing the nitrogen content of the case.

NITRIDING. The nature of the nitriding process used to obtain a casehardened product is very different from that of the carburizing process. Nitrogen, instead of carbon, is added to the surface of the steel. Carbon does not play any part in the nitriding operation but influences the machinability of the steel and the properties of the core in the finished nitrided steel. The temperatures used in nitriding are much lower than those used in carburizing and below the critical temperature of the steel.

Simple carbon steels, which are often used for carburizing, are not used for nitriding. Steels used in the process are special alloy steels. With the nitriding developing rather thin cases, a high core hardness is required to withstand any high crushing loads. High tempering temperatures call for a steel with a higher carbon content in order to develop this increase in core hardness. In addition to higher carbon content, various alloying elements are called for in the steel to bring about an increase in the formation of these nitrides. Aluminum seems to display the strongest tendency in the formation of these nitrides. The aluminum precipitates the compound AlN in a finely divided state, accounting for the extreme hardness of these nitriding steels. Chromium, molybdenum, vanadium, and tungsten, all being nitride formers, also are used in nitriding steels. Nickel in nitriding steels hardens and strengthens the core and toughens the case with but slight loss in its hardness.

In general, steels used in the nitriding process contain the elements within the percentage range given in Table 1.

Table 1. Nitriding Steels*

Element	N 125 (Type H)	N 125N† (Type H with Nickel)	N 135 (Type G)	N 135 Modified†	N 230
Carbon	0.20–0.30	0.20–0.27	0.30–0.40	0.38–0.45	0.25–0.35
Manganese	0.40–0.60	0.40–0.70	0.40–0.60	0.40–0.70	0.40–0.60
Silicon	0.20–0.30	....	0.20–0.30	....	0.20–0.30
Aluminum	0.90–1.40	1.10–1.40	0.90–1.40	0.95–1.35	1.00–1.50
Chromium	0.90–1.40	1.00–1.30	0.90–1.40	1.40–1.80	....
Molybdenum	0.15–0.25	0.20–0.30	0.15–0.25	0.30–0.45	0.60–1.00
Nickel	....	3.25–3.75	....	....	....

*"N" preceding a number indicates nitralloy steels.
†Aircraft specifications.

Nitriding Operation. In the nitriding process, nitrogen is introduced to the steel by passing ammonia gas through a muffle furnace containing the steel to be nitrided. The ammonia is purchased in tanks as a liquid and introduced into the furnace as a gas at slightly greater than atmospheric pressure. With the nitriding furnace operating at a temperature of 900° to 1000° F., the ammonia gas partially dissociates into a nitrogen and hydrogen gas mixture. The dissociation of ammonia is shown by the following equation:

$$2NH_3 \rightleftarrows 2N + 3H_2$$

The operation of the nitriding cycle is usually controlled so that the dissociation of the ammonia gas is held to approximately 30% but may be varied from 15% to 95%, depending upon operating conditions. The gas mixture leaving the furnace consists of hydrogen, nitrogen, and undissociated ammonia. The undissociated ammonia, which is soluble in water, is usually discharged into water and disposed of in this manner.

The free nitrogen formed by this dissociation is very active, uniting with the iron and other elements in the steel to form nitrides. These nitrides are more or less soluble in the iron and form a solid solution or, more likely, are in a fine state of dispersion, imparting hardness to the surface of the steel. From the surface the nitrides diffuse slowly, and the hardness decreases inwardly until the unaffected core is reached. The depth of penetration depends largely upon the length of time spent at the nitriding temperature. Diffusion of these nitrides is much slower than diffusion of carbon in the carburizing operation, so a much longer time is required to develop similar penetration. The case depth specified in nitriding is usually a very shallow one but requires from 18 to 90 hours to obtain. Nitriding at 960° F. for 18 hours results in about 0.010-inch case depth; 48 hours yields approximately 0.020-inch depth of case; 90 hours, approximately 0.030-inch depth of case.

Nitriding is usually carried out in muffle-type furnaces designed to operate within the temperature range of the nitriding cycle (800° to 1200° F.). The muffle or chamber is frequently made from a high

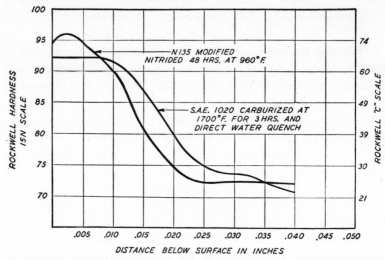

Fig. 14. Comparison of the Hardness at Various Depths below the Surfaces of Nitrided and Carburized Steels

alloy metal containing various amounts of chromium, 12% to 25%, with nickel from 20% to 80%. In order to obtain uniform dissociation of the ammonia gas in the nitriding chamber, the furnace should be designed to provide means of gas circulation. This may be accomplished by a fan built into the muffle or nitriding chamber.

The Nitrided Case. The depth hardness that may be expected from a nitriding operation as compared to a carburized and hardened steel is illustrated in Fig. 14. In general, the surface hardness is much greater after nitriding than it is after carburizing and hardening. The maximum hardness obtained from a carburized and hardened case runs around 67 Rockwell C; whereas, it is possible to

obtain surface hardness values in excess of 74 Rockwell C by nitriding.
The surface hardness of the nitrided case cannot be measured by the
Rockwell C scale due to the extreme brittleness and shallowness of the
case; it is usually measured by the Rockwell superficial scale such as
the 15N or 30N scale. The hardness value on the Rockwell C scale
may be estimated from a hardness conversion table.

The nitrided case is made up of three zones. The first zone is a
thin white layer; the second zone, the effective nitrided case; and the
third zone, a zone of gradation of hardness from that of the effective
case to the core. The thin white layer, see Fig. 15, forms on the surface of the steel at the beginning of the nitriding cycle. This white
layer is extremely brittle and is usually ground off after the nitriding
operation so as to avoid failure by chipping which may occur in handling or during service, particularly where sharp corners exist in the
work. The white layer has good corrosion-resistant characteristics,
and from this standpoint it is desirable not to remove it.

Protection Against Nitriding. In order to obtain localized nitriding of parts or to stop nitriding on some surface areas, the best
method is to use tin as a protecting agent against the nitriding action.
Tin, in the form of a paste or paint made from tin powder, or tin oxide
mixed with glycerine or shellac, may be applied to the areas to be
protected against nitriding. A thin tin electroplate may be applied
as a satisfactory stop-off method. Although tin melts at a lower
temperature than that used in nitriding, ample protection is provided by the thin layer of tin that is held to the surface by surface
tension. Care should be exercised to apply the tin paint or electroplate to a clean surface and to avoid a thick layer of tin which may
run or drip onto surfaces where protection is not desired. A tin plate
of 0.0005 inch is sufficient to prevent nitriding.

Heat Treatment in Nitriding. All heat treatments, such as the
quench hardening of steel in the nitriding process, are carried out
before the nitriding operation. After a rough machining operation,
the steel is heated to about 1750° F., held for the necessary length of
time at this temperature, and then quenched in oil. This high hardening temperature is necessary in order to have the alloying elements
go into solution in the austenite, thereby imparting core strength
and toughness after quenching and tempering. Tempering is

usually done slightly below 1100° F., before and after finish machining, to produce a sorbitic structure which has a tough case and eliminates any brittleness resulting from any free ferrite. This tempering also relieves internal stresses resulting from machining and hardening, thus reducing distortion during nitriding. After tempering,

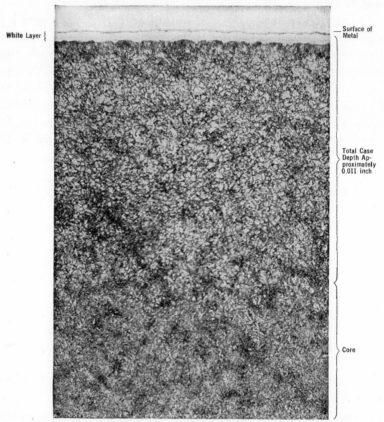

Fig. 15. N135 Modified Steel, Nitrided at 960° F. for 18 Hours, Illustrating White Layer and Case Depth. Magnified 250 Times

all oxide film and any traces of decarburization are removed. Any decarburization left on the surfaces of the steel to be nitrided will usually result in failure of the nitrided surfaces by peeling or spalling off. The steel is then nitrided and allowed to cool slowly to room temperature in the nitriding box or chamber. No quenching is required; the steel develops its maximum hardness without necessitating a further quenching operation.

The advantages of nitriding as a hard-surfacing operation are listed as follows:

1. Greater surface hardness.
2. Greater resistance to wear and corrosion.
3. Better retention of hardness at elevated temperatures.
4. Less warping or distortion of parts treated.
5. Higher endurance limit under bending stresses.
6. Greater fatigue strength under corrosive conditions.

Factors limiting its application include:

1. High furnace costs due to the long time of treatment.
2. Necessity of using special alloy steels.
3. Necessity of using high alloy containers to resist the nitriding action.
4. Expense of medium used.

QUIZ QUESTIONS

1. For what purposes are surface treatments of metal carried out?
2. Name several kinds of surface treatments for metals.
3. Name four methods of plating metals.
4. How is flame hardening carried on?
5. How much time is required for the operation of induction heating for hardening?
6. As applied to case carburizing and hardening, what does "case" mean? What is the core?
7. During the carburizing process, what is considered the best carbon pickup?
8. Describe the low-cost treatment after carburizing. What disadvantages has this treatment?
9. What treatment will refine and fully harden the case of steel?
10. Describe the double heat treatment which is used following carburizing to give a refined core of steel.
11. Name the special advantages of the newer grain-controlled carbon and special alloy steels.
12. What type of work is carburized and hardened in cyanide liquid baths?
13. What percentage of sodium cyanide is used in cyanide liquid baths in steel casehardening?
14. Why must all parts placed in the molten bath be free from moisture? What safety equipment should the operator use?
15. Describe the nitriding process for steel.
16. How much time is required in the nitriding operation of steel for a shallow case?
17. Name the advantages of nitriding.

NORMALIZING 40 TONS OF FORGED CRANK CASES MADE OF ALLOY STEEL
Courtesy of Massachusetts Steel Treating Corporation

CHAPTER XIII

Alloy or Special Steels

ALTHOUGH by far the largest tonnage of steel manufactured is of the plain carbon steel type, a greater and greater tonnage of so-called **alloy** or **special** steels is being manufactured each year. We may think of the alloy steel as a plain carbon steel to which have been added elements, other than iron or carbon, in large enough percentage to slightly or markedly alter the characteristics and properties of the steel. Carbon steel does contain other elements besides carbon and iron, such as silicon and manganese; however, unless these other elements are increased in percentage beyond the usual amounts found in carbon steel, the steel is not considered an alloy or special steel.

We may assume that carbon is the most important element in either carbon or alloy steels. The carbon content determines the hardness of any steel as measured by the standard hardness testing machines. In other words, the hardness of any steel will depend chiefly upon its carbon content and heat treatments, regardless of the amount of special alloying element present in the steel. A Rockwell hardness of 67C is about the maximum hardness that any plain carbon or alloy steel develops. However, although the maximum hardness of steel may not be materially increased by the addition of any alloying element, the properties such as ductility, magnetic properties, machinability, hardenability, etc., may be very materially changed. In general, it is easier to harden alloy steels than plain carbon steels, and, because of this ease of hardening and the greater uniformity from any heat treatment operation, alloy steels are often selected for a job in preference to the plain carbon steel. Some of the reasons for the selection of alloy steels may include the following:

1. Alloy steels often may be hardened by quenching in oil, or even in air, and produce their maximum hardness.

2. Because of oil- or air-hardening characteristics, alloy steels are less apt to crack and are in less danger from warping.

3. Alloy steels are deeper hardening, and hardening heavy sections is apt to be more satisfactory with them than with a carbon steel.

4. The martensitic structure formed in alloy steels is more stable and resistant to tempering effects. This property allows the use of hardened alloy steels in dies and tools subjected to heating.

5. Some alloy steels develop high resistance to shock loading due, no doubt, to a greater ductility with the same tensile properties exhibited by carbon steels.

6. Some alloy steels exhibit a marked resistance to grain growth and oxidation at elevated temperatures.

7. Alloy steels may exhibit less sensitivity to effects of subnormal temperatures or elevated temperatures, and perform better than carbon steels.

8. The stainless characteristics of certain alloy steels is a well-known advantage.

BEHAVIOR AND INFLUENCE OF SPECIAL ELEMENT. With the addition of a special element to steel, the added element may combine with the steel in four ways:

1. Dissolve in both the liquid and solid states of the iron, and thus be retained in solid solution in the iron at room temperature.

2. Combine with the carbon or cementite to form a compound.

3. Form an oxide.

4. Remain "uncombined" or in a free form in the steel.

Elements such as nickel, copper, and silicon combine with the iron at all temperatures forming a solid solution—the first-mentioned behavior of the alloying element. Solid solution-forming elements, in general, increase the strength and hardness and lower the ductility of steel; however, some reports indicate that nickel and also copper, in moderate amounts, decrease the ductility very slightly, hence the importance of nickel steels.

The elements such as manganese, chromium, tungsten, vanadium, and molybdenum combine with the cementitic constituent in the steel, thus forming a carbide with the iron and carbon. Because of their hardness and relative brittleness, the carbide-forming elements, which separate out from solid solution during slow cooling of the steel, seldom develop the desired properties when the carbides exist as free carbides. The value of the carbide-forming steels depends upon the ability to heat-treat the steel so as to dissolve the carbides and retain them in solution upon quenching.

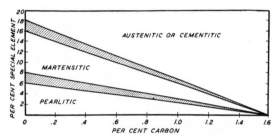

Fig. 1. Constitutional Diagram of Alloy Steels (After Guillet)

In the third behavior, elements such as aluminum, silicon, and zirconium may readily oxidize upon being added to steel, and the oxides of these elements may appear as inclusions in the steel. The

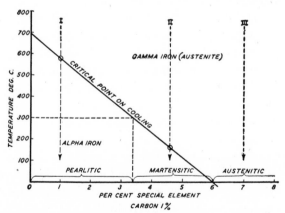

Fig. 2. Influence of Special Element on the Position of the Critical Point (After Sauveur)

effect of inclusions seems to be largely one of lower plasticity, and, perhaps, contributory to formation of cracks and ultimate failures.

Graphitic carbon, lead, and excess copper may all be present in the steel as free constituents, or uncombined. The principal influence of the uncombined constituents is to break up the continuity of the steel and thus weaken its structure. However, this usually improves the machinability. Also, constituents such as MnS, formed from sulphur and manganese, may be classified as similar to uncombined constituents in action.

The steels produced by the addition of alloying elements develop structures and properties that may be divided into four classifications. These four groups are indicated in Figs. 1 and 2 and are discussed briefly here.

GROUP I. PEARLITIC ALLOY STEELS. The pearlitic type of alloy steel contains a relatively small percentage of the special element, although with a low percentage of carbon the amount of the special element may be as high as 6%, as indicated by Fig. 1. The structure and characteristics of pearlitic alloy steels are similar to carbon steels, and the microscopic analysis may reveal all pearlite, or a mixture of pearlite and free ferrite, or a mixture of pearlite and free cementite, all depending upon the amount of carbon and special element. Generally, the special element lowers the eutectoid ratio of carbon to iron, and it therefore requires less than 0.85% carbon in a special steel to produce 100% pearlite or eutectoid steel. The lower carbon alloy steels of this group usually are used for structural purposes; however, they may be hardened by casehardening methods and used for tools. The medium-to-high carbon steels of this group are subjected to heat treatments and used in highly stressed parts of structures and machines, or find many applications in tools. Because a great many of these alloy steels have a slower rate of transformation from austenite to pearlite during cooling, they are more easily made martensitic and may often be quenched in oil in place of water or brine. Fig. 3 illustrates this effect and indicates the rate of cooling needed in order to produce martensite with a carbon steel as compared with a chromium and nickel steel. Because they may be hardened fully by oil quenching, these steels are hardened with less danger of warping and cracking. However, due to their slower rate of transformation these steels are apt to be hardened through their section leaving no soft core, which, in a tool, may increase the danger of breakage in service.

GROUP II. MARTENSITIC ALLOY STEELS. As indicated in Fig. 1, when the carbon content and amount of special element exceed that of the pearlitic type of alloy, a series of compositions are found that form a natural martensitic structure upon air cooling. The addition of a greater amount of special element than found in the pearlitic alloy steels has resulted in the slowing up of the transformation rate so as to allow undercooling of the austenitic structure to around 200° F. even when cooled in still air. The alloying element acts as a fast quench in the lowering of the transformation from austenite to pearlite. This effect is indicated in Fig. 2, which illustrates the influence of the special element upon the transformation tempera-

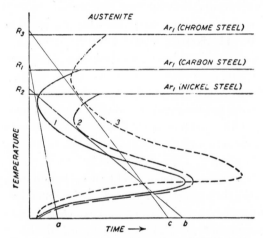

Fig. 3. Comparative Reaction Rate Curves for Plain Carbon
Steel, Nickel Steel, and Chromium Steel (Bain)

ture. If the transformation from austenite takes place above 600° F., a pearlitic structure is formed. If the transformation upon cooling takes place below 400° F. but above room temperature, a martensitic type of structure is formed. The properties of martensitic alloy steel are not unlike those of fully-hardened and martensitic carbon steel, although they are much more stable above room temperature and resist tempering effects and are therefore used for tools and dies that are subjected to heating. These steels are usually hardened by air cooling from above their critical temperature and annealed by unusually slow cooling in a furnace.

GROUP III. AUSTENITIC ALLOY STEELS. Austenitic alloy steels, as indicated in Figs. 1 and 2, are steels that remain austenitic in structure (gamma iron) upon slow cooling from the temperature of solidification. These steels do not undergo any change in the condition of the iron and therefore exhibit no critical temperature upon cooling. These steels cannot be hardened by heat treatment although they may be cold work-hardened and annealed. Also, if any precipitate occurs with these steels upon slow cooling from a high temperature, they may be reheated and quenched to redissolve the precipitate and keep it in solution. These austenitic steels exhibit great shock strength and low elastic strength and are very ductile. They work-harden very rapidly and develop great resistance to wear by abrasion. The chrome-nickel austenitic steels are very resistant to corrosion.

GROUP IV. CEMENTITIC ALLOY STEELS. As indicated in Fig. 1, some alloying elements on being added to steel in increasing amounts fail to convert the steel into an austenitic type. A steel containing 18.0% of a special element and 0.6% of carbon, upon slow cooling from above its critical temperature, would have a structure of ferrite or martensite with numerous particles of cementite embedded in the ferritic or martensitic matrix. Such a steel has been referred to as a **cementitic** or Group IV type of steel. The cementitic type of alloy steel is usually a difficult type of steel to use. It requires special care to properly anneal the steel so as to make it machinable. Also, these steels are subjected to such hardening heat treatments as to cause most of the cementite or carbides to be absorbed and retained in a martensitic structure. The excess cementite or carbides add to the wear resistance of the martensitic structure. These steels are largely used in tools, particularly where hardness and resistance to wear are important.

SPECIFIC ALLOY STEELS

NICKEL STEELS. The use of nickel as an alloy in steel dates back about 50 years although the occurrence of nickel in meteorites and the working of this material into swords by the ancients may account for the first use of nickel. In 1891, the U.S. Navy conducted tests on the use of carbon steel and nickel steel for armor plate. These tests proved decisively the superiority of the nickel and stimulated worldwide interest in this metal.

Nickel, when added to steel, dissolves to form a solid solution with iron, lowering the critical range to a marked degree, and thus forms a steel that may be made pearlitic, martensitic, or austenitic by simply varying the percentage of nickel. The lower carbon pearlitic-nickel steels contain from 0.5% to 6.0% nickel, and are particularly suited for structural applications because of greater toughness, strength, and resistance to corrosion.

Martensitic-nickel steels, because of brittleness and hardness, are little used. They contain from 10% to 22% nickel. This range of nickel compositions was selected as the most probable to form martensitic structures upon slow cooling. It is only an approximate range.

The diagrams in Figs. 1 and 2 are only working diagrams which serve as a working theory of the metallic behavior of special elements in iron-carbon alloys. These diagrams should not be used to determine the structural composition of any specific composition of alloy steel if the analysis is to be very accurate. If accuracy is wanted, a student should consult a constitutional diagram involving the particular composition of alloy steel being studied. Constitutional diagrams of many of the common industrial alloy steels are now available. The diagrams in Figs. 1 and 2 may be considered as introductory diagrams to the study of special alloy steels.

The tonnage nickel steels have a microstructure similar to the plain carbon steels; i.e., the structure consists of ferrite, pearlite, and cementite in various amounts, depending upon the ratio of nickel to carbon in the steel. Low carbon steel may contain up to about 10% nickel and remain pearlitic, whereas with higher carbon contents, the nickel is decreased to about 1% and the steel remains pearlitic. In pearlitic nickel steels (nickel from 0.5% to 5.0%), nickel has a marked effect in slowing down the rate of transformation from austenite to pearlite during the cooling cycle from above the critical range. This retarding of the transformation rate, as indicated by curve 2, Fig. 3, allows the use of a slower cooling rate during the hardening operation. These steels can be fully hardened by oil quenching or use of hot salt bath quenches which reduce the warping and danger from cracking during the hardening operation. Also, the slower transformation rate of these nickel steels makes it possible to heat-treat successfully heavy sections and obtain uniform hardening results. The addition of other elements, such as molybdenum and chromium, to the nickel steel increases the effectiveness of the nickel.

Nickel also retards the rate of grain growth at elevated temperatures. This effect is valuable when low-carbon nickel steels are subjected to carburizing treatments for purposes of casehardening. Very little grain growth may occur in nickel steels during the carburizing cycle, thus preventing the formation of a coarse-grained core in the finished casehardened part. By maintaining a fine grain in the core during the carburizing cycle, the necessity of a regenerative heat treatment can be avoided, and the use of a single quench and draw can be employed to finish the carburized part.

Nickel in steel also improves the resistance to fatigue failure, increases the resistance to corrosion, and improves the toughness and impact properties of steel. Nickel steels are harder than carbon steels, a characteristic which is of value in parts that are used for wear resistance.

Nickel steels, with nickel from 1.5% to 3%, are used for structural applications. These steels, as forgings or castings, develop excellent mechanical properties after a simple annealing or normalizing operation. Steels containing approximately 5% nickel are famous for their superior behavior in parts that are subjected to severe impact loads. These steels, low in carbon, may be casehardened and make an excellent gear; in the higher carbon contents these steels are hardened and tempered before using.

Although many straight nickel alloy steels are used, the value of nickel as an alloying element may be emphasized by the addition of other alloying elements. Both chromium and molybdenum are used with nickel in some of these special steels. The nickel-chromium, and nickel-chromium-molybdenum alloy steels are capable of developing superior mechanical properties and respond very well to heat treatments. In the higher alloy compositions, 2% nickel, 0.8% chromium, 0.25% molybdenum, these steels have excellent hardening characteristics and develop a uniform hardness in heavy sections.

Many corrosion-resistant steels will be found within the range of 10% to 22% nickel, but the nickel is usually combined with chromium producing an austenitic steel.

The austenitic nickel steels present a most fascinating study. Research engineers are constantly finding new alloys of this group.

A few of the most common are as follows:

1. 25% to 30% nickel is used for corrosion resistance.

2. 20% to 30% nickel-iron alloys are non-magnetic by normal cooling and can be made magnetic by cooling to liquid air temperatures.

3. 30% to 40% nickel has a very low coefficient of expansion and is called **Invar.**

4. 36% nickel and 12% chromium alloy is called **Elinvar** and has a nonvariant elastic modulus with temperature change.

5. With over 50% nickel, steel develops high magnetic properties.

CHROMIUM STEELS. Of all the special elements in steel, none is used for such a wide range of applications as chromium. Chromium dissolves in both gamma iron and alpha iron, but in the presence of carbon it combines with the carbon to form a very hard carbide. To steel, chromium imparts hardness, wear resistance, and useful magnetic properties, permits a deeper penetration of hardness, and increases the resistance to corrosion.

Chromium content in steels varies from a small percentage to approximately 35%. Chromium is the principal alloying element in many of the alloy or special steels. Also, a large tonnage of steels is manufactured in which other alloying elements than chromium are added, such as vanadium, molybdenum, tungsten, etc.

The low carbon or pearlitic-chromium steels are the most important of the chromium steels although stainless steels containing chromium from 12% to 35% are becoming more and more important.

When chromium is used in amounts up to 2% in medium and high carbon steels, it is usually for the hardening and toughening effects and for increased wear resistance and increased resistance to fatigue failure. Chromium, when added to steel, raises the critical temperature and slows up the rate of transformation from austenite to pearlite during the hardening process. This slower transformation rate allows the use of a slow quench in hardening and produces deep-hardening effects. With additions of less than 0.50% chromium to the steel, there is a tendency to bring about a refinement of grain and to impart slightly greater hardenability and toughness. Chromium is added to the low carbon steels for the purpose of effecting greater toughness and impact resistance at sub-zero temperatures, rather than for reasons of increased hardenability. The lower-carbon chromium steels can be casehardened, resulting in greater surface hardness and wear resistance. The S.A.E. 5120 type of steel is used in the casehardened condition for general purposes. Engineering steels of the S.A.E. 52100 class find many applications where deep and uniform hardening from oil quenching is needed. These steels develop good wear resistance and fatigue resistance with moderately high strength. Steels of this type, the S.A.E. 52100 series, are used for gears, pistons, springs, pins, bearings, rolls, etc.

Chromium is used quite frequently in tool steels to obtain extreme hardness. Applications of such include files, drills, chisels, roll thread dies, and steels commonly used for ball bearings, which contain approximately 1% carbon and 1.5% chromium. The extreme hardness and resistance to wear associated with the chromium steels seems to be a specific property of the chromium carbides such as Cr_7C_3, Cr_4C, and $(FeCr)3C$ found in these steels. Increasing the chromium content of steels beyond 2% and up to 14% increases the hardenability, the wear resistance, the heat resistance in steels used for hot work, and the corrosion resistance. The high-carbon high-chromium steels, with chromium from 12% to 14% and carbon from 1.50% to 2.50%, are used when wear resistance is of prime importance, as in knives, shear blades, drawing dies, lathe centers, etc.

Although high percentages of chromium, such as those in the high-carbon high-chromium steels, lead to the property of corrosion resistance, this property requires that the chromium carbides be dissolved at a high temperature and retained in solution by quenching. In order to obtain corrosion resistance, it is necessary to keep the chromium carbides in solution or to lower the carbon content to a value that will reduce the formation of chromium carbides. So-called **stainless** steel is a chromium alloy steel with a relatively low carbon content.

Stainless Steels. Stainless, or corrosion-resistant, steels include a large number of different alloys. However, modern stainless steel is an alloy made principally from iron and chromium, referred to as **straight chromium steel** and identified as the 400 series of steels, see Table 1. Nickel is added to the chromium-iron alloys to form a series of stainless or corrosion-resistant alloys identified by the 300 series of steels, see Table 1. Nickel improves the corrosion resistance of the

Table I. Stainless Steel Specifications

Alloy Type	Chromium—%	Nickel—%	Other Elements (See Note 4)	Carbon—%	Manganese—%	Silicon—%	Structure Annealed
502	4.0-6.0	0.5 Max.	....	0.10 Max.	0.60 Max.	0.75 Max.	Pearlite-Ferrite
501+Mo	4.0-6.0	0.5 Max.	0.50 Mo	Over 0.10	0.60 Max.	0.75 Max.	Pearlite-Ferrite
410	11.5-13.5	0.5 Max.	....	0.15 Max.	0.60 Max.	0.75 Max.	Pearlite-Ferrite
414	11.5-13.5	2.0 Max.	....	0.15 Max.	0.60 Max.	0.75 Max.	Pearlite-Ferrite
416	12.0-14.0	0.5 Max.	0.45-0.60 Mo	0.15 Max	0.75-1.20	0.75 Max.	Pearlite-Ferrite
420	12.0-14.0	0.5 Max.	....	0.30-0.40	0.50 Max.	0.75 Max.	Pearlite
431	14.0-18.0	2.0 Max.	....	0.15 Max.	0.50 Max.	0.75 Max.	Pearlite-Ferrite
430	16.0-18.0	0.5 Max.	....	0.12 Max.	0.50 Max.	0.75 Max.	Pearlite-Ferrite
430-F	16.0-18.0	....	S,Se .07 Min.	0.12 Max.	0.75-1.20	0.30-0.75	Pearlite-Ferrite
440	16.0-18.0	0.5 Max.	0.45-0.60 Mo	0.65-0.70	0.35-0.50	0.75 Max.	Pearlite
440	16.0-18.0	0.5 Max.	....	1.00-1.10	0.35-0.50	0.75 Max.	Pearlite-Carbide
446	23.0-30.0	1.0 Max.	....	0.35 Max.	1.50 Max.	0.75 Max.	Ferrite-Carbide
301	16.0-18.0	7.0-9.0	....	0.09-0.20	1.25 Max.	....	Austenitic
302	17.5-20.0	8.0-10.0	....	0.08-0.20	1.25 Max.	0.75 Max.	Austenitic
304	18.0-20.0	8.0-10.0	....	0.08 Max.	2.00 Max.	0.75 Max.	Austenitic
303	17.5-20.0	8.0-10.0	S,Se,P (Note 1)	0.20 Max.	1.25 Max.	0.75 Max.	Austenitic
316	16.0-18.0	10.0-14.0	2.00-3.00 Mo	0.10 Max.	2.00 Max.	0.75 Max.	Austenitic
317	18.0-20.0	10.0-14.0	2.00-4.00 Mo	0.10 Max.	2.00 Max.	0.75 Max.	Austenitic
321	17.0-20.0	7.0-10.0	Ti (Note 2)	0.10 Max.	0.75 Max.	0.75 Max.	Austenitic
347	17.0-20.0	8.0-12.0	Cb (Note 3)	0.10 Max.	2.00 Max.	0.75 Max.	Austenitic
309	22.0-26.0	12.0-14.0	....	0.20 Max.	1.25 Max.	0.75 Max.	Austenitic
310	24.0-26.0	19.0-21.0	....	0.25 Max.	1.25-1.75	0.75 Max.	Austenitic

Note 1—Sulphur or Selenium .07 Minimum. Phosphorus .03–.17
Note 2—Minimum Titanium content=4 times % Carbon.
Note 3—Minimum Columbium content=10 times % carbon.
Note 4—Sulphur and Phosphorus shown in this column when sufficient; not shown if normal.
From data contained in the pamphlet *Stainless Steels, an Elementary Discussion* published
by the Allegheny Ludlum Steel Corp.

basic iron-chromium alloys and greatly increases their mechanical
properties by improving their plasticity, toughness, and welding
characteristics. Stainless steel, originally intended for high-grade
cutlery and tools, has since developed into a steel of inestimable
value for engineering purposes and is of great economic value in
present-day ferrous metallurgy because of its resistance to a wide
range of corroding media. Metal waste due to corrosion has become
an important engineering problem. It has been stated that no waste,

except of human life, is more important. Besides corrosion-resistant and stainless characteristics, other attributes of stainless steels are the property of resisting oxidation and scaling, and the maintenance of strength at elevated temperatures. Types 309 and 310 in Table 1 are primarily heat-resistant alloys in which the chromium content is sufficiently high to obtain resistance to scaling up to approximately 2000° F., with sufficient nickel to maintain this type of steel in its austenitic condition.

The oxide-film theory is offered in an effort to explain the corrosion resistance of chromium alloys. It is believed that an oxide film forms naturally on the surfaces of all metals and protects them to some degree, at least temporarily, from corrosive action. The oxide film that forms under normal atmospheric conditions on the surface of stainless steels of the high chromium-iron type is said to be very stable, tough, and self-healing. If the oxide film is maintained, stainless steels are very effective against any corrosive media. Ordinary compositions of stainless steels do not satisfactorily resist common acids such as hydrochloric, hydrofluoric, sulphuric, or sulphurous, although special compositions that resist such attack have been developed.

Iron-Chromium Alloys. Stainless steels containing from 14% to 18% chromium and a maximum of 0.12% carbon are magnetic and consist structurally of a solid solution of iron and chromium. They are a ferritic type of stainless steel used for general requirements where resistance to corrosion and heat is needed, but where service conditions are not too severe and where slight discoloration of the surface during service can be tolerated. Steels of this type, that contain less than 0.10% carbon with chromium from 14% to 20%, are not heat treatable except for an annealing treatment. They cannot be hardened by heat treatment as they do not transform into austenite when heated to an elevated temperature. These steels are susceptible to grain growth at elevated temperatures, and with a larger grain size they suffer a loss in toughness. The ferritic stainless steels may be cast and forged hot or cold, but they do not machine easily—a characteristic of all stainless steels. They possess a high resistance to corrosion in an ordinary atmosphere, providing they have been highly polished and are free from foreign particles. Improvement in their machinability can be obtained by additions of molybdenum and sulphur, or phosphorus and selenium. Although sulphur improves machinability, it reduces toughness, ductility, and corrosion resistance. The additions of phosphorus and selenium are less detrimental than sulphur so far as the corrosion resistance of these steels is concerned.

Iron-Chromium-Carbon Alloys (Martensitic Stainless Steels).
Everyone is familiar with cutlery stainless steels which give hardness, resistance to abrasion, high strength, and cutting qualities. These steels contain enough carbon so that when they are quenched from the austenitic condition, they develop a martensitic structure that has a hardness value dependent upon the carbon-chromium ratio. Steels of this type are called **martensitic** stainless steels. These martensitic steels transform to austenite at elevated temperatures and therefore are essentially austenitic at the quench-hardening temperature. The chromium dissolved in the austenite slows up the transformation rate so that steels of this type can be made fully hard, or martensitic, by oil quenching. Some compositions can be hardened by air cooling from the austenitic temperature range. The structure of the hardened steel is similar to that of other steels.

Following a quench-hardening treatment, the fully-hardened steel is usually tempered or drawn within a range up to 1000° F., depending upon the toughness requirements. The annealed condition of this type of steel, after slow cooling from the austenitic temperature range, consists of complex carbides in an alpha-iron structure. Corrosion resistance of the steel in this condition is poor, and it is therefore necessary to heat the steel into the austenitic range and dissolve the chromium carbides and retain this solution condition by quenching. Because of this requirement with this type of stainless steel, it has been replaced for structural purposes by the low carbon type of steel that is naturally stainless and does not require a solution heat treatment. However, when a relatively hard stainless steel is required, a higher carbon content is essential, as in the 420 and 440 types shown in Table 1. The type 420 steel containing 12% chromium and 0.35% carbon is known as the regular cutlery grade steel. In the hardened martensitic condition, it develops a hardness of about 55 Rockwell C and attains its maximum corrosion resistance. The

440 type is a general purpose hardenable stainless steel used for hardened steel balls and pump parts and is particularly adapted to resist corrosion for parts of machinery used in the oil industry.

Chromium-Nickel-Iron Stainless Alloys. The 300 series of stainless steels listed in Table 1, contain considerable nickel in addition to chromium. The addition of nickel to these steels is sufficient to render the alloy austenitic at room temperature; these steels are often referred to as **austenitic stainless steels.** Austenitic stainless steels are highly resistant to a large variety of corrosive agents and find a wide range of applications.

The most important of the austenitic stainless steels is the so-called **18-8** type containing 18% chromium and 8% nickel and including the modifications represented by the types 301, 303, 316, 321, and 347, Table 1. These steels possess extraordinary toughness and ductility, but they are nonmagnetic (gamma iron) and cannot be hardened by heat treatment. They are used in their natural condition as cast, forged, cold worked, and annealed. The only heat treatment given these steels is that of annealing after cold working or annealing for the purpose of stabilization.

Cold working of these austenitic stainless steels may be employed to develop high strengths and increased hardness. The strength of the 18-8 type may be varied from that of 90,000 lbs. per sq. in. in the annealed condition to as high as 260,000 lbs. per sq. in. in the cold work-hardened condition, with the hardness varying from 120 to 480 Brinell. The extreme high toughness of austenitic steels results in poor machining qualities which, however, may be somewhat improved by the addition of phosphorus and selenium, or through the addition of sulphur, as in the free-machining austenitic steels (type 303).

The austenitic chromium-nickel steels, when heated in the temperature range of 800°–1500° F. for a sufficiently long period, suffer from a precipitation of chromium carbides, largely forming at the grain boundaries of the austenitic grains. The precipitated carbides are less resistant to corrosion than the balance of the austenitic structure, and under conditions of marked precipitation of carbides at the grain boundaries, the steel may disintegrate when exposed to a corrosive medium. Fig. 4 illustrates a condition of severe intergranular corrosion resulting from exposing a piece of 18–8 austenitic stainless steel to a sulphuric acid and copper sulphate solution after the steel had been subjected to a long heating cycle at 1400° F. The corrosive medium has disintegrated the steel along the austenitic grain boundaries. The susceptibility of this type of steel to intergranular corrosion after heating to a red heat is influenced by the combined chromium and nickel contents with respect to the carbon content. Carbide precipitation diminishes rapidly with the reduction in carbon content, but it is difficult to manufacture stainless steels with the carbon content low enough to completely eliminate the possibility of intergranular precipitation. To prevent the precipitation of chromium carbides, elements such as columbium and titanium are added to the steel. Both columbium and titanium are strong carbide formers and combine with the carbon, using it up as special carbides and thus preventing the formation of the detrimental chromium carbides.

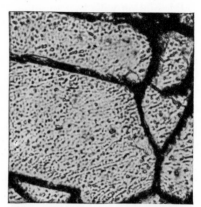

Fig. 4. Photomicrograph of Stainless Steel, No. 301 Type, That Has Been Subjected to the Sulphuric Acid and Copper Sulphate Etching Solution (Strauss Etch). This Photomicrograph Shows an Extreme Case of Intergranular Attack Resulting from Carbide Precipitation. Magnified 500 Times

The carbides of columbium and titanium are not considered harmful to the corrosion resistance of the steel.

Subjecting austenitic stainless steels that have not been treated with either columbium or titanium to a heating cycle, as in welding or forging operations, is dangerous with regard to an intergranular corrosion attack. Stabilization of such steels and the removal of the danger from corrosion may be obtained by a solution heat treatment. The stabilization, or solution heat treatment, usually consists of heating the steel to a temperature range of 1850°–2100° F., depending upon the composition, for a sufficient length of time (approximately ½ hr.) to get the carbides back into solution, and then cooling rapidly down to below the carbide precipitation range in less than three minutes. The cooling is usually accomplished by a water quench. A microscopic examination of the structure of the steel after this treatment will reveal a homogeneous austenitic structure free from any carbide precipitate, as seen in Fig. 5.

MANGANESE STEELS. Manganese is always used in steel, having a beneficial effect in the steel both directly and indirectly, and is always added to steel during its manufacture. Manganese combines with sulphur, iron, and carbon. With no carbon present, it forms a solid solution with both gamma and alpha iron. Manganese has only a mild tendency to combine with the carbon and therefore to form a

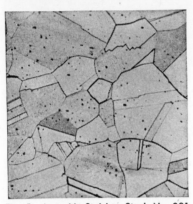

carbide (Mn_3C), which accounts for one of the principal advantages obtained from alloying manganese with steels: viz., the manganese dissolves in the ferrite matrix, adding materially to its strength. All steels contain manganese from a few hundredths of one per cent in many of the low carbon structural and machine steels to about 2% in steels that remain pearlitic in structure.

Fig. 5. Austenitic Stainless Steel, No. 301 Type, Containing 16.0%–18.0% Chromium and 7.0%–9.0% Nickel. Magnified 250 Times

As the manganese content of the steel is increased, the steel changes from a pearlitic to a martensitic, to an austenitic steel. The pearlitic steels are the most important. A very important steel is one containing up to 1.5% manganese. This type is oil hardening and retains its shape; therefore, it is known as **nondeforming** steel. It is used in many types of tools and dies that are to be hardened fully.

Manganese structural steel contains from 1% to 2% manganese, and from 0.08% to 0.55% carbon.

In tool steels, increasing the manganese content from 0.30% to 1.0% changes the steel from water hardening to oil hardening, due to the greater hardenability of the steel with the higher manganese content.

Martensitic manganese steels are not used because of great brittleness and hardness.

Austenitic manganese steels, sometimes called **Hadfield** steels, contain up to 15% manganese and 1% to 1.5% carbon. In the cast condition, this steel is very weak and brittle because of the presence of free carbides, and it is necessary to subject it to a heat treatment. The cast steel is heated to about 1900° F. and quenched in water, which increases the strength to 160,000 lbs. per sq. in., with an elongation of 60% to 70% in 2 in. The properties are those of austenite, with a low elastic limit, but it possesses great wearing power combined with much ductility. The wearing power is due to work hardening under cold deformation. Tests have shown that the initial wear of steel crusher jaws made from this type of steel is greater than the rate of wear after a few tons of stone have been crushed.

TUNGSTEN STEELS. Tungsten, like chromium and other alloying elements, dissolves in iron and forms a carbide with the cementite. The carbide formed in steels containing carbon and tungsten is thought to be Fe_4W_2C or Fe_3W_3C. It is apparent that this complex carbide is present in the commercial tungsten steels. The complex carbide formed in tungsten steels is very hard and brittle and imparts hardness to the steel. The tungsten carbide, like many of the other hard carbides found in alloy steels, resists tempering or softening of the martensite upon heating. When this carbide is present in sufficient quantities, it imparts high strength and hardness to steels subjected to elevated temperatures, or the property of hot hardness.

Tungsten has the following influences on steel:

1. Makes a dense and fine structure in steel.
2. Increases strength and toughness at high temperature.
3. Increases hardenability of steel.
4. Stabilizes martensite, imparting the property of **red hardness,** the ability of a cutting tool to maintain a cutting edge even at a red heat.

Tungsten forms two general types of steel:

1. Carbon type, with the tungsten under 1% for general purposes, tungsten from 1% to 2.5% for special tools, and 2.5% to 7% tungsten for fast finishing tool steels. Parts can be cut at much higher speeds with this steel than with carbon cutting tools, but it cannot be used when subjected to much heating, as can the high-speed steels.

2. Special type, which includes the tungsten-magnet steel, drawing-die steels, steels for pneumatic tools, hot-working steels and high-speed steels.

MOLYBDENUM STEELS. Molybdenum is considered one of the most recent alloys to be used in steel. However, Dr. Sargent reports that the Germans learned that some famous Japanese swords were made during the fourteenth century from a certain Japanese ore. Following this discovery, the Germans are said to have imported Japanese iron in large quantities. Although the element molybdenum was unknown prior to 1790, the superiority of the iron, which is now known to have contained molybdenum, was recognized about six hundred years ago.

Molybdenum dissolves in both gamma and alpha iron, but in the presence of carbon it combines to form a carbide. The behavior of molybdenum in steel is about the same as tungsten, but twice as effective. Since large deposits of molybdenum were discovered in this country, the commercial development has been rapid.

Molybdenum, like tungsten, improves the hot strength and hardness of steels. The complex carbide formed by the addition of molybdenum acts to stabilize martensite and resist softening upon heating, similar to the action from additions of tungsten. Molybdenum reduces the tendency toward grain growth at elevated temperatures and slows up the transformation rate from austenite to pearlite. This characteristic of molybdenum steels, increased hardenability, allows the use of air quenching of many of the alloy tool steels instead of oil quenching in the hardening operation. The sluggishness of the molybdenum steels to any structural change during heat-treating operations leads to longer soaking periods for annealing or hardening and slower cooling rates in order to obtain a well-annealed structure. Molybdenum is often combined with other alloying elements in commercial alloy steels. The addition of other special elements seems to enhance the value of molybdenum in steels. Molybdenum-chromium, molybdenum-nickel, molybdenum-tungsten, and molybdenum-nickel-chromium are common combinations used. The use of molybdenum as a supplementary element in steel is more extensive than its use alone.

Molybdenum structural steels of the SAE 4000 series find many applications intended for heat-treated parts. The molybdenum in these steels strengthens the steels both statically and dynamically, eliminates temper brittleness almost completely, refines the structure, and widens the critical range.

Molybdenum is alloyed with both structural steel and tool steel. The low-carbon molybdenum steels are often subjected to case-hardening heat treatments. Medium-carbon molybdenum steels are heat treated for parts including such applications as gears, roller bearings, and aircraft and automobile parts that are subjected to high stresses. Tool steels for general use and for tools for hot working are often alloyed with molybdenum. Greater hardenability and improvements in physical properties are outstanding reasons for the selection of a tool steel containing molybdenum. As a stabilizer for martensite, molybdenum can be used as a substitute for tungsten in hot working and high-speed steels.

HIGH-SPEED STEELS. High-speed steels are so named because, when used as tools such as machine cutting tools, they remove metal much faster than ordinary steel. Their chief superiority over other steels lies in their ability to maintain their hardness even at a dull red heat (about 1100° F.). Due to this property, such tools can operate satisfactorily at speeds which cause the cutting edges to reach a temperature that would ruin the hardness of ordinary tool steels. Table 2, Chapter XIV, contains a list of the most commonly used high-speed steels along with their chemical composition. It will be seen from this table that the principal alloying elements are tungsten, molybdenum, chromium, and vanadium. The tungsten type of high-speed steel contains up to 20% tungsten, from 2% to 5% chromium, usually from 1% to 2% vanadium, and sometimes cobalt which is added for special properties. More recently, molybdenum has been successfully substituted for tungsten in these steels, with molybdenum up to 9% and no tungsten, although a more common high-speed steel contains approximately equal amounts of molybdenum and tungsten, 5% of each. The most commonly used high-speed steel is referred to as 18–4–1, which means that it contains 18% tungsten, 4% chromium, and 1% vanadium. The carbon content in the usual high-speed steel runs about 0.65% to 0.75% although in some grades the carbon content may run as high as 1.30% (see Table 2, Chapter XIV).

The molybdenum or molybdenum-tungsten high-speed steels have been largely substituted for the straight tungsten high-speed steels of the 18–4–1 type. Actual shop tests made with heavy and light lathe tools, planer tools, and milling reamers demonstrated that particularly the heavy planer and lathe tools stood up, on the average, as well as or better than tungsten or the tungsten-cobalt tools. The molybdenum grades of high-speed steels have one drawback to their use: viz., they are much more sensitive to decarburization than the tungsten steels during the hot-working and heat-treating operations. This problem can be overcome by the use of borax which is fused in a thin coating over the steel, forming a protective film during the heating and hot forging and during subsequent forging operations. The borax may also be used during the heat-treating operations, but it causes a cleaning problem and is injurious to the furnace hearth. In the place of borax, a furnace designed with the correct atmosphere will prevent any serious decarburization. Also, it has been found that it is practical to use salt baths for the heat-treating operations since the molten salt protects the surfaces of the molybdenum high-speed steel from decarburization or carburization.

Heat Treating of High-Speed Steels. Heating for hardening may be carried out in controlled-atmosphere furnaces or in salt baths, or the tools, before heating, may be dipped in a saturated solution of borax and water that is heated to between 150° and 180° F. Tools dipped in this warm solution will dry when removed and will be covered with a thin powdery film of borax that will not rub off if the tools are handled with moderate care. If too much borax is used, blister may form on the surface of the hardened tools. After hardening, the tools will be found coated with a thin layer of borax, which can be removed with a wire brush, sand blast, or a 10% solution of acetic acid.

Salt baths offer one of the best methods available for the heat treating of high-speed steels, particularly when the maximum temperature for hardening does not exceed 2300° F. Some compositions of high-speed steel require a hardening temperature in excess of 2300° F., and therefore it may be found inadvisable to use a salt bath. Some other heating medium may prove more satisfactory. The straight tungsten types and those containing cobalt require higher hardening temperatures than the molybdenum and molybdenum-tungsten steels.

Salt bath furnaces are usually complete in themselves, consisting of a preheat, a high-heat, and a quench bath. The preheat salt operates at about 1500° F., and the steel is placed in this bath for a period of time that allows it to reach the heat of the bath. From the preheat salt, the work is placed in the high-heat bath and held in this bath for a predetermined length of time. The time in the high heat is determined by the usual trial and error method although with the use of hardness tests and microscopic examination of the treated steel, the correct time can be determined accurately. The time and temperature of the high heat are governed by the amount of carbide solution and the grain size developed. Fig. 6 illustrates the type of microstructure obtained from heating a piece of 6–6–2 type (molybdenum-tungsten) high-speed steel to 2250° F. for 5 minutes and quenching in hot salt. The structure consists of undissolved carbides and aus-

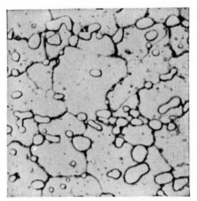

Fig. 6. Molybdenum-Tungsten (6–6–2 Type) High-Speed Steel in the As-Quench-hardened Condition. Undissolved Carbides (Light), Austenitic Grain Boundaries (Dark). Magnified 1000 Times

tenitic grain boundary markings. The grain size is on the coarse side, with about 10 grains per 5-inch length at 1000 magnifications (No. 10 grain size). From the high-heat bath, the work is quenched in a salt bath held at 1100° F. The hot salt quenching bath acts as a quenching medium, undercooling the austenitic structure formed at the high heat and also helping in the removal of the salt that adheres to the work from the high-heat bath. The high-heat salt is very hard to remove from the work without the aid of the hot-salt quench. Under ideal operating conditions, the salt-bath method of heat treating for high-speed steels furnishes full protection against any surface skin such as decarburization or carburization. Fig. 7 illustrates a slight skin of about 0.0003 in. that was formed in a salt-bath treatment for hardening of high-speed steel. This slight skin is negligible insofar as it influences the useful properties of the steel for tools.

Frequently, high-speed steel is heated for hardening in a standard type of oven furnace with protection offered by a suitable gaseous atmosphere. The atmosphere commonly used is rich in carbon monoxide, running about 34% and with only a trace of CO_2. With

the proper controlled atmosphere, high-speed steels of any composition can be successfully hardened without any detrimental effects from either carburization or decarburization. Hardening of the tungsten type (18–4–1) or cobalt high-speed steels can be carried out successfully in the gas or electric-fired furnaces with a suitable gaseous atmosphere.

Carburization of the surfaces of high-speed steels, particularly of the tungsten type, may occur when a rich CO atmosphere is used as protection. Carburized surfaces will cause the austenitic structure to become quite stable

Fig. 7. Decarburized Skin (Dark) on Molybdenum-Tungsten (6–6–2) Type of High-Speed Steel, Hardened from a Salt-Bath Furnace. Magnified 1000 Times

and prevent its breaking down to martensite in the drawing or tempering operation. Fig. 8 illustrates a soft skin formed on the surface of the 18–4–1 type of high-speed steel by carburization during the hardening operation. The austenitic layer (light in photomicrograph) resists transformation to martensite during the tempering operation and remains relatively soft. This condition is undesirable and should be avoided by reducing the CO content in the atmosphere surrounding the steel during the hardening operation.

Preheating for Hardening. It is recommended that high-speed steels be preheated to a temperature range from 1400° to 1500° F. before placing them in the hardening furnace. This preheating should be carried out in a furnace separate from the one used for the hardening heat. The molybdenum high-speed steels can be preheated to a lower temperature than the tungsten high-speed steels. This apparently helps to avoid decarburization. Small tools of light section, under ¼ inch, can be hardened without preheating.

Hardening Temperatures for High-Speed Steels. The straight tungsten type of high-speed steel, such as the 18–4–1, can be hardened by heating to a temperature range from 2300° to 2375° F., followed by quenching in an oil bath. The time required to heat will depend upon the size of the section and upon the type of heating medium. The timing should be such as to allow the steel to come up to the temperature of the furnace, or nearly so. For light sections, this may take only a few minutes, whereas for a section of 1 to 2 inches, it may require a heating time of 20 minutes. Careful observation of the steel during the heating cycle will allow the hardener to judge the time needed for heating.

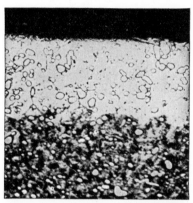

Fig. 8. High-Speed Steel of the 18–4–1 Type, Hardened and Double-drawn to 1050° F. Surface Layer (White) Is a Layer of Retained Austenite, Resulting from Heating in a Carburizing Atmosphere during the Hardening Operation. Surface Hardness—Rockwell C 56. Magnified 500 Times

Anyone who has hardened the 18–4–1 type of tungsten high-speed steel can harden molybdenum high-speed steel. The hardening is carried out in a similar way, preheating at 1200° to 1500° F. and transferring the steel to the high-temperature furnace for hardening. Quenching and drawing are carried out as with the 18–4–1 type. The steel should never be soaked excessively at the hardening temperature but should be removed from the furnace and quenched shortly after it is up to heat. The temperatures recommended for the hardening of the molydenum type of high-speed steels are somewhat lower than for the tungsten steels, i.e., 2150° to 2250° F. Overheating of the molybdenum type will put it in a somewhat brittle condition, whereas the 18–4–1 type may be overheated 75° F. and still make a reasonably satisfactory tool.

Overheating of high-speed steel may ruin the steel for further use, making it weak and relatively soft. The structure resulting from severe overheating is illustrated in Fig. 9. This structure shows large austenitic grains with fused grain boundaries (dark), and coarse needle-like martensitic markings. Practically all of the carbides are dissolved when high-speed steels are overheated.

Quenching of High-Speed Steels. The quenching may be done in oil, salt bath, or air for both the tungsten and molybdenum steels.

Fig. 9. Photomicrograph of High-Speed Steel That Was Severely Overheated in the Hardening Operation. Note the Coarse Martensitic Markings (Needle-like) with a Network Structure Resulting from Slight Fusion. Note also Freedom from Carbides. Magnified 500 Times

Oil is the most common quenching medium. However, if warping and cracking become a problem, it is recommended that hot quenching be used, quenching in molten salts held at a temperature range from 1100° to 1200° F., or quenching in air if scaling is not serious and the section hardens satisfactorily. A practice that may be tried is to quench in oil for a short time, then to place the tool in the pre-heat furnace held at 1200° F. until the temperature becomes equalized, and finally to air-cool to room temperature. The time in the oil quench should be such as to cool the steel from the high heat to around 1200° F., or a very dull heat.

Tempering or Drawing of High-Speed Steels. High-speed steels, after hardening, do not develop their full hardness and toughness without tempering or drawing. Drawing may be carried out successfully by heating the hardened steel to a temperature range extending from 1000° to 1100° F. for at least 1 hour, preferably 2 hours. The steel, before tempering, should be cooled to at least 200° F. from the quench and reheated slowly to the temperature used in drawing. The cooling from the drawing temperature may be done in air but *not* in water. Multiple tempering is recommended when maximum toughness is required; i.e., the tempering operation should be repeated.

The Microstructure of High-Speed Steels. Microscopic examination of annealed high-speed steels shows the structure to consist of a large quantity of carbides in a matrix of ferrite. The structure of annealed high-speed steel is shown in Fig. 10. The carbides (light particles) are made up of a complex mixture of carbon, tungsten, molybdenum, chromium, vanadium, etc. The complex carbides found in high-speed steels give these steels outstanding properties. In the hardening process, the steel is heated to a relatively high temperature in order to dissolve a large percentage of these carbides.

However, the austenitic structure formed at the high temperature does not dissolve all of these carbides, and it is not desirable to do so. The carbides remaining out of solution add to the wear resistance and the cutting ability of this steel. Upon quenching from the high heat to room temperature in either oil, air, or hot salt, the austenite transforms to martensite, but not completely, so that the hardened high-speed steel always retains at room temperature some austenite from the

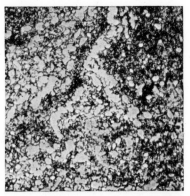

Fig. 10. Photomicrograph of Annealed High-Speed Steel of the Molybdenum-Tungsten Type (6–6–2). Carbides (Light). Magnified 500 Times

quench. In fact, as much as 30% austenite may be retained in the quenched high-speed steel. Microscopic examination of the quench-hardened steel shows a structure that appears to be austenitic with undissolved carbides (see Fig. 6). The original austenitic grain outlines can be plainly seen. The size of the austenitic grain is one of the factors that influence the properties of the finished tool or die and is a criterion of the correct temperature-time factor used in the hardening operation.

Because of the retained austenite in the hardened steel, it becomes necessary to temper or draw the steel after hardening. The objective of the drawing treatment is largely to transform the remaining austenite to martensite. This is accomplished by reheating the hardened steel between 1000° and 1100° F., usually 1050° F., followed by slow cooling to room temperature. By this treatment, the retained austenite of the quench-hardened steel is transformed to martensite, and the internal stresses in the hardened steel are removed. The fresh-born martensite of the tempered or drawn steel should now be drawn to relieve any stresses set up by its birth. This is accomplished by repeating the drawing operation, i.e., heating to 1050° F., followed by slow cooling to room temperature. The steel is now in the best condition for use. The microscopic appearance of high-speed steel after a double draw following hardening is shown in Fig. 11.

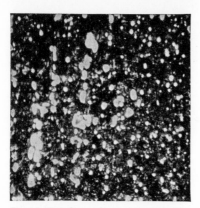

Fig. 11. High-Speed Steel of the Molybdenum-Tungsten (6–6–2) Type in the Hardened and Double-drawn Condition. Magnified 1000 Times

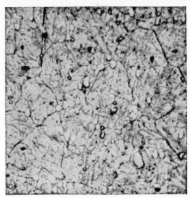

Fig. 12. High-Speed Steel in the Hardened and Drawn Condition, Etched to Bring Out the Original Austenitic Grain Size. Etching Solution Is HC_1—10 ml.; Alcohol—100 ml.; HNO_3—3 ml. Magnified 1000 Times

The structure consists of white carbides in a dark martensitic matrix, with the austenitic grain outlines, as seen in the hardened steel, completely gone. The grain size of the original austenite may be brought out in the drawn high-speed steel by means of a special etching treatment, as shown in Fig. 12, which shows the structure of hardened and drawn high-speed steel with the grain outlines of the original austenite appearing in the photomicrograph.

Hardness of High-Speed Steels. High-speed steel in the fully annealed condition will run between Rockwell C-10 and C-20 and is machinable. In the hardened condition, as quenched, the hardness should run between Rockwell C-63 and C-65 for satisfactory results. After drawing, the hardness should run between C-64 and C-66.

Forging of High-Speed Steels. Forging should be carried out from 2100° to about 1800° F. in order to obtain a good condition in the final forged shape. In most applications, the user of high-speed steel buys the steel in the forged condition, such as forged or rolled bars and forged blanks. However, if some shaping is required, it may be carried out successfully if the necessary precautions are taken. In the manufacture of high-speed cutters, where the outside diameter is greater than 4 inches, it is recommended that upset-forged blanks be used. The blanks may be made by buying a small-diameter bar and upset-forging a section of the bar to make the size cutter required. The upset-forging operation produces a better condition of structure in the high-speed steel than can be obtained from a rolled or hammered bar of large diameter.

Annealing of High-Speed Steels. Annealing may be carried out by slowly heating the high-speed steel to a temperature from 1550° to 1675° F. for about 6 to 8 hours, followed by very slow cooling of the steel. The cooling cycle should require about 24 hours. The steel must be protected from oxidation and decarburization by packing in cast-iron chips or a suitable reducing agent such as charcoal and ashes mixed. As most high-speed steel is purchased in the annealed condition for machining, it is not necessary to anneal this type of steel unless reannealing and rehardening of a used tool are required. In the event that this is the case, the steel should be reannealed before hardening; otherwise a brittle condition of the rehardened tool will result.

Decarburization or Carburization in High-Speed Steels. Successfully hardened and tempered high-speed steels should not have more than 0.001 inch of soft skin of decarburization or carburization. However, if hardening of the molybdenum type is carried out in a standard oven-type furnace without the necessary controlled and protective atmosphere, decarburization may become a very serious factor. Decarburization and soft skin on the surface of tools hardened in this manner may extend to a depth of more than 0.010 inch, and if the allowance for finishing or grinding does not remove all of this skin, a poor tool will result. Fig. 13 illustrates a satisfactorily hardened piece of high-speed steel having no skin.

HOT-WORKING STEELS. Steels containing from 5% to 15% tungsten and several per cent of chromium resemble high-speed steels in that they have a tendency to retain their hardness when heated. These steels are used as hot-working tools, such as forging dies or extrusion dies. They need not be as hard as cutting tools, and their carbon content is somewhat lower than that of high-speed steels.

Part or all of the tungsten present in hot-working steels may be replaced by molybdenum, similar to the substitution that may be used in the high-speed steels. Hot-working steels resemble high-speed steels, with this type of steel containing a lower carbon content and somewhat lower percentages of all of the alloying elements. These steels are deep hardening and are of the oil- or air-hardening type.

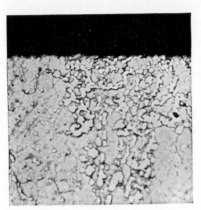

Fig. 13. Photomicrograph of the Edge of a Sample of Hardened High-Speed Steel, Showing Practically No Surface Skin. Magnified 500 Times

VANADIUM STEELS. Although vanadium is not a major alloy in many of the special alloy steels, the role it plays as a minor alloying element is very important. Vanadium has a strong affinity for carbon, and when added to steel, it is found partly combined with the ferrite but principally with the carbide or cementite. The presence of vanadium greatly increases the strength, toughness, and hardness of the ferrite matrix of steels. The carbide, or cementite, formed with vanadium is likewise greatly strengthened and hardened and shows little tendency to segregate into large masses.

The most important effect of vanadium in steels is to produce a very small grain size and induce grain control in the steel. The vanadium steels are inherently fine-grained, and this fine grain size is maintained throughout the usual heat-treating temperature range. Steels containing vanadium are also shallow hardening because they have a faster transformation rate from austenite to pearlite during the cooling cycle from the hardening temperature. However, due to the grain-control characteristics imparted by the addition of vanadium, steels may be heated over a wide range of temperatures during the hardening operation without danger of developing a coarse and weak structure.

Another important effect resulting from the presence of vanadium carbides is that these carbides are extremely stable, and, when in solution, resist precipitation from the solution. As a result, after vanadium steels have been quench-hardened from the heat-treating temperature, they exhibit a marked tendency to resist loss of hardness during the tempering cycle. This characteristic is of major importance with steels that are used for hot work and contributes to the hot hardness of the special high-speed steels. This carbide stability is important in constructional steels and in cast irons used at elevated temperatures.

Vanadium is effective in steels in amounts as low as 0.05%, and in many of the common alloy steels the vanadium content runs under 0.30%. Alloy steels designed for use at elevated temperatures, such as hot-work steels and high-speed cutting tools, contain up to 4.0% vanadium.

SILICON STEELS. Silicon as an alloying element dissolves in both gamma iron and alpha iron and does not form a carbide. The solubility of silicon in the gamma iron is approximately 2%, whereas it is soluble in the alpha iron up to 18% and remains highly soluble even in the presence of carbon. Silicon is present in all steels as a result of the manufacturing process. In low carbon structural steel and machine steel, the silicon content runs around 0.25% to 0.35%. Silicon in this range does not influence the properties of the steel to any extent. With the additions of silicon above .50% to more than 2%, we find improvement in tensile strength and yield point of steels. A popular spring steel contains approximately 2% silicon, 0.7% manganese, and 0.5% carbon. This steel, after heat treatment, develops excellent strength and toughness and is widely used for coil and leaf springs. Combinations of silicon-chromium and silicon-chromium-manganese are also used for spring steels.

Silicon has been alloyed to steels of the stainless and heat-resisting type, with improvements noted in their ability to resist certain types of corrosion and oxidation at elevated temperatures. The 18–8 (austenitic) type of stainless steel has been improved for some uses by the addition of silicon up to 4%. Steels used for gas-engine valves in the automotive and airplane industry often contain appreciable amounts of silicon. These steels contain from 1% to 4% silicon, 6% to 9% chromium, 0.15% vanadium, and approximately 0.5% carbon. This steel is highly resistant to oxidation and retains high strength and hardness at elevated temperatures.

Alloys of iron and silicon, containing but a very small amount of carbon as an impurity, are used in transformer cores due to their good magnetic properties and high electrical resistance. Such steels contain from 2% to 5% silicon and usually are used in sheet form.

MAGNET STEELS. Carbon, chromium, tungsten, and cobalt steels are used for permanent magnets. The superiority, as well as the price, increases in the order given above. These steels are used in the hardened condition. The carbon steels contain from 0.80% to 1.20% carbon and are, in fact, carbon tool steels. The chromium magnet steels contain from 0.70% to 1.00% carbon and 2% or 3% chromium. The tungsten steels contain about 0.70% carbon and 5% tungsten. The best and most expensive cobalt steels contain 35% cobalt, together with several per cent of both chromium and tungsten. A permanent magnet alloy (Alnico), recently developed, contains approximately 60% iron, 20% nickel, 8% cobalt and 12% aluminum. This alloy cannot be forged and is used as a casting hardened by precipitation heat treatments. Alloys of this type have great magnetic strength and permanence.

QUIZ QUESTIONS

1. Describe plain carbon steel.
2. What is the approximate maximum hardness developed by plain carbon or alloy steel?
3. Name the reasons for the selection of alloy steels in preference to carbon steels.
4. Name the four ways in which an element added to steel may combine with it.
5. What improvements in steel are contributed by the addition of elements which form a solid solution with the iron?
6. What property makes carbide-forming steels valuable?
7. What effect does the formation of oxides have upon steel?
8. What improvement results from the addition to steel of elements that remain uncombined?
9. In general, what percentages of special element and carbon are contained in pearlitic alloy steels?
10. Name the uses of steels in the pearlitic alloy group.

11. *How do percentages of carbon and special element in steels in the martensitic group compare with those in the pearlitic group?*

12. *Name the uses of martensitic alloy steels.*

13. *Why have austenitic alloy steels no critical temperature on cooling?*

14. *What characteristics do austenitic alloy steels have?*

15. *What use is made of cementitic alloy steels?*

16. *What qualities make nickel steels suitable for structural applications?*

17. *What other elements are alloyed with nickel alloy steels to make special steels?*

18. *Give the composition of five nickel alloy steels and name a particular property for which each is noted.*

19. *What use is made of low-carbon chromium steels that have been case-hardened?*

20. *What important property does a high percentage of chromium give to steel?*

21. *For what is high-carbon chromium steel used?*

22. *What percentages of carbon and chromium are used in cutlery stainless steels?*

23. *Why is sulphur added to some stainless steels?*

24. *What is the strength of the stainless steel known as "18-8" in the annealed and work-hardened conditions? What is the hardness?*

25. *What use is made of so-called "nondeforming" steel?*

26. *Name the special properties of Hadfield steels?*

27. *What four improvements does tungsten make on the characteristics of steel?*

28. *What are the two types of tungsten steel?*

29. *Name one disadvantage of molybdenum high-speed steels.*

30. *For what are "hot-working" steels used?*

31. *How does the addition of vanadium to steel affect its physical properties?*

32. *Name some uses of silicon steels.*

CHARACTERISTICS OF SPARKS GENERATED BY THE GRINDING OF METALS

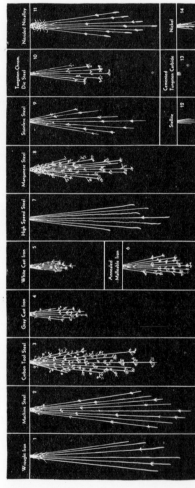

Metal	Volume of Stream	Relative Length of Stream, Inches†	Color of Stream Close to Wheel	Color of Streaks Near End of Stream	Quantity of Sparks	Nature of Sparks
1. Wrought iron	Large	65	Straw	White	Very few	Forked
2. Machine steel	Large	70	White	White	Few	Forked
3. Carbon tool steel	Moderately large	55	White	White	Very many	Fine, repeating
4. Gray cast iron	Small	25	Red	Straw	Many	Fine, repeating
5. White cast iron	Very small	20	Red	Straw	Few	Fine, repeating
6. Annealed mall. iron	Moderate	30	Red	Straw	Many	Fine, repeating
7. High speed steel	Small	60	Red	Straw	Extremely few	Forked
8. Manganese steel	Moderately large	45	White	White	Many	Fine, repeating
9. Stainless steel	Moderate	50	Straw	White	Moderate	Forked
10. Tungsten-chromium die steel	Small	35	Red	Straw*	Many	Fine, repeating*
11. Nitrided Nitralloy	Large (curved)	55	White	White	Moderate	Forked
12. Stellite	Very small	10	Orange	Orange	None	
13. Cemented tungsten carbide	Extremely small	2	Light Orange	Light Orange	None	
14. Nickel	Very small**	10	Orange	Orange:	None	
15. Copper, brass, aluminum	None				None	

†Figures obtained with 12" wheel on bench stand and are relative only. Actual length in each instance will vary with grinding wheel, pressure, etc. *Blue-white sparks. **Some wavy streaks.

Courtesy of Norton Company, Worcester, Massachusetts

CHAPTER XIV

Classification of Steels

MANY attempts have been made to classify and standardize the many different types and compositions of steels used throughout industry. Steel makers have worked out charts and tables in an effort to simplify the selection of steels so that the average user may find it easier to make a selection. Those most commonly referred to are the tables and specifications of the Society for Automotive Engineers, specifications of American Iron and Steel Institute, the classification of American Tool Steels by Gill and the American Society for Metals, and the classification by Chambers of Tool Steels by Wear-Toughness Ratio. These specifications and tables are available in many different forms (see Table 1) and may be used to advantage by anyone using structural and tool steels.

S.A.E. STEELS. The steel specifications and compositions by the Society for Automotive Engineers are very well known and are in general use. Although these specifications were intended for use in the automotive industry, their use has spread into all industries where steels, and particularly alloy steels, are being used. The specifications are mainly intended for structural applications, as in machines, but they include a limited number of high carbon and alloy steels that can be used for tools. In the selection of any of these steels, the user may consult the specifications and select a number of different steels with different compositions that may be applied to the same usage. No definite applications for the different steels are included in the specifications. However, the complete specifications include compositions, heat treatments, and conservative physical properties that might be expected from the steels, so that the user may make an intelligent selection.

S.A.E. Steel Numbering System. A numeral index system is used to identify the compositions of the S.A.E. and A.I.S.I. steels,

Table 1. Standard Steel Compositions

Jointly Issued by the American Iron and Steel Institute and Society of Automotive Engineers

A.I.S.I. Standard Steel Compositions—Revised Feb. 1, 1943

CODE FOR PREFIXES:

A is basic openhearth alloy steel.
B is acid bessemer carbon steel.
C is basic openhearth carbon steel.
D is acid openhearth carbon steel.
E is electric furnace steel.

NE is National Emergency standard steel; designation promulgated by W.P.B.
Q is forging quality, or special requirement quality.
R is re-rolling quality billets.

Openhearth Alloy and Electric Furnace Carbon and Alloy Steels
(Blooms, Billets, Slabs, Bars and Hot-Rolled Strip)

AISI Number	C	Mn	P Max.*	S Max.*	Si*	Ni	Cr	Mo	'42 SAE Number
A 1330	0.28-0.33	1.60-1.90	0.040	0.040	0.20-0.35	.....	.....	.....	1330
A 1335	0.33-0.38	1.60-1.90	0.040	0.040	0.20-0.35	.....	.....	.....	1335
A 1340	0.38-0.43	1.60-1.90	0.040	0.040	0.20-0.35	.....	.....	.....	1340
A 1345	.43-0.48	1.60-1.90	0.040	0.040	0.20-0.35	.....	.....	.....	.....
A 1350	0.48-0.53	1.60-1.90	0.040	0.040	0.20-0.35	.....	.....	.....	.....
A 2317	0.15-0.20	0.40-0.60	0.040	0.040	0.20-0.35	3.25-3.75	.....	.....	{2315, 2317
A 2330	0.28-0.33	0.60-0.80	0.040	0.040	0.20-0.35	3.25-3.75	.....	.....	2330
A 2335	0.33-0.38	0.60-0.80	0.040	0.040	0.20-0.35	3.25-3.75	.....	.....	.....
A 2340	0.38-0.43	0.70-0.90	0.040	0.040	0.20-0.35	3.25-3.75	.....	.....	2340
A 2345	0.43-0.48	0.70-0.90	0.040	0.040	0.20-0.35	3.25-3.75	.....	.....	2345
E 2512	0.09-0.14	0.45-0.60	0.025	0.025	0.20-0.35	4.75-5.25	.....	.....	.....
A 2515	0.12-0.17	0.40-0.60	0.040	0.040	0.20-0.35	4.75-5.25	.....	.....	2515
E 2517	0.15-0.20	0.45-0.60	0.025	0.025	0.20-0.35	4.75-5.25	.....	.....	.....
A 3115	0.13-0.18	0.40-0.60	0.040	0.040	0.20-0.35	1.10-1.40	0.55-0.75	.....	3115
A 3120	0.17-0.22	0.60-0.80	0.040	0.040	0.20-0.35	1.10-1.40	0.55-0.75	.....	3120
A 3130	0.28-0.33	0.60-0.80	0.040	0.040	0.20-0.35	1.10-1.40	0.55-0.75	.....	3130
A 3135	0.33-0.38	0.60-0.80	0.040	0.040	0.20-0.35	1.10-1.40	0.55-0.75	.....	3135
A 3140	0.38-0.43	0.70-0.90	0.040	0.040	0.20-0.35	1.10-1.40	0.55-0.75	.....	3140
A 3141	0.38-0.43	0.70-0.90	0.040	0.040	0.20-0.35	1.10-1.40	0.70-0.90	.....	X3140, 3141
A 3145	0.43-0.48	0.70-0.90	0.040	0.040	0.20-0.35	1.10-1.40	0.70-0.90	.....	3145
A 3150	0.48-0.53	0.70-0.90	0.040	0.040	0.20-0.35	1.10-1.40	0.70-0.90	.....	3150
A 3240	0.38-0.45	0.40-0.60	0.040	0.040	0.20-0.35	1.65-2.00	0.90-1.20	.....	3240
E 3310	0.08-0.13	0.45-0.60	0.025	0.025	0.20-0.35	3.25-3.75	1.40-1.75	.....	{3310, 3312

Type	SAE No.	C	Mn	P max	S max	Si	Ni	Cr	Mo	AISI No.
E	3316	0.14–0.19	0.45–0.60	0.025	0.025	0.20–0.35	3.25–3.75	1.40–1.75		
A	4023	0.20–0.25	0.70–0.90	0.040	0.040	0.20–0.35			0.20–0.30	4023
A	4024	0.20–0.25	0.70–0.90	0.040	(a)	0.20–0.35			0.20–0.30	
A	4027	0.25–0.30	0.70–0.90	0.040	0.040	0.20–0.35			0.20–0.30	4027
A	4028	0.25–0.30	0.70–0.90	0.040	(a)	0.20–0.35			0.20–0.30	
A	4032	0.30–0.35	0.70–0.90	0.040	0.040	0.20–0.35			0.20–0.30	4032
A	4037	0.35–0.40	0.70–0.90	0.040	0.040	0.20–0.35			0.20–0.30	4037
A	4042	0.40–0.45	0.75–1.00	0.040	0.040	0.20–0.35			0.20–0.30	4042
A	4047	0.45–0.50	0.75–1.00	0.040	0.040	0.20–0.35			0.20–0.30	4047
A	4063	0.60–0.67	0.75–1.00	0.040	0.040	0.20–0.35			0.20–0.30	4063
A	4068	0.64–0.72	0.75–1.00	0.040	0.040	0.20–0.35			0.20–0.30	4068
A	4119	0.17–0.22	0.70–0.90	0.040	0.040	0.20–0.35		0.40–0.60	0.20–0.30	4119
A	4120	0.17–0.22	0.70–0.90	0.040	0.040	0.20–0.35		0.60–0.80	0.15–0.25	
A	4125	0.23–0.28	0.70–0.90	0.040	0.040	0.20–0.35		0.40–0.60	0.14–0.19	4125
A	4130	0.28–0.33	0.40–0.60	0.040	0.040	0.20–0.35		0.80–1.10	0.18–0.25	X4130, 4130
A	4131	0.28–0.33	0.50–0.70	0.040	0.040	0.20–0.35		0.80–1.10	0.15–0.25	
E	4132	0.30–0.35	0.40–0.60	0.025	0.025	0.20–0.35		0.80–1.10	0.18–0.25	
A	4134	0.32–0.37	0.40–0.60	0.040	0.040	0.20–0.35		0.80–1.10	0.18–0.25	
E	4135	0.33–0.38	0.70–0.90	0.025	0.025	0.20–0.35		0.80–1.10	0.15–0.25	
A	4137	0.35–0.40	0.70–0.90	0.040	0.040	0.20–0.35		0.80–1.10	0.14–0.19	4137
E	4137	0.35–0.40	0.70–0.90	0.025	0.025	0.20–0.35		0.80–1.10	0.15–0.25	
A	4140	0.38–0.43	0.75–1.00	0.040	0.040	0.20–0.35		0.80–1.10	0.15–0.25	4140
A	4141	0.38–0.43	0.75–1.00	0.040	0.040	0.20–0.35		0.80–1.10	0.30–0.40	
A	4142	0.40–0.45	0.75–1.00	0.040	0.040	0.20–0.35		0.80–1.10	0.15–0.25	
A	4143	0.40–0.45	0.75–1.00	0.040	0.040	0.20–0.35		0.80–1.10	0.15–0.25	
A	4145	0.43–0.48	0.75–1.00	0.040	0.040	0.20–0.35		0.80–1.10	0.20–0.27	4145
A	4147	0.45–0.52	0.75–1.00	0.040	0.040	0.20–0.35		0.80–1.10	0.20–0.30	
A	4150	0.46–0.53	0.75–1.00	0.040	0.040	0.20–0.35		0.80–1.10	0.20–0.30	4150
E	4150	0.48–0.53	0.70–0.90	0.025	0.025	0.20–0.35		0.80–1.10	0.30–0.40	
A	4317	0.15–0.20	0.45–0.65	0.040	0.040	0.20–0.35	1.65–2.00	0.40–0.60	0.23–0.30	
A	4320	0.17–0.22	0.45–0.65	0.040	0.040	0.20–0.35	1.65–2.00	0.40–0.60	0.23–0.30	4320
A	4337	0.35–0.40	0.60–0.80	0.040	0.040	0.20–0.35	1.65–2.00	0.60–0.80	0.15–0.25	
E	4340	0.38–0.43	0.60–0.80	0.025	0.025	0.20–0.35	1.65–2.00	0.70–0.90	0.20–0.30	X4340, 4340
A	4342	0.40–0.45	0.60–0.80	0.025	0.025	0.20–0.35	1.65–2.00	0.70–0.90	0.20–0.30	
E	4608	0.06–0.11	0.40 max.	0.025	0.025	0.25 max.	1.40–1.75		0.20–0.27	
A	4615	0.13–0.18	0.45–0.65	0.040	0.040	0.20–0.35	1.65–2.00		0.20–0.30	4615
E	4617	0.15–0.20	0.45–0.65	0.025	0.025	0.20–0.35	1.65–2.00		0.20–0.30	
A	4620	0.17–0.22	0.45–0.65	0.040	0.040	0.20–0.35	1.65–2.00		0.20–0.30	4620
E	4620	0.17–0.22	0.45–0.60	0.025	0.025	0.20–0.35	1.65–2.00		0.20–0.27	
A	4621	0.18–0.23	0.70–0.90	0.040	0.040	0.20–0.35	1.65–2.00		0.20–0.30	
A	4640	0.38–0.43	0.60–0.80	0.040	0.040	0.20–0.35	1.65–2.00		0.20–0.30	4640

[Continued on following page]

Table 1—*Continued*

Openhearth Alloy and Electric Furnace Carbon and Alloy Steels—*Concluded*

AISI Number	C	Mn	P Max.*	S Max.*	Si*	Ni	Cr	Mo	'42 SAE Number
E 4640	0.38–0.43	0.60–0.80	0.025	0.025	0.20–0.35	1.65–2.00	....	0.20–0.27	....
A 4645	0.43–0.48	0.60–0.80	0.040	0.040	0.20–0.35	1.65–2.00	....	0.20–0.30	....
A 4815	0.13–0.18	0.40–0.60	0.040	0.040	0.20–0.35	3.25–3.75	....	0.20–0.30	4815
A 4820	0.18–0.23	0.50–0.70	0.040	0.040	0.20–0.35	3.25–3.75	....	0.20–0.30	4820
A 5120	0.17–0.22	0.70–0.90	0.040	0.040	0.20–0.35	....	0.70–0.90	....	5120
A 5130	0.28–0.33	0.70–0.90	0.040	0.040	0.20–0.35	....	0.80–1.10	....	....
A 5140	0.38–0.43	0.70–0.90	0.040	0.040	0.20–0.35	....	0.70–0.90	....	5140
A 5145	0.43–0.48	0.70–0.90	0.040	0.040	0.20–0.35	....	0.70–0.90	....	....
A 5150	0.48–0.55	0.70–0.90	0.040	0.040	0.20–0.35	....	0.70–0.90	....	5150
A 5152	0.45–0.55	0.70–0.90	0.040	0.040	0.20–0.35	....	0.90–1.20	....	....
E 52095	0.95–1.10	0.25–0.45	0.025	0.025	0.20–0.35	....	0.40–0.60	....	....
E 52098	0.95–1.10	0.25–0.45	0.025	0.025	0.20–0.35	....	0.90–1.15	....	....
E 52100	0.95–1.10	0.25–0.45	0.025	0.025	0.20–0.35	....	1.20–1.50	....	....
E 52101	0.95–1.10	0.25–0.45	0.025	0.025	0.20–0.35	....	1.30–1.60	....	....
A 6120	0.17–0.22	0.70–0.90	0.040	0.040	0.20–0.35	....	0.70–0.90	0.10 min. V	....
A 6145	0.43–0.48	0.70–0.90	0.040	0.040	0.20–0.35	....	0.80–1.10	0.15 min. V	....
SAE 6150	0.48–0.55	0.65–0.90	0.025	0.025	0.20–0.35	....	0.80–1.10	0.15 min. V	6150
E 6151	0.47–0.53	0.70–0.90	0.040	0.040	0.20–0.35	....	0.80–1.10	0.15 min. V	....
A 6152	0.48–0.55	0.70–0.90	0.040	0.040	0.20–0.35	....	0.80–1.10	0.10 min. V	....
A 9255	0.50–0.60	0.70–0.95	0.040	0.040	1.80–2.20	....	....	....	....
A 9260	0.55–0.65	0.75–1.00	0.040	0.040	1.80–2.20	....	....	....	....
A 9262	0.55–0.65	0.75–1.00	0.040	0.040	1.80–2.20	....	0.20–0.40	....	....

*Lowest standard maximum phosphorus or sulphur content for acid openhearth or acid electric furnace alloy steel is 0.05% each; silicon is 0.15% min.

NOTE (a).—Sulphur range: 0.035 to 0.050%.

Basic Openhearth and Acid Bessemer Carbon Steels

AISI Number	Semifinish	Bars	Wire Rods	C	Mn	P (b)	S (b)	'42 SAE Number
C 1005	–	–	√	0.06 max.	0.35 max.	0.04	0.05	....
C 1006*	Q. R.	√	√	0.08 max.	0.25–0.40	0.04	0.05	....
C 1008*	Q. R.	√	√	0.10 max.	0.30–0.50	0.04	0.05	1008
CB 1008	–	√	√	0.10 max.	....	....	....	....
C 1009	Q.	–	–	0.07–0.12	0.25–0.40	0.04	0.05	....
C 1010*	Q. R.	√	√	0.08–0.13	0.30–0.50	0.04	0.05	1010
C 1012	Q	√	√	0.10–0.15	0.30–0.50	0.04	0.05	....
CB 1012	–	√	–	0.15 max.	....	....	....	....

AISI No.	Former designation	P max	S max	Mn	C	(1)	(2)	Process
C 1013		0.04	0.05	0.60–0.90	0.11–0.16	✓		—
C 1014		0.04	0.05	0.40–0.60	0.13–0.18	✓	✓	Q
C 1015*	1015	0.04	0.05	0.30–0.50	0.13–0.18	✓	✓	Q, R.
C 1016	X1015, 1016	0.04	0.05	0.60–0.90	0.13–0.18	✓	✓	—
CB 1017		0.04	0.05		0.10–0.25		✓	—
C 1017		0.04	0.05	0.40–0.60	0.15–0.20	✓	✓	Q
C 1018		0.04	0.05	0.60–0.90	0.15–0.20	✓	✓	Q
C 1019		0.04	0.05	0.70–1.00	0.15–0.20	✓	✓	Q
C 1020*	1020	0.04	0.05	0.30–0.50	0.18–0.23	✓	✓	Q, R.
C 1021		0.04	0.05	0.40–0.60	0.18–0.23	✓	✓	Q
C 1022	X1020, 1022	0.04	0.05	0.70–1.00	0.18–0.23	✓	✓	Q
C 1023		0.04	0.05	0.30–0.50	0.20–0.25	✓	✓	Q
C 1024	1024	0.04	0.05	1.35–1.65	0.20–0.26	✓	✓	—
C 1025*	1025	0.04	0.05	0.30–0.50	0.22–0.28		✓	Q, R.
C 1026		0.04	0.05	0.40–0.60	0.22–0.28	✓		Q
C 1027		0.04	0.05	0.40–0.60	0.24–0.30	✓	✓	—
C 1029		0.04	0.05	0.60–0.90	0.25–0.31	✓	✓	Q
C 1030	1030	0.04	0.05	0.60–0.90	0.28–0.34			Q
C 1031		0.04	0.05	0.40–0.60	0.28–0.34	✓	✓	Q
CB 1032		0.04	0.05		0.25–0.40		✓	R
C 1033		0.04	0.05	0.60–0.90	0.30–0.36			Q
C 1034		0.04	0.05	0.50–0.70	0.32–0.38			—
D 1034		0.05	0.05	0.50–0.70	0.32–0.38	✓	✓	—
C 1035	1035	0.04	0.05	0.60–0.90	0.32–0.38	✓	✓	Q
C 1036	1036	0.04	0.05	1.20–1.50	0.32–0.39			—
C 1037		0.04	0.05	0.40–0.60	0.32–0.38		✓	C.r. strip
C 1038		0.04	0.05	0.60–0.90	0.35–0.42	✓		Q
C 1039		0.04	0.05	0.40–0.60	0.37–0.44		✓	C.r. strip
C 1040	1040	0.04	0.05	0.60–0.90	0.37–0.44	✓	✓	—
C 1041		0.04	0.05	1.35–1.65	0.36–0.44	✓		Q
C 1042		0.04	0.05	0.60–0.90	0.40–0.47		✓	Q
C 1043		0.04	0.05	0.70–1.00	0.40–0.47			—
C 1044		0.04	0.05	0.50–0.70	0.43–0.50	✓		Q
C 1045	1045	0.04	0.05	0.60–0.90	0.43–0.50		✓	Q
C 1046		0.04	0.05	0.70–1.00	0.43–0.50	✓		—
C 1047		0.04	0.05	0.40–0.60	0.43–0.50	✓	✓	Q
C 1049		0.04	0.05	0.40–0.60	0.48–0.55			C.r. strip
D 1049		0.05	0.05	0.50–0.70	0.43–0.50			C.r. strip
C 1050	1050	0.04	0.05	0.60–0.90	0.48–0.55	✓	✓	—
C 1051		0.04	0.05	0.85–1.15	0.45–0.56			Q
C 1052	1052	0.04	0.05	1.20–1.50	0.47–0.55		✓	—
C 1054		0.04	0.05	0.50–0.70	0.50–0.60	✓		—
D 1054		0.05	0.05	0.50–0.70	0.50–0.60	✓		—
C 1055	1055	0.04	0.05	0.60–0.90	0.50–0.60		✓	Q

[Continued on following page]

Table 1—*Continued*

Basic Openhearth and Acid Bessemer Carbon Steels—*Continued*

AISI Number	Semifinish	Bars	Wire Rods	C	Mn	P (b)	S (b)	'42 SAE Number
C 1056	C.r. strip	—		0.50-0.60	0.40-0.60	0.04	0.05	
C 1057	—		✓	0.50-0.61	0.85-1.15	0.04	0.05	
C 1058	C.r. strip			0.55-0.65	0.40-0.60	0.04	0.05	
D 1059		✓	✓	0.55-0.65	0.50-0.70	0.05	0.05	
C 1059		✓	✓	0.55-0.65	0.50-0.70	0.04	0.05	
C 1060			✓	0.60-0.70	0.60-0.90	0.04	0.05	1060
C 1061		✓		0.54-0.65	0.75-1.05	0.04	0.05	
C 1062		✓	✓	0.54-0.65	0.85-1.15	0.04	0.05	
C 1063				0.57-0.67	0.60-0.85	0.04	0.05	
C 1064		✓	✓	0.60-0.70	0.50-0.70	0.04	0.05	
D 1064			✓	0.60-0.70	0.50-0.70	0.05	0.05	
C 1065	Strip			0.60-0.70	0.60-0.90	0.04	0.05	X1065, 1066
C 1066		✓	✓	0.60-0.71	0.80-1.10	0.04	0.05	
C 1068		✓		0.65-0.75	0.50 max.	0.04	0.05	
C 1069			✓	0.65-0.75	0.50-0.70	0.04	0.05	
D 1069		✓	✓	0.65-0.75	0.40-0.60	0.05	0.05	
C 1070				0.70-0.80	0.70-1.00	0.04	0.05	1070
C 1074		✓	✓	0.70-0.80	0.50-0.70	0.04	0.05	
D 1074	Q		✓	0.70-0.80	0.40-0.60	0.05	0.05	
C 1075			✓	0.70-0.80	0.60-0.80	0.04	0.05	
C 1076		✓		0.65-0.85	0.60-0.85	0.04	0.05	
C 1078		✓	✓	0.72-0.85	0.30-0.50	0.04	0.05	
D 1078			✓	0.70-0.85	0.30-0.50	0.05	0.05	
C 1080		✓		0.75-0.88	0.60-0.90	0.04	0.05	1080
D 1083	Q		✓	0.80-0.95	0.30-0.50	0.05	0.05	
C 1084	Q	✓	✓	0.80-0.93	0.60-0.90	0.04	0.05	
C 1085			✓	0.80-0.93	0.70-1.10	0.04	0.05	1085
C 1086	Q	✓		0.82-0.95	0.30-0.50	0.04	0.05	
C 1090			✓	0.85-1.00	0.60-0.90	0.04	0.05	
C 1095		✓		0.90-1.05	0.30-0.50	0.04	0.05	1035
D 1095		✓	✓	0.90-1.05	0.30-0.50	0.05	0.05	
B 1006	R		✓	0.08 max.	0.45 max.	0.11 max.	0.06 max.	
B 1008	R	✓	✓	0.10 max.	0.30-0.50	0.11 max.	0.06 max.	
B 1011		✓	✓	0.13 max.	0.50-0.70	0.11 max.	0.06 max.	

*Compositions given are for forging quality; re-rolling quality differs slightly in analysis.

NOTE 1: When silicon is specified in standard basic openhearth steels, silicon may be ordered only as 0.10% maximum; or as 0.10% to 0.20%; or as 0.15% to 0.30%. In the case of many grades of basic openhearth steel, special practice is necessary in order to comply with a specification including silicon.

NOTE 2: Acid bessemer steel is not furnished with specified silicon content.

Sulphurized or Phosphorized Carbon Steels

AISI Number	Semi-finish	Bars	Wire Rods	C	Mn	P (b)	S (b)	'42 SAE Number
B 1106	—	—	—	0.09 max.	0.50 max.	0.11 max.	0.04-0.09	....
C 1108	—	—	✓	0.08-0.13	0.50-0.70	0.045 max.	0.07-0.12	....
C 1109	Q	✓	✓	0.08-0.13	0.60-0.90	0.045 max.	0.08-0.13	....
B 1110	—	✓	✓	0.13 max.	0.60 max.	0.11 max.	0.045-0.075	....
C 1110	—	✓	✓	0.08-0.13	0.60-0.90	0.045 max.	0.10-0.15	....
B 1111	—	✓	✓	0.08-0.13	0.60-0.90	0.09-0.13	0.10-0.15	1111
C 1111	—	—	✓	0.08-0.13	0.60-0.90	0.045 max.	0.16-0.23	1111
B 1112	—	✓	✓	0.08-0.13	0.60-0.90	0.09-0.13	0.16-0.23	....
C 1112	—	✓	—	0.10-0.16	1.00-1.30	0.045 max.	0.08-0.13	1112
B 1113	Q	✓	✓	0.08-0.13	0.60-0.90	0.09-0.13	0.24-0.33	X1112, 1113
C 1113	R	✓	—	0.10-0.16	1.00-1.30	0.045 max.	0.24-0.33	....
C 1114	Q	—	—	0.12-0.18	0.45-0.65	0.045 max.	0.075-0.15	....
C 1115	Q	✓	✓	0.13-0.18	0.70-1.00	0.045 max.	0.10-0.15	1115
C 1116	—	✓	✓	0.14-0.20	1.10-1.40	0.045 max.	0.16-0.23	....
C 1117	Q	✓	✓	0.14-0.20	1.00-1.30	0.045 max.	0.08-0.13	X1314, 1117
C 1118	—	—	✓	0.14-0.20	1.30-1.60	0.045 max.	0.08-0.13	X1315, 1118
C 1119	Q.R.	✓	✓	0.14-0.20	1.35-1.65	0.045 max.	0.16-0.23	....
C 1120*	Q	✓	✓	0.18-0.23	0.60-0.90	0.045 max.	0.08-0.13	....
C 1121	Q	✓	✓	0.18-0.23	0.70-1.00	0.045 max.	0.08-0.13	....
C 1122	Q	✓	✓	0.17-0.23	1.35-1.65	0.045 max.	0.08-0.13	....
C 1132	Q	✓	✓	0.27-0.34	1.35-1.65	0.045 max.	0.08-0.13	X1330, 1132
C 1137	Q	✓	✓	0.32-0.39	1.35-1.65	0.045 max.	0.08-0.13	X1335, 1137
C 1140‡	Q	—	—	0.37-0.44	0.60-0.90	0.045 max.	0.04-0.07	....
C 1141	—	✓	—	0.37-0.45	1.35-1.65	0.045 max.	0.08-0.13	{X1340, 1141
C 1144	—	✓	—	0.40-0.48	1.35-1.65	0.045 max.	0.24-0.33	....
C 1145‡	Q	—	—	0.42-0.49	0.70-1.00	0.045 max.	0.04-0.07	1145
C 1205	Q	—	✓	0.08 max.	0.25-0.40	0.04-0.07	0.05 max.	....
C 1206	R	—	✓	0.08 max.	0.25-0.40	0.06-0.10	0.05 max.	....
C 1209	R	—	✓	0.08-0.13	0.30-0.50	0.04-0.07	0.05 max.	....
C 1210	Q	—	✓	0.08-0.13	0.30-0.50	0.06-0.10	0.05 max.	....
C 1217	—	✓	—	0.14-0.19	0.70-1.00	0.09-0.13	0.20-0.29	....

*Compositions given are for forging quality; re-rolling quality differs slightly in analysis.

(b)—Phosphorus and sulphur are maximum for basic openhearth and acid bessemer steels; sulphurized or phosphorized steels are not subject to check analysis for S or P.

NOTES: Acid bessemer steels (B series) are not furnished with specified silicon content.

‡Standard steels C1140 and C1145 may be ordered with silicon content either as 0.10% max., 0.10 to 0.20%, or 0.15 to 0.30%.

which makes it possible to use numerals on shop drawings and blue-prints that are partially descriptive of the composition of material covered by such numbers. The first digit indicates the type to which the steel belongs; thus *1* indicates a carbon steel, *2*, a nickel steel, and *3*, a nickel-chromium steel. In the case of the simple alloy steels the second digit generally indicates the approximate percentage of the predominant alloying element. Usually the last two or three digits indicate the average carbon content in points, or hundredths of 1%. Thus *2340* indicates a nickel steel of approximately 3% nickel (3.25% to 3.75%) and 0.40% carbon (0.38% to 0.43%).

In some instances, in order to avoid confusion, it has been found necessary to depart from this system of identifying the approximate alloy composition of a steel, by varying the second and third digits of the number. An instance of such departure is the steel numbers selected for several of the corrosion and heat-resisting alloys.

The basic numerals for the various types of S.A.E. and A.I.S.I. steel are*:

Type of Steel	Numerals (and Digits)
Carbon Steels	1xxx
Plain Carbon	10xx
Free Cutting, (Screw Stock)	11xx
Manganese Steels	13xx
Nickel Steels	2xxx
3.50% Nickel	23xx
5.00% Nickel	25xx
Nickel-Chromium Steels	3xxx
1.25% Nickel, 0.60% Chromium	31xx
1.75% Nickel, 1.00% Chromium	32xx
3.50% Nickel, 1.50% Chromium	33xx
Corrosion- and Heat-Resisting Steels	30xxx
Molybdenum Steels	4xxx
Carbon-Molybdenum	40xx
Chromium-Molybdenum	41xx
Chromium-Nickel-Molybdenum	43xx
Nickel-Molybdenum	46xx and 48xx
Chromium Steels	5xxx

*Reprinted by permission of Society of Automotive Engineers, Inc., from *1942 S.A.E. Handbook*.

Chromium Steels—*Continued*
    Low Chromium.......................51xx
    Medium Chromium...................52xxx
    Corrosion- and Heat-Resisting.........51xxx
Chromium-Vanadium Steels...............6xxx
1% Chromium...........................61xx
Silicon-Manganese Steels..................9xxx
2% Silicon.............................92xx

NATIONAL EMERGENCY (N.E.) STEELS. With the beginning of
World War II, alloy-steel producers all felt the strain of war requirements for alloy steels and discovered that there would be a
serious shortage of all alloying elements used in the manufacture of
alloy steel if the alloy content should be maintained at the point or
amount that was required to manufacture the standard steels, such
as S.A.E. or A.I.S.I. steels. Accordingly, steel compositions had to
be changed to meet the emergency, which resulted in changes in
composition that allowed the manufacture of large tonnages of alloy
steels with much less alloy content than in the older standard steels.
These new steels were classified as **National Emergency (N.E.) Steels.**

Many of these new steels were used successfully as substitutes
for many of the standard alloy steels despite the fact that they contained less alloy than the standard and older compositions. It was
determined subsequently that the first small addition of an alloy is
most effective, and increasing the alloy content to twice the amount
does not double its effectiveness. Small additions of several alloys
have proved to be more effective than a comparatively large addition of a single alloy. Many of the N.E. steels contained relatively
small percentages of several elements, such as nickel, chromium,
molybdenum. This has led to investigating alloys using small
amounts of several elements rather than larger amounts of one or
two. The use of small quantities of several alloys is a practice that
will continue to influence alloy-steel metallurgy.

The N.E. steels are classified in a manner similar to the S.A.E.
and A.I.S.I. steels through the use of a numerical index system such
as *N.E. 8740* or *N.E. 9415*. The compositions and specifications for
these steels may be obtained from any of the data tables supplied by
the various steel manufacturers and users.

Table 2. Tool Steels Classified by Wear-Toughness Ratio

By Harold B. Chambers

Each of the three groups arranged in order of increasing toughness and decreasing wear resistance. Figures indicated as max. are optional and may be present up to amount noted. Since the difference in relative wear-toughness capacities of adjacent classes is small to negligible, the many brands covered by each class may be expected to give competitive performance except when highly standardized operating conditions require that consideration be given to the footnotes.

Class	Conventional Type Names	Carbon	Manganese	Silicon	Tungsten	Chromium	Vanadium	Molybdenum	Cobalt	Nickel	Notes
	Water-Hardening Steels										
1A	Tungsten finishing.	1.25–1.50	0.15–0.35	0.15–0.50	2.50–6.00	1.80 max.	0.30 max.	0.50 max.			A,B,C
1B	Carbon or carbon-vanadium.	1.30–1.45	0.15–0.35	0.15–0.35		0.35 max.	0.30 max.				A,C
2A	High carbon, low tungsten.	1.10–1.30	0.15–0.35	0.15–0.35	1.00–2.50	0.35 max.	0.30 max.				A,B
2B	Low chromium or chrome-vanadium.	1.10–1.30	0.15–0.35	0.15–0.35		0.10–1.20	0.30 max.				A,C
2C	Carbon or carbon-vanadium.	1.10–1.30	0.15–0.35	0.15–0.35			0.30 max.				A
3A	High carbon, low tungsten.	0.90–1.10	0.15–0.35	0.15–0.35	1.00–2.50	0.75 max.	0.30 max.				A,B,C
3B	Low chromium or chrome-vanadium.	0.90–1.10	0.15–0.35	0.15–0.35		0.10–1.50	0.30 max.				A,C
3C	Carbon or carbon-vanadium.	0.90–1.10	0.15–0.35	0.15–0.50			0.50 max.				A,D
4A	Chrome-molybdenum or chrome-vanadium.	0.55–0.90	0.15–0.35	0.15–0.35		0.40–1.20	0.35 max.	0.25 max.		0.50 max.	A,C
4B	Carbon or carbon-vanadium.	0.70–0.90	0.15–0.35	0.15–0.35			0.30 max.				A
4C	Silico-manganese or silico-molybdenum.	0.45–0.75	0.35–1.00	0.75–2.25		0.60 max.	0.35 max.	0.60 max.			A,E
	Oil-Hardening and Air-Hardening Steels (Tools of Intricate Design)										
5A	High carbon, high chromium.	1.80–2.50	0.15–1.20	0.15–1.00	2.00 max.	10.50–14.00	1.25 max.	0.30 max.	1.00 max.	1.00 max.	A,F,G
5B	High carbon, high chromium.	1.80–2.40	0.15–0.60	0.15–0.50		10.50–14.00	1.20 max.	0.70–1.00	0.60 max.		A,F,G
5C	High carbon, high chromium.	1.30–1.70	0.15–0.60	0.15–0.50		10.50–14.00	1.20 max.	0.50–1.25	4.00 max.	1.00 max.	A,F,G
5D	High carbon, high chromium.	1.10–1.40	0.15–1.20	0.15–1.10		5.00–13.00	0.75 max.	0.70–1.50	0.60 max.		A,F,G
6A	Chrome-molybdenum.	1.10–1.30	0.35–0.95	0.15–0.35		0.40–1.75	0.30 max.	0.25–0.75			A,E
6B	High carbon, low tungsten.	1.10–1.30	0.15–0.70	0.15–0.35	1.00–2.50	0.35–1.25	0.30 max.				A,B,C
6C	Low chromium or chrome-vanadium.	1.10–1.30	0.35–0.70	0.15–0.35		0.40–1.50	0.30 max.				A,C
7A	Cr-Mo, Mn-Cr, or Mn-Mo non-deforming.	0.90–1.10	0.35–3.00	0.15–1.00		0.80–5.50	0.50 max.	0.80–1.75			A,E
7B	Chromium non-deforming.	0.90–1.10	0.35–1.10	0.15–0.50	1.10 max.	0.90–1.60	0.30 max.	0.50 max.			A,E

No.	Type										Heat treatment
7C	Manganese non-deforming	0.80–1.10	0.85–1.80	0.15–0.50	0.70 max.	0.90 max.	0.30 max.	0.35 max.			A,E
8A	Low tungsten-chromium	0.40–0.65	0.15–0.35	0.15–1.50	0.75–3.00	0.50–2.00	0.50 max.	0.35 max.		1.50 max.	A,E
8B	Chrome-nickel or chrome-nickel-molybdenum	0.50–0.80	0.35–0.90	0.15–0.35		0.50–1.25	0.50–1.25	0.80 max.		1.00–2.50	A,E
8C	Chrome-molybdenum, chrome-vanadium, or manganese-molybdenum	0.50–0.90	0.35–0.90			1.20 max.	0.35 max.	0.40 max.		0.50 max.	A,E
8D	Silico-molybdenum	0.45–0.60	0.35–1.25	0.75–2.25	0.50	0.75 max.	0.60 max.	0.15–2.20			A,E
	High-Speed (H.S.) Steels and Hot-Work (H.W.) Steels (Tools Which Heat Up)										
9A	Tungsten-cobalt high speed	0.70–0.90	0.15–0.35		18.00–23.00	3.50–4.75	1.25–2.50	1.25 max.	9.00–15.00		A,G,H
9B	Tungsten-cobalt high speed	0.65–0.90	0.15–0.35		17.00–21.00	3.50–4.75	1.00–2.50	1.25 max.	5.00–9.00		A,G,H
9C	Tungsten-cobalt high speed	0.65–0.80	0.15–0.35		17.00–20.00	3.50–4.75	0.75–1.50	1.00 max.	2.00–5.00		A,G,H
9D*	Tungsten-cobalt high speed	0.65–0.85	0.15–0.35		12.00–15.00	3.50–4.75	1.25–2.25	0.75 max.	3.00–8.00		A,G,H
9E*	Molybdenum-cobalt H.S.	0.75–0.90	0.15–0.35		2.00 max.	3.50–4.75	1.00–2.50	6.00–10.00	3.00–8.00		A,G,H
10A	18-4-4 and 18-4-3 high speed	0.90–1.30	0.15–0.35		17.00–19.00	3.50–4.75	2.50–4.25	1.00 max.			A,H
10B	18-4-2 high speed	0.75–0.90	0.15–0.35		17.00–19.00	3.50–4.75	1.50–2.50	1.00 max.			A,H
10C	18-4-1 high speed	0.55–0.80	0.15–0.35		16.00–19.00	3.50–4.75	0.50–1.50				A,H
10D	14-4-2 and 14-4-1 high speed	0.55–0.90	0.15–0.35		13.00–15.00	3.50–4.75	0.75–2.25				A,H
10E*	Mo-W or Mo-V high speed	0.65–1.30	0.15–0.35		6.50 max.	3.50–4.75	0.75–4.25	3.50–9.50			A,H
11A	Low carbon high speed	0.45–0.60	0.15–0.35		16.00–19.00	3.00–4.50	0.50–1.25				A,H,I
11B	High tungsten hot work	0.25–0.50	0.15–0.35		12.00–16.00	2.50–4.50	0.30–0.75		3.00 max.		A,H,I
11C	Tungsten hot work	0.25–0.50	0.15–0.35		8.00–12.00	1.25–3.50	0.60 max.	2.00 max.	2.25 max.		A,H,I
11D*	Mo, or Mo-W hot work	0.30–0.65	0.15–0.35		3.00 max.	2.00–5.50	0.30–1.25	2.50–9.00	1.75 max.		A,H,I
11E	Tungsten-chromium H.W.	0.30–0.60	0.35–0.75	0.35–1.75	4.00–7.50	4.50–7.50	0.60 max.	1.00 max.	0.50 max.		A,H,I
12A	Chrome-molybdenum H.W.	0.30–0.50	0.80–1.10		1.50 max.	4.00–7.50	0.50 max.	0.45–1.75	1.75 max.		A,H
12B	Low tungsten-chromium H.W.	0.35–0.65	0.15–1.10		1.50–4.25	0.75–2.20	0.50 max.	0.60 max.	1.50 max.		A,H
12C	Chrome-molybdenum H.W. or chromium hot work	0.30–1.00	0.15–0.75		1.00 max.	2.25–4.50	1.00 max.	1.00 max.	0.50 max.		A,H
12D	Cr-Ni, or Cr-Ni-Mo hot work	0.25–0.60	0.15–1.00			0.50–2.50			1.25–5.00		A,H

A. Wear resistance increases and toughness decreases as carbon content increases.

B. Wear resistance increases and toughness decreases as tungsten content increases.

C. Hardenability increases, wear resistance increases, toughness decreases, movement in hardening decreases, and tendency for soft spots in hardening decreases as chromium increases.

D. Some special applications (silverware striking dies, certain header dies, etc.) may occasionally require extra penetration of hardness, which may be produced by adjusting manganese and silicon contents.

E. Hardenability increases, wear resistance increases and toughness decreases as total alloy content increases.

F. Machining difficulties increase as total alloy content increases.

G. Red hardness properties increase and toughness decreases as cobalt content increases.

H. Red hardness properties increase and toughness decreases as total alloy content increases.

I. Water cooling surface in operation, particularly when intermittent, tends to promote heat checking approximately in proportion to tungsten and/or molybdenum content.

*Not divided into classes. The relative position of a specific molybdenum steel is just below its tungsten steel counterpart. The tungsten counterpart is indicated by adding twice the molybdenum content to the tungsten in a molybdenum steel having 0.05–0.10% higher carbon than the tungsten steel.

Reprinted by Permission from *Metal Progress* 1941 Reference Issue, Published by American Society for Metals.

CLASSIFICATION OF TOOL STEELS. Tool steels are sold largely under trade names, a practice that grew up with the industry and has proved satisfactory. However, in recent years the user of tool steels has become more interested in the composition of the steels he is using, and he has become familiar with the different types and compositions available. Although there are many variations in composition, most tool steels that are commonly used may be identified and classified by their composition and properties. Such a classification is illustrated in Table 2 by Chambers, in which tool steels are classified by their wear-toughness ratio. Also, in this table the steels fall into three general classifications, such as (1) water-hardening steels, (2) oil- and air-hardening steels, (3) high-speed steels and steels for hot work. The applications for these steels are not indicated, and the user must rely upon past practice and performance with which he may be familiar in order to make a satisfactory selection of a steel for some specific application.

The water-hardening steels are the plain carbon steels, or the so-called low alloy steels, in which the alloying element is not present in large enough percentage to change the heat-treatment characteristics of the steel. The water-hardening steels require a water or brine quenching in order to produce maximum hardness. However, it should be recalled that thin sections cool much faster than heavy sections, and it is possible to quench a thin section of water-hardening steel in oil and obtain satisfactory results.

The oil- and air-hardening steels are the steels that may be cooled in oil or air from the hardening temperature to attain the maximum hardness. These steels are usually of the higher alloy type, containing such elements as manganese, molybdenum, and chromium, all of which retard the transformations during cooling and thus allow a slower quench to obtain the maximum hardness. All of the steels in this group may be hardened by quenching in oil, and a few of the higher alloyed compositions may be hardened by quenching in air when the section is such as to allow fast enough cooling. None of these steels may be safely hardened by quenching in water or brine without the danger of hardening cracks.

CLASSIFICATION BY HARDENABILITY. Alloy steels as well as plain carbon steels may be classified according to their ability to harden or be made martensitic. The ability to harden has been defined as the *hardenability* of the steel. The rôle played by the hardenability of steels is one of great importance, and any test that can be made to check this characteristic of steel will prove of value in the selection and qualification of any steel for a given application.

It has been determined that the hardenability of steels is dependent upon factors other than chemical composition or alloy content of the steel. Such factors as methods of manufacture, practice in shaping, and variables in treating, all influence the hardenability of steels. Because these variables will influence the hardenability, the usual methods of testing, without carrying out a test for hardenability, may not reveal the complete story about the steel. This being true, several methods have been designed to measure the ability of the steel to harden. The principle behind all of the hardenability tests is to measure the maximum section or thickness of steel that can be made hard or martensitic successfully. The Jominy end-quench test is recommended as a hardenability test for alloy structural and tool steels. This test can be used for both shallow- and deep-hardening steels.

The type of test piece used in the Jominy end-quench test is illustrated in Fig. 1. The test specimen is heated to the hardening temperature and dropped into a fixture that holds the lower end of the specimen above a spray nozzle. The quenching medium is water, which, by means of a suitable spray nozzle, hits only the bottom of the specimen. By this method, practically all of the heat is extracted from the face of the quenched end of the test piece. After the specimen has been cooled, it is ground with a small flat surface 0.015 inch deep along the entire length of the test bar, and Rockwell hardness readings are made at $\frac{1}{8}$-inch intervals from the hard end.

The results of the Jominy end-quench test can be plotted as illustrated in Fig. 2. This test can be used to check the hardenability of steels before they are used, or it can be used to test the hardenability of one steel against another and in this way determine a suitable steel.

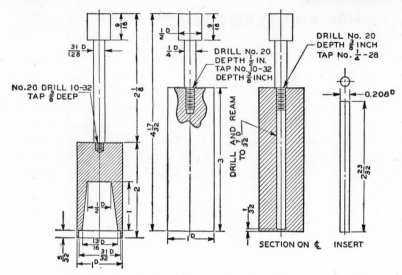

Fig. 1. Test Specimens for End-Quench Method of Determining Hardenability. Usual Specimen at Center; "L" Bar for Steels of Low Hardenability at Left; Drilled Bar at Right for Steels Available in Small Sizes Only

Reprinted by Permission, from *Metal Progress*, Article by Walter E. Jominy, Published by Metallurgical Dept., Research Laboratories of General Motors Corporation, Detroit, Michigan

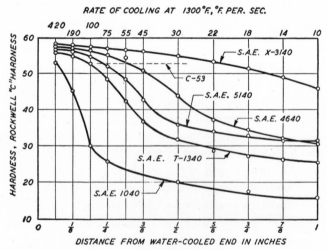

Fig. 2. Hardenability Curves (End-Quench Bars) of Five Steels Containing 0.40% Carbon

Reprinted by Permission, from *Metal Progress*, Article by Walter E. Jominy, Published by Metallurgical Dept., Research Laboratories of General Motors Corporation, Detroit, Michigan

QUIZ QUESTIONS

1. *Explain the S.A.E. numbering system for steels.*

2. *What are the three general classes of steel when classified by their wear-toughness ratio?*

3. *Under what conditions is it possible to quench a water-hardening steel in oil?*

4. *If oil- and air-hardening steels were quenched in water or brine, what would be the danger?*

5. *What characteristic of steel is of value in the selection and qualification of any steel for a given application?*

6. *Describe the Jominy end-quench test.*

TAPPING PIG IRON FROM A BLAST FURNACE
Courtesy of Ford Motor Co.

CHAPTER XV

Cast Iron

THE principal difference between steel and cast iron is that steel is plastic and forgeable whereas cast iron is not plastic enough to be forgeable within any temperature range. Many of our modern cast irons do, however, develop fair amounts of plasticity and toughness with relatively high strength.

Cast iron is a more complex alloy than steel and is much harder to define. However, we may consider cast iron as essentially an alloy of iron, carbon, and silicon. The carbon content is much higher than found in ordinary steels, running around 2.5% to 4.0%, with the element silicon playing a most important part. Silicon affects the structure and properties of cast iron more than it does those of steel. Varying percentages of manganese, sulphur, and phosphorus are also present in all cast irons, and sometimes special alloying elements such as copper, molybdenum, nickel, and chromium are added for the purpose of altering the chemical and mechanical properties of the iron. There are many variations in structure and properties available in cast iron. However, we may classify all cast irons into one of three main groups, namely, **grey cast iron, white cast iron, and malleable cast iron.** The terms *grey* and *white*, when applied to cast iron, refer to the appearance of the fracture of a casting. The grey cast iron fractures with a dark grey fracture, whereas the white cast iron shows a light grey fracture, almost white, as illustrated in Fig. 1. Malleable iron gets its name from the ability of this type of cast iron to bend or undergo permanent deformation before it fractures. It is much more ductile and tough than either white or grey cast iron. In each group or classification of cast irons, many variations in composition and in the foundry practice used in the manufacture may result in a great many variations in the structure and physical properties of the cast metal.

GREY CAST IRON. Although the greatest tonnage of grey iron is produced by cupola melting, other furnaces such as the air furnace, electric furnace, and rocking-type furnace are also used in its manufacture. The cupola is the oldest and cheapest melting method used but is the most difficult to control as to the composition and structure of the final product. In the production of a casting, the molten metal is taken from the furnace and poured into a mold usually made from sand. After the mold has been poured and the metal has cooled sufficiently, the casting is removed from the mold and taken to the cleaning room where adhering sand is removed by one of several processes,

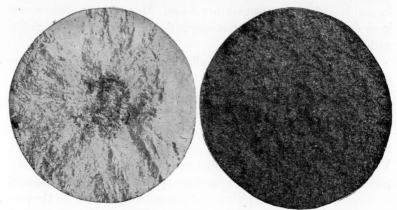

Fig. 1. Fracture Appearance of White Cast Iron, Left; Grey Cast Iron, Right

and the castings are chipped and ground. Inspection of the castings takes place at several points during cleaning, with a final inspection after the finishing operations. Heat treating, when required, is performed after cleaning.

Metallurgy of Grey Iron. Carbon in cast iron, as in steel, plays the most important part in the metallurgical control of the properties developed in the cast metal. Some of the carbon in grey cast iron is in the combined form similar to the form that carbon assumes in steel, but by far the larger percentage of the total carbon is present in the iron as flakes of graphitic carbon. To control the properties of grey iron, one must control the amount, size, shape, and distribution of the graphitic and combined forms of carbon. The metallurgist tries to control the effect of carbon largely by controlling the composition of the iron, particularly the percentage of carbon and silicon, and by controlling other factors that influence the formation of combined and graphitic carbon. Some of the variables that influence the carbon control include:

1. Melting method used, such as cupola, air furnace, etc. The cupola melting method is not as easily controlled as the air or electric furnaces, and its use may result in undesirable amounts of carbon.

2. Chemical composition. The chemistry of the charge placed in the furnace and the composition of the final product largely determine the properties of this product.

3. Temperatures throughout the entire process are factors that have an important bearing on the final structure and properties of the cast metal.

4. The cooling rate from the temperature at the pouring of the casting to room temperature is a very important factor, as this has a marked influence upon the final structure developed in the casting.

5. Heat treatments that may be applied to the final casting.

Other variables that may have a marked effect upon the characteristics of any casting are factors of casting design and the workmanship relative to the entire process of making a casting. From these established facts, it should be apparent that to make a grey iron casting to meet certain structural and physical requirements is rather a difficult task, and it can be accomplished only with accurate control of all of the variables that are encountered in the process. Control of composition alone will not necessarily result in satisfactory castings; however, if all of the variables including melting and foundry technique can be controlled accurately, then the foundryman can expect to regulate his results by control of composition. The chemical composition, with all other factors remaining constant, largely determines the type of structure and therefore the properties of the final product.

Structure of Grey Iron. Grey cast iron can be varied in its structural composition within wide limits and develop a wide range of properties and applications. There is no one structure or set of properties for this iron. Microscopic examination of grey iron will reveal the presence of the following structural constituents in varying percentages, depending upon the character of the iron: graphite, pearlite, ferrite, cementite, steadite, and manganese sulphide. The constituents, graphite and pearlite, are present in varying percentages in all of the grades of grey iron. The presence of ferrite or cementite, in a free condition, depends upon the amount of combined carbon present in the casting. If the amount of combined carbon is below the eutectoid ratio (pearlite), free ferrite will be found in the structure. On the other hand, if the combined carbon content is above the amount necessary to form pearlite, then free cementite will be present in the final structure of the casting. The presence of steadite and manganese sulphide depends upon the amount of phosphorus and sulphur present in the casting.

Graphite in Grey Iron. Graphite is by far the most important constituent of grey iron. The amount, size, shape, and distribution of the graphite flakes found in this iron largely control the final properties of the iron. The carbon present in grey iron is largely in the form of graphite, which has a relatively low density and therefore occupies more volume than indicated by the weight percentage determination. A grey iron with 3% of its total carbon present as graphite actually has 9.6% or more graphite by volume in its structure. Besides the large percentage of graphite by volume present in the grey iron, the effect of the graphite is also magnified by its flake-like shape. Due to its flake-like shape, the graphite breaks up the continuity of the iron and greatly weakens it. If the graphite is present in small, round, well-distributed particles, its weakening effect is much less pronounced, and the iron develops much higher mechanical properties. If the foundry could control the graphitic constituent of grey iron, almost complete control would be exercised over the properties of the metal. The condition of the graphitic carbon may easily be determined by a microscopic examination of the polished surface of the iron.

Large flakes of graphitic carbon produce a soft, weak casting; whereas, fine and short flakes of graphitic carbon result in a stronger casting. This difference in graphitic carbon is illustrated in Figs. 2 and 3. The nodular shape of graphitic carbon is desired, as illustrated in Fig. 4, but this shape of graphite is obtained in annealing of white cast iron, thus producing malleable cast iron. The graphitic phase of carbon in grey cast iron may be influenced by many factors. Included among them are: (1) Ratio of carbon to silicon. Silicon acts as a graphitizer, and the more silicon present the more and larger will be the flakes of graphite. (2) Additions of steel to the melt. Steel additions reduce the total carbon and dilute the graphitic carbon present in the melt. This reduces the opportunity for the carbon to graphitize and develop many and large flakes of graphite. (3) Temperature used in melting. Very high melting temperatures seem to dissolve the graphite present in the melt and thus reduce the tendency to graphitize. (4) Fast cooling. Rapid solidification of the casting will reduce the action of graphitization. The cooling rate is largely controlled by

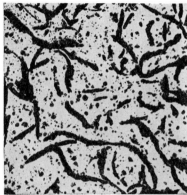

Fig. 2. Grey Cast Iron with Tensile Strength of 15,000 lb. per sq. in. and Brinell Hardness of 140. Large Flakes of Graphitic Carbon Are Responsible for Low Hardness and Strength (Polished, Not Etched). Magnified 100 Times

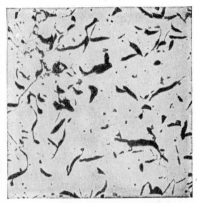

Fig. 3. Grey Cast Iron with Tensile Strength of 35,000 lb. per sq. in. and Brinell Hardness of 195. Note Much Smaller Flakes of Graphitic Carbon than in Fig. 2 (Polished, Not Etched). Magnified 100 Times

the size of the cast section. This is one of the most prominent factors affecting the character of a casting. Indeed, if the foundry is asked to cast a section that is wedge shaped, or that has a very obvious change in section from thin to thick, this causes more difficulty in controlling the graphitic carbon constituent than any other single factor. The thin sections may not graphitize at all and therefore will be hard and difficult to machine, whereas the thick section of the same casting will graphitize nearly completely into large flakes of graphite and cause a very weak, soft condition. (5) Special alloys added to melt. The principal effect of alloys used in the foundry is the control they exert over the formation of graphitic carbon. Nickel added helps to graphitize the carbon in a thin section, whereas chromium reduces the graphitization in a heavy section.

Pearlite in Grey Iron. The constituent pearlite in grey iron is the same as the pearlite present in steel. Carbon present in the combined form (Fe_3C) will combine with the ferrite constituent upon cooling through the critical range of the iron, thus developing the pearlitic constituent. Due to the presence of phosphorus, silicon, and manganese, a combined carbon content ranging from 0.50% to 0.89% may develop a structural matrix in the iron which is largely pearlitic. It is

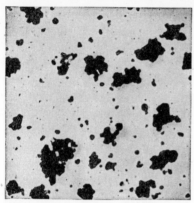

Fig. 4. Malleable Cast Iron, Shows Nodular Shape of Graphitic Carbon (Polished, Not Etched); Tensile Strength, 52,000 lb. per sq. in.; Elongation 16% in 2 in.; Brinell Hardness, 118. Magnified 100 Times

possible to have all of the carbon present in the grey iron as graphite, in which case a structure of ferrite and graphite results with no pearlite, and the iron is soft and weak. As the amount of combined carbon increases, the iron changes from all ferrite and graphite to pearlite and graphite. A casting consisting of pearlite and graphite is known as a **pearlitic grey iron** and is considered the best possible structure for strength, yet it maintains good machinability. Fig. 5 illustrates the type of structure referred to as a pearlitic grey iron, consisting of graphite flakes with a matrix of pearlite.

The pearlite constituent influences the properties of grey iron as follows:

a) The strength of grey iron increases as the amount of pearlite increases.

b) The finer the constituents in pearlite (i.e., ferrite and cementite layers), the stronger the iron.

c) Finer grain size gives increased strength.

d) The Brinell hardness increases with the increase in the fineness and amount of pearlite in going from a ferritic to a pearlitic condition.

e) Increase in the fineness and the amount of the pearlite and decrease in grain size result in some increase in toughness, noticeable in machining operations, but produce a correspondingly smoother finish.

If more combined carbon is present than can form with the pearlite during slow cooling through the critical range of the iron, a free cementite is present which adds materially to the hardness.

Free Cementite in Grey Iron. The presence of free cementite in grey iron will increase the difficulty of machining and lower the

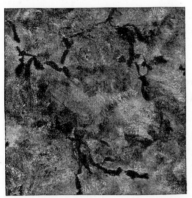 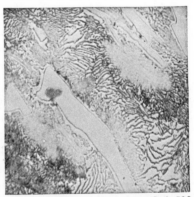

Fig. 5. Pearlitic Grey Iron, Etched to Bring Out the Fine Pearlitic Structure which Forms the Matrix of This Iron. Magnified 250 Times

Fig. 6. White Cast Iron, Magnified 500 Times. Same as Fig. 16. Pearlite, Dark; Cementite, White

strength of the iron. Cementite is very hard and brittle and its presence in the free form as cementite particles may be accidental or may be for the purpose of increasing the hardness and wear resistance of the iron. Ordinarily, free cementite in large amounts is found only in hard, white iron or in chilled irons. Fig. 6 illustrates the large percentage of free cementite found in a white iron casting.

Ferrite in Grey Iron. Ferrite is a naturally soft, ductile constituent possessing good tensile properties. There is no free ferrite present in grey iron unless the combined carbon content is below that which produces a pearlitic matrix. The presence of free ferrite does not impart ductility to the grey iron because the continuity of the ferrite matrix is broken by graphite flakes. A highly ferritic grey iron is not ductile as it means less pearlite and more graphitic carbon, resulting in a grey iron of less strength and softer than those containing a pearlitic matrix.

Steadite in Grey Iron. Steadite is a eutectic constituent formed from the presence of phosphorus, which, as an iron phosphide, combines with the iron to form a low-melting-point constituent, which melts at about 1750°–1800° F. Steadite is hard and brittle and is considered undesirable in irons when good mechanical properties are required. Steadite contains about 10% phosphorus, and a 1% phosphorus iron forms about 10% steadite. Phosphorus increases the fluidity of the molten iron, which is desirable in some types of castings, such as ornamental iron castings. However, while phosphorus increases the fluidity, it also decreases the strength, and for this reason it is better to obtain fluidity by higher tapping and pouring temperatures when strength is desired.

Minor Constituents of Grey Iron. Minor constituents of grey iron include manganese sulphide (MnS), oxides, and gases. Manganese sulphide is present as relatively small inclusions scattered throughout the iron and has no appreciable effect on the strength of the iron. Oxides and gases weaken the iron and promote lack of density and soundness. Oxidation of cast iron results in a marked growth in the volume of the iron, which causes trouble when the iron is subjected to elevated temperatures.

Influence of Rate of Cooling upon Structure of Grey Iron. The rate at which the cast metal cools from the beginning of freezing to below the critical range determines to a large degree the type of structure developed in the final casting. Fast cooling through the cooling zone and down to a relatively low temperature will result in the formation of little or no graphitic carbon. Such an iron will be hard and brittle. Very slow cooling will allow for marked graphitization with little or no combined carbon and result in a soft and weak iron. There is no easy way to control the relative rates of cooling of castings cast in sand molds, as the rate of cooling is largely governed by the volume and surface area of the individual castings. Light sections with large surface area will, of necessity, cool much faster than heavy sections with small surface area. The effect of the cooling rate upon the structure developed in an iron casting can be illustrated by casting a section in the shape of a wedge, see Fig. 7. The thin point of the wedge will cool relatively fast and will consist structurally of a white iron, cementite, and pearlite. If the cooling rate is fast through the critical range of the iron, a martensitic matrix will be formed. The heavy end of the wedge, which cools relatively slowly, will contain a structure of ferrite and graphite with no combined carbon. This end will be very soft and weak. From this illustration, it should be appreciated that any marked change in section in any given casting design may cause trouble for the foundry when a uniform structure throughout the entire casting is specified. The foundryman can avoid a marked difference in the structure and properties of a casting with thin and thick sections by employing various foundry

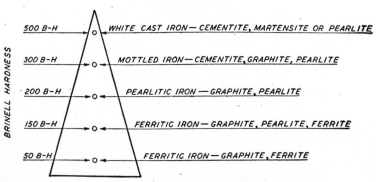

Fig. 7. General Influence of Section on Structure and Brinell Hardness

techniques, most of which are largely those of composition control. It is possible to obtain a uniform structure in castings of varying section thickness; however, it is much better to design a casting with as uniform a section as possible.

Carbon-Silicon Ratio in Grey Iron. One of the most important factors affecting the structure and properties of a casting is the amount of carbon and silicon used and the ratio of the carbon to the silicon. This factor of foundry control is illustrated in Fig. 8 which points out the ratio of carbon to silicon required for irons that fall in the grey iron, mottled iron, and white iron classes. The ratio of carbon to silicon in Fig. 8 has to be modified, depending upon the section size of the casting and the presence and amount of other elements or alloys contained in the iron. However, silicon is by far the strongest graphitizer of all of the elements that may be added to cast iron, and, consequently, it is the predominant element in determining the relative proportions of combined and graphitic carbon that will be present in the final casting. Thus, the foundryman controls the structure and properties of his casting largely by adjusting the silicon content relative to the amount of carbon and section size of the casting. In general, the foundryman uses less silicon for a high carbon iron and more silicon for a low carbon iron. High-strength grey irons are of the pearlitic type, with the graphitic carbon in fine, well-distributed

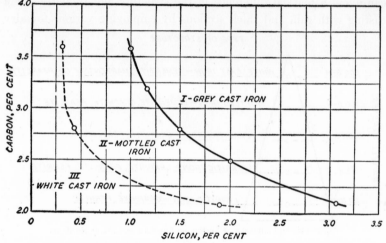

Fig. 8. Composition Limits for Grey, Mottled, and White Cast Irons (Tanimura)

flakes. These high-strength grey irons usually have a low carbon content, around 2.50 to 2.65%, with the silicon running around 1.50 to 1.70%. The structure of such an iron is illustrated in Figs. 5 and 9. The following indicates the range of chemicals that might be available in grey cast irons:

Carbon............................2.50 to 3.50%
Silicon............................0.60 to 2.40%
Manganese........................0.50 to 1.20%
Phosphorus.......................0.05 to 1.00%
Sulphur..........................0.04 to 0.25%

plus special alloying elements, including nickel, chromium, molybdenum, and copper.

Effect of Nickel on Grey Iron. Nickel is added to grey cast iron in amounts from 0.25 to 5.0%. Nickel will assist in the graphitizing of the carbon, but it is only about one-half as effective as silicon in this respect. However, about 3.0% silicon seems to be the limit in the addition of this constituent in preventing the formation of free cementite or hard iron, whereas the effect of nickel extends beyond that percentage so that greater additions of this constituent act as a great aid in rendering iron grey that otherwise would be hard and con-

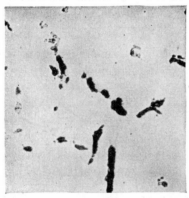

Composition

Total Carbon	2.65%
Silicon	1.62%
Manganese	0.96%
Sulphur	0.11%
Phosphorus	0.15%
Tensile Strength	46,000 lbs. per sq. in.
Brinell Hardness	207 to 217

Fig. 9. Polished Grey Iron (Same as in Fig. 5 but Not Etched), Showing the Type of Graphite Flakes Present in High-Strength Iron. Magnified 250 Times

tain free cementite. Additions of nickel in small amounts will reduce the effects of chilling or rapid cooling and soften thin cast sections by eliminating hard, free cementite, thus promoting machineability. Nickel promotes density and freedom from porosity by permitting the use of a lower silicon content without causing chill or hard spots to appear in light sections. As nickel is increased up to 4%, the hardness and strength of heavy sections increases slightly, and the lighter sections become progressively more grey and more machinable. Unlike silicon, nickel progressively and uniformly hardens the matrix of the iron by changing the structure of coarse pearlite to a finer and harder pearlite and finally to martensite. Nickel also helps in refining the grain and promotes dispersion of the graphite in a finely divided state, thus improving the strength and toughness of the iron.

Effect of Chromium on Grey Iron. Chromium is a carbide-forming element, and chromium carbide is much more stable than the iron carbide (cementite) found in plain cast iron. By stabilizing the carbide (cementite), chromium acts opposite to the graphite-forming elements, silicon and nickel. Chromium increases the chill effect, i.e., retards graphite formation and increases the hardness and strength.

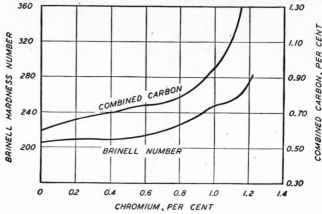

Fig. 10. Effect of Chromium on Brinell Hardness and Combined Carbons of Arbitration Bars (2.5% Silicon; 3.3% Carbon) (Trantin)

Reprinted by Permission, from *Cast Metals Handbook*, 1935 Edition, Published by American Foundrymen's Association, Chicago, Illinois

This effect of chromium is illustrated in Fig. 10. Chromium additions promote the formation of more finely laminated and harder pearlite, thus increasing the strength and hardness of the iron matrix. Experience has shown that combinations of nickel and chromium develop better results than if they are used alone as alloying elements. Nickel, which is a graphitizer, and chromium, which is a carbide stabilizer, seem to supplement each other very usefully.

Effect of Molybdenum on Grey Iron. Molybdenum as an alloying element in grey iron has but little effect in stabilizing the carbide (cementite) but is used to increase the strength of iron, due to its effect upon the decomposition of austenite to pearlite. Molybdenum decreases the rate of change from austenite to pearlite during the cooling cycle in cast iron similar to the way it does in steel. This results in developing a harder and stronger iron due to the formation of a much finer pearlite, approaching a martensitic-type structure. In grey irons, molybdenum improves the strength, hardness, impact strength, fatigue strength, and the strength of iron at elevated temperatures.

Effect of Copper on Grey Iron. Copper, like silicon, when alloyed in cast iron functions primarily as a graphitizing agent. However, its ability to act as a graphitizer is only about one-tenth that of silicon. Copper may be added to grey iron in amounts up to 3%. A large percentage of the copper is thought to dissolve, forming a solid solution with the ferrite. The remaining copper, in excess of its limits of solid solubility, is dispersed as microscopic or submicroscopic particles in the iron. The addition of copper refines the pearlite and increases the tensile strength and the Brinell hardness. It improves the wear resistance of the iron, its resistance to acid and atmospheric corrosion, and, combined with chromium, improves the strength and resistance to oxidation at elevated temperatures.

Properties of Grey Cast Iron. Grey cast iron is widely used in the machine tool field and in general engineering and industrial applications, because of its ability to be cast in intricate shapes, its low cost, and its wide range of useful properties. Included among its outstanding properties are the following:

1. Excellent machinability.
2. Excellent wear resistance.
3. Tensile strength in the as-cast condition varying from 20,000 lbs. per sq. in. for the soft, weak irons to 70,000 lbs. per sq. in. for the high-strength cast irons.
4. Compressive strength is usually three to four times the tensile strength, ranging from 70,000 to 200,000 lbs. per sq. in.
5. Grey cast iron has no well-defined elastic limit and may be loaded up to 80% or more of its maximum strength.
6. It is the only ferrous alloy that may be varied in stiffness. Its modulus of elasticity, at a load of 25% of ultimate strength, ranges from 12,000,000 to 21,000,000 lbs. per sq. in.
7. The hardness of cast iron can be controlled within certain limits and may extend from 100 to 350 Brinell hardness.

8. Included in its properties are its valuable damping capacity for vibrations and its good resistance to corrosion.

The tensile strength of grey iron is important from an engineering design viewpoint. Tensile strengths may be varied from 20,000 psi* for soft, weak irons, to over 70,000 psi for the high-strength grey irons and irons in the heat-treated condition. Modern practice classifies grey cast irons according to their minimum tensile strengths. Classification by tensile strength prepared by the American Society for Testing Materials as their specification *A48-41* is shown in Table 1.

Table 1. Classification of Grey Cast Irons
A.S.T.M. Specification A48-41

Class	Tensile Strength Minimum psi	Class	Tensile Strength Minimum psi
No. 20............	20,000	No. 40..........	40,000
No. 25............	25,000	No. 50..........	50,000
No. 30............	30,000	No. 60..........	60,000
No. 35............	35,000	....	....

Compressive Strength of Grey Iron. The compressive strength of grey iron is one of its most valuable properties. Compressive strengths developed are from three to five times the tensile strength and will run from 70,000 psi to over 200,000 psi for some of the higher strength irons.

Hardness. The hardness of grey iron may be varied within wide limits and may run from 100 Brinell to over 700 Brinell for iron that has received heat treatments, such as surface hardening. Grey irons with a Brinell hardness value of 180 to 200 constitute the major group and are more commonly used than any other class.

Transverse Strength. A method for testing cast iron that is readily made in the foundry without elaborate equipment and with a test bar in the unmachined condition is known as the **transverse bend test.** A test bar of standard dimensions is cast and broken on supports spaced 12, 18, or 24 inches apart. The load required to rupture the bar is measured, and the value obtained can be reasonably correlated with the tensile strength of the iron. Also, the maximum deflection taken at the center of the bar indicates the ductility and toughness of the iron. The A.S.T.M. classification or grading of grey iron by the transverse bend test is shown in Table 2.

*Abbreviation for pounds per square inch.

Table 2. Average Values for Transverse Strength of Grey Cast Irons
(A.S.T.M. Standard Specification A48-41)

Transverse Test Bar............... Span Length.......... Class	0.875 in. Diam 12-in. Supports Load at Center, lb.	1.2 in. Diam. 18-in. Supports Load at Center, lb.	2.0 in. Diam. 24-in. Supports Load at Center, lb.
No. 20............	900	1800	6000
No. 25............	1025	2000	6800
No. 30............	1150	2200	7600
No. 35............	1275	2400	8300
No. 40............	1400	2600	9100
No. 50............	1670	3000	10,300
No. 60............	1925	3400	....

Fatigue Strength. The fatigue strength, or endurance limit, for grey iron follows the values for tensile strength. The ratio of fatigue strength to tensile strength runs about 0.40 to 0.57. For the common grey irons, this would be about 9,000 to 26,000 psi. It has been demonstrated during endurance tests that soft grey irons were less sensitive to notches and grooves or other surface discontinuities than expected for most materials. Grey iron is also apparently less sensitive to notch brittleness than most materials. This has been explained by pointing out that grey irons contain many internal notches caused by the presence of graphite flakes; therefore, the addition of external notches does not make so much difference. Also, grey irons are less rigid with lower stiffness values, i.e., lower modulus of elasticity, than other iron alloys; this reduces the effect of stress concentrations so that the effect of a notch as a stress raiser in producing fatigue failure is less apparent. Usually the modulus of elasticity, at 25% of the ultimate strength, ranges from 12,000,000 to 18,000,000 psi, whereas steel has a modulus of elasticity of 30,000,000 psi.

The lower modulus of elasticity or stiffness developed in grey irons results in an iron having greater damping effects to vibrations set up in service. This characteristic of grey iron makes it desirable for parts of machine tools where vibrations cause trouble in accurate machining operations, producing inaccuracies and rough finishes. The stiffer the iron, the lower the damping capacity. With a material of high strength and high modulus of elasticity, the vibrations may be allowed to build up to a serious intensity, whereas a high damping material with a fair strength will damp them out.

Wear Resistance. Grey cast iron is widely used for machinery parts to resist wear. The graphitic carbon in grey irons acts as a lubricant and prevents galling when metal to metal contact occurs. Increasing the hardness of the iron improves its resistance to wear. A minimum hardness of 200 Brinell is usually specified for parts that are manufactured for wear resistance. However, Brinell hardness is not an accurate criterion of wear resistance for the type of micro-structure, and alloys used in the iron seem to have far more influence upon this important property. Increasing the hardness by heat treatments is often practiced for parts such as ways of lathes, cylinder liners, cams, gears, sprockets, etc., and this practice does increase the wear resistance of the iron. In the hardening process, however, only the pearlitic constituent is changed to a harder structure. The graphite flakes remain as they were in the as-cast condition.

Heat Resistance. Very little change in the strength of grey iron is observed at elevated temperatures up to 800° F. Above this tem-perature, in the average types of grey iron, there is a sharp drop in the strength and hardness, and in most cases a permanent loss in strength occurs. Alloyed grey irons, with a fine grain size and small graphite flake size, suffer less from loss of strength at elevated tem-peratures. Grey irons subjected to elevated temperatures up to 700° F. show good resistance to wear and galling, which makes them useful for applications in automobile, steam, and Diesel engines. However, grey irons grow or develop a permanent increase in volume when subjected to repeated cycles of heating and cooling in excess of 700° F. Growth of cast iron is largely due to graphitization of the combined carbon in the iron and to corrosion and oxidation in the iron. It is thought that oxidizing gases penetrate the iron by way of the graphite flakes and attack the constituents of the iron, especially the silicon. This growth is serious as it reduces the strength and causes a very weak, brittle condition.

Heat Treatments of Grey Iron. Grey cast iron may be subjected to various heat treatments for the purpose of increasing its usefulness and improving its mechanical properties. The heat treatments usually applied to grey iron include (1) stress-relief annealing, (2) annealing, (3) hardening and tempering, and (4) nitriding.

Stress-Relief Annealing. Grey cast iron for machine parts is often subjected to a stress-relief annealing treatment for the purpose of removing any of the residual internal stresses present in the castings as they are received from the foundry. Also, the treatment tends to soften any hard spots and hard corners that occur in the castings, resulting from chills. The stress-relief annealing treatment consists of heating the castings to within a temperature range of 750° to 1250° F. for a period of sev-

eral hours, followed by slow cooling to below 700° F. After reaching this low temperature, the doors of the furnace may be opened and the castings cooled to room temperature in air. Fig. 11 illustrates a furnace loaded with grey iron castings for machine tool parts that are being treated in this manner. This treatment will remove the internal stresses and allow the castings to be finish-machined to accurate dimensions without the fear of warping. Also, this treatment will improve the machineability of castings having hard corners and hard spots by breaking down the combined carbon.

Fig. 11. Grey Iron Castings for Machine Tool Parts Being Given a Stress-Relief Annealing to Remove Internal Stresses and to Improve Machineability
Courtesy of Massachusetts Steel Treating Corporation.

Annealing. The purpose of annealing grey cast iron is to increase the softness of the iron for economy in machining. Castings that are hard and difficult to machine because of the amount of combined carbon in their structure can be annealed so as to graphitize the combined carbon and restore easy machineability. The process consists in controlling the degree of transformation of the combined carbon to graphitic or free carbon. The annealing treatment selected depends upon the structure and composition of the iron being treated and the degree of softening desired. The usual practice is to heat the

castings in a furnace to around 1500°–1600° F., hold the castings at
this temperature for an hour or more, depending upon the maximum
section of the casting, and follow by a slow cool to around 700° F., at
which temperature the doors of the furnace may be opened and the
castings removed. The maximum temperature used in this treatment
depends upon the composition of the casting. Annealing temperatures from 1200° to 1800° F. have been used. The time at heat influ-

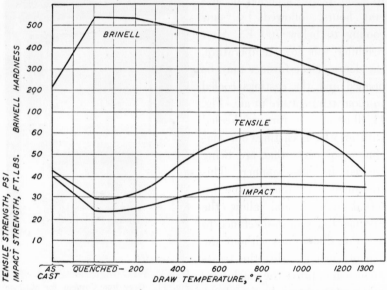

Fig. 12. Effects of Tempering Temperatures on the Properties of Grey Cast Iron

Reproduced by Permission, from *Cast Metals Handbook*, 3d Edition, Published by the American Foundrymen's Association, Chicago, Illinois

ences the degree of graphitization and is governed by the required
softness.

Hardening and Tempering. Grey irons of the pearlitic type can
be hardened and tempered just as steels can. The pearlite in the
structure of the iron can be changed to austenite upon heating to
above the critical temperature of the iron, and, upon rapid cooling
(quenching), transformed to martensite. The casting thus treated
can be tempered to relieve the quenching stresses, increase the toughness of the iron, and reduce the maximum hardness. The purpose of
hardening and tempering grey iron is to strengthen and to increase

the wear and abrasion resistance of the iron. Ordinary pearlitic grey irons are heated to 1500° F. and oil quenched although water is used as a quenching medium to a limited extent. Water quenching will cause more warping and danger from hardening cracks. The hardening of ordinary grey irons by this treatment will increase the Brinell hardness from around 180–200 to 400–500. Following the hardening operation, the casting may be tempered from 400° to 800° F., depending upon the desired properties. Fig. 12 illustrates

Fig. 13. Fractured Section of Flame-hardened Grey Cast Iron. Light Edge at Top Shows the Depth of Hardness. Surface Hardness, Rockwell C 55

the change in tensile strength and hardness that might be expected from hardening a pearlitic iron and tempering within a temperature range of 200° to 1200° F.

Grey iron castings can be locally hardened by either the flame-hardening or induction-hardening method. Local heating of massive castings can be carried out safely by either process. If this is followed by local quench-hardening, the heat treater is able to harden surfaces without heating the entire casting to the quenching temperature. This insures a very hard surface without the danger of cracking and marked distortion that would occur if an attempt should be made to heat and quench the entire casting. Fig. 13 shows a fractured section of grey iron that has had one surface hardened by local heating and quenching, using the flame-hardening method. Fig. 14 illustrates the type of pearlitic structure in this iron before hardening, and Fig. 15 shows the martensitic structure found in the hardened region of the casting after treatment. It will be seen from Fig. 15 that the hardening operation did not affect the graphitic constituent of the casting; it only changed the pearlite to martensite.

Fig. 14. Photomicrograph of Grey Cast Iron, Polished and Etched. This Iron Is the Same as That Shown in Fig. 2. Structure Consists of Graphite Flakes, Matrix of Pearlite, with a Small Percentage of Ferrite (White). Magnified 500 Times

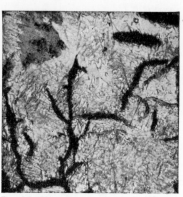

Fig. 15. Photomicrograph of the Edge of Flame-hardened Grey Cast Iron. Structure Is Martensitic with Graphite Flakes. Magnified 500 Times

Nitriding of Grey Iron. Grey cast irons suitable for surface hardening by the nitriding process are essentially alloy irons containing aluminum and chromium. A typical analysis contains:

Total Carbon	2.62%
Graphitic Carbon	1.63%
Combined Carbon	0.99%
Silicon	2.44%
Manganese	0.60%
Chromium	1.58%
Aluminum	1.37%

Castings of this composition are usually given a hardening and stabilizing heat treatment prior to the nitriding operation. This consists of an oil quench from 1550°–1600° F., followed by a draw at 1100°–1200° F. for two hours. The nitriding is carried out in the usual way, heating to 950° F. in an atmosphere of approximately 30% dissociated ammonia for a period up to 90 hours. A case depth of 0.015 inch may be expected with this treatment. A surface hardness of 800 to 900 Vickers diamond hardness test using 10-kg. load is obtained after nitriding a finish-machined casting of this type. To obtain local nitriding, a thin coating of tin paint may be used as a stop-off material similar to the treatment used for steels.

WHITE AND CHILLED CAST IRONS. Iron castings that are classified as white or chilled iron have practically all of their carbon in the combined condition as cementite. These castings are relatively hard and brittle due to the high carbon content which forms a large percentage of hard and brittle cementite. Cast irons that contain low carbon, 2.0%–2.5%, and low silicon (see Fig. 8), when cast in sand molds and cooled slowly, solidify and cool to room temperature without graphitizing any of their carbon. These irons are naturally white irons.

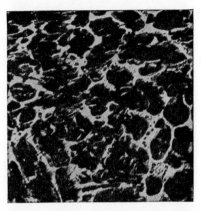

Fig. 16. White Cast Iron, Polished and Etched. White Constituent Is Free Cementite, and the Dark Constituent Is Pearlite. Magnified 100 Times

A white cast iron that has been slowly cooled in the mold has a structure of pearlite and free cementite similar to that of a high carbon steel, except that the white cast iron contains much more free cementite. The microstructure of this type of iron is illustrated in Figs. 6 and 16. The greatest tonnage of this type of iron is used for the manufacture of malleable iron. The addition of alloys such as nickel, molybdenum, and chromium to white iron results in the formation of a much harder iron. The type of structure formed by the alloy additions is usually martensite and free cementite, with the alloys acting as hardening agents and thus preventing the formation of pearlite from austenite during the cooling cycle. The structure of an alloyed white iron is illustrated in Figs. 17 and 18. Irons of this type are used for parts of machinery and industrial equipment where extreme hardness and excellent wear resistance are required, such as in crusher jaws and hammers, wearing plates, cams, and balls and liners for ball mills.

White cast iron can also be made by rapid cooling or chilling of an iron which, if cooled slowly, would be graphitic and grey. If cast iron is cooled relatively fast in the mold, the carbon does not have an opportunity to graphitize and remains combined. Also, rapid cooling prevents the formation of a coarse, soft pearlite and adds to the hard-

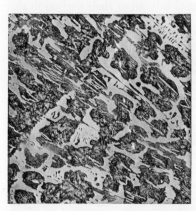 

Fig. 17. Photomicrograph of the Structure of White Cast Iron Alloyed with Molybdenum. Structure Is Martensitic with Cementite. Rockwell C 58. Magnified 100 Times

Fig. 18. Same as Fig. 17. Magnified 1000 Times. Structure Martensitic with Cementite

ness of the casting. If the cooling is fast enough, martensite may be formed instead of pearlite.

Local hardening effects may be produced by a local chill in the molds, which results in a hard, white iron surface on a casting that might ordinarily be soft and grey if cooled slowly. Fig. 19 illustrates this effect. Factors that influence the depth of the chill obtained include the ratio of carbon to silicon (high silicon content decreases the depth of chill), thickness of the casting, thickness and temperature of the metal placed in the mold to act as a chill, the time that the cast metal is in contact with the metal chiller, and the use of alloy additions.

Chilled iron castings are extensively used for railroad car wheels and for many diversified applications where resistance to wear and compressive strength are major requirements. Applications for chilled iron include rolls for crushing grain and ore, rolling mills for shaping metals, farm implements, and cement-grinding machinery.

MALLEABLE CAST IRON. Malleable cast iron is made by a process involving the annealing of hard, brittle white iron which, as the name implies, results in an iron that is much more ductile (malleable) than either white or grey cast iron. Malleable cast iron is not malleable in the sense that it is as forgeable as steel or wrought iron, but it does exhibit greater toughness and ductility as compared to other forms of cast iron. Also, malleable iron is softer than grey cast iron and exhibits easier machining characteristics. Because of these characteristics, malleable iron can be used in applications where greater

Approximate Hardness		Approximate Combined Carbon and Graphitic Carbon
Scleroscope, 64 Brinell, 450 Rockwell, "C" scale 44		Chill Comb. carbon, 3.30% Graph. carbon, 0.20%
Scleroscope, 45 Brinell, 300 Rockwell, "C" scale, 30		Mottle Comb. carbon, 2.00% Graph. carbon, 1.50%
Scleroscope, 28 Brinell, 150 Rockwell, "B" scale, 87		Grey Iron Comb. carbon, 0.80% Graph. carbon, 2.70%

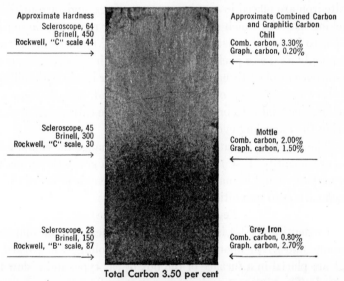

Total Carbon 3.50 per cent

Fig. 19. Fracture of a Chilled Casting, Showing the Approximate Combined Carbon Content, Graphitic Carbon Content, and Hardness of the White, Mottled, and Grey Iron in the As-Cast Condition

Reproduced by Permission, from *Cast Metals Handbook* 3rd Edition, Published by the American Foundrymen's Association, Chicago, Illinois

toughness and resistance to shock are required, such as in farm implements, plows, tractors, harrows, rakes, etc., and finds many applications in automobile parts, hardware, small tools, and pipe fittings in spite of its greater cost as compared to grey cast iron.

Malleable iron is made from white iron castings by a high-temperature, long-time annealing treatment. The original white iron castings are made of a low carbon, low silicon type of iron—an iron that will solidify in a mold and cool without the formation of graphitic carbon. The iron is usually melted in a reverberatory type of furnace, commonly known as an air furnace. Occasional heats of white iron are melted in the electric furnace or the open-hearth furnace. Some heats are melted in the cupola, but it is difficult to melt irons of this composition due to the high temperatures required for them.

Annealing or Malleableizing. A white iron casting is first made by casting a controlled composition of metal into a sand mold. Upon cooling, this casting is hard and brittle because of its structure of combined carbon (Fe_3C). In the annealing process, the castings of white iron are placed in cast iron pots, or rings, and surrounded by a packing material which should be sufficiently refractory in nature so as not to fuse to the castings at the annealing temperatures. Sand is commonly used as a packing material although squeezer slag, crushed air-furnace or blast-furnace slag (used alone or mixed with mill scale), or other forms of iron oxide may also be used. The purpose of the packing material is to protect and support the castings from warping during the annealing cycle.

The object of the annealing cycle is to change the combined carbon or cementite (Fe_3C) of the white iron to a graphitic carbon (temper carbon) found in malleable iron. The decomposition of the combined carbon to graphitic carbon is as follows:

$$Fe_3C \rightarrow 3Fe + C \text{ (graphite)}$$

Cementite (Fe_3C) is unstable at a red heat and decomposes to graphite and ferrite upon heating and slow cooling. The packed castings are placed in a furnace of the box or car type, and a slow fire is started. The temperature is increased at such a rate as may require two days to reach an annealing temperature of 1550° to 1600° F. After reaching this temperature range, the castings are held there from 48 to 60 hours. The castings are then cooled slowly at a rate of not more than 8° to 10° F. per hour until the temperature has dropped to around 1300° F. The castings may be held at this temperature, 1250° to 1300° F., for a period up to 24 hours, or the doors of the furnace may be opened after the castings have been slow-cooled to 1250° F. and the pots removed and allowed to air-cool. The castings are shaken out as soon as their temperature permits handling.

The annealing cycle should result in all of the combined carbon in the original white iron being completely decomposed to a graphitic or temper carbon condition, and the final structure of the iron should consist of ferrite and graphite. The graphitization of the combined carbon starts as soon as the castings reach a red heat. The initial heating to 1600° F. for 48 hours causes the free or excess cementite of the white iron to graphitize, and the slow cooling cycle to 1250°–1300° F. allows the graphitization of the cementite that is precipitated from solution during this period. When the temperature of the iron falls below the critical temperature on cooling or the Ar_1 point (1250°–1300° F.), the balance of the cementite dissolved by the iron is precipitated with the formation of pearlite. A soaking period or a very slow cool while this change is taking place will allow the graphitization of the cementite portion of the pearlite. This will complete the graphitization of all the possible cementite contained in the original white iron.

Fig. 20. Black-Heart Malleable Cast Iron Showing Picture-Frame Fracture Formed by Decarburized Surface. Magnified 2½ Times (Roys)

The time required for the complete annealing cycle varies from five to seven days. A so-called accelerated annealing cycle that requires from one-third to one-half the time required by the large annealing ovens in general use has been used successfully. The shorter annealing cycle is accomplished by the use of better designed furnaces of the gas or electric-fired type and, because of the rapid temperature changes and the accurate control possible with these newer furnaces, requires much less total time. Furnaces used in the shorter annealing cycle are the smaller batch-type, continuous car-type, or kiln-type furnaces. Also, if the annealing can be carried out without the use of a packing material, considerable reduction in the annealing time is gained. This is

because of more rapid and even heating and cooling of the metal.
Black-Heart Malleable Iron. Because of the ductile nature of
malleable iron, and due to the presence of graphitic carbon, the structure appearance upon fracturing will show dark or black with a light
decarburized surface; thus the fracture will appear with a white edge
and black core. This is known as **black-heart malleable iron,** the
structure appearance of which is illustrated in Fig. 20. The white

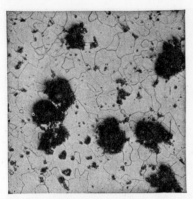

picture-frame edge is due to a
decarburized surface. The graphite present in a fully annealed
malleable iron differs from the
flake-like graphite found in grey
cast irons in that it is formed
into a nodular shape called **temper
carbon.** The principal constituents of malleable iron are ferrite
and nodular graphite, see Fig. 21.
The ferrite matrix of fully annealed malleable iron contains
the silicon, manganese, and phosphorus in a solid solution condition.

Fig. 21. Photomicrograph of Malleable Iron Etched to Show Ferrite Grains. The Dark Spots Are Graphitic (Temper) Carbon. Magnified 100 Times

The decarburized or white surface found in malleable iron results
from a decarburization or burn-out of the carbon during the annealing cycle. Decarburization can be avoided by the use of a carbonaceous packing material or by annealing in a controlled atmosphere.
If annealing is carried out using an iron oxide such as mill scale or
iron ore for packing material, it is possible to completely decarburize
or burn out all of the carbon in the original iron. This will result in a
malleable iron that fractures with a light fracture appearance and is
known as **white-heart malleable iron.** Such a type of iron is seldom
manufactured as it is difficult to machine, and its mechanical properties are inferior to those of the black-heart malleable iron.

Properties of Malleable Iron. The chemical composition of malleable iron is controlled within the limits specified for the various
grades manufactured. The average chemical composition is as follows:

Carbon........................1.00 to 2.00%
Silicon.........................0.60 to 1.10%
Manganese.......................under 0.30%
Phosphorus......................under 0.20%
Sulphur ....0.06 to 0.15%

This composition is only approximate and is changed to suit the requirements of the final product. All of the carbon should be in the graphitic form, with no combined carbon present. The amount of phosphorus and sulphur is not objectionable in that the phosphorus does not produce any marked cold-brittleness, and, as the iron is not hot-worked, hot-shortness or brittleness caused by the sulphur has no appreciable effect.

The average properties of malleable iron are as follows:

Tensile Strength...................54,000 lbs. per sq. in.
Yield Point.......................36,000 lbs. per sq. in.
Elongation, 2 inches...............15% minimum
Brinell Hardness...................115
Izod Impact Strength...............9.3 foot lbs.
Fatigue Endurance Limit...........25,000 lbs. per sq. in.

Modifications in composition and heat treatment may alter these properties, and malleable irons that exhibit much higher mechanical properties are made. One of the modern developments in metallurgy has been the manufacture of high-strength malleable irons known as pearlitic malleable irons.

Alloy Malleable Irons. Some producers of straight malleable iron are also manufacturing a malleable iron to which they add a small amount of copper and molybdenum. These alloy malleable iron castings have numerous applications since they have a yield point that approximates 45,000 psi and an ultimate strength that often exceeds 60,000 psi, accompanied by an elongation in some instances as high as 20% or more in 2 inches. These irons are reported as exhibiting excellent machining properties even when the hardness exceeds 200 Brinell, and a very fine surface finish is obtained. Castings for use in valve and pump parts render very good service, showing excellent resistance to wear and corrosion.

The addition of copper to malleable iron apparently accelerates graphitization during annealing treatments and also strengthens the ferrite, while at the same time greatly improving the iron by increasing its susceptibility to heat treatments following the usual annealing cycle. Copper additions from 0.70 to over 2.0% will make possible an improvement in the physical properties by a precipitation heat treatment that consists of heating the annealed iron to 1290°–1330° F., quenching and then drawing at about 940° F. for three to five hours. The quenching temperature is not high enough to redissolve the graphitic carbon but dissolves much of the copper which is precipitated in a finely divided form by reheating to 940° F. At this temperature copper is relatively insoluble and precipitation occurs at a fast rate. The precipitated copper increases the hardness and strength without much loss in ductility. Precipitation hardening, due to the copper precipitation, also occurs in the regular annealing cycle during the malleabilizing treatment. By controlling the original composition of the casting, marked improvement in physical properties is obtained as compared with the straight malleable iron compositions. The structure of malleable iron alloys with copper, or copper-molybdenum malleable irons, consists of nodular graphitic carbon with a matrix of ferrite, in which we find a precipitate of copper.

Pearlitic Malleable Cast Irons. Straight malleable irons have all of their carbon in the graphitic or temper carbon condition, whereas the so-called pearlite malleable iron retains some of its carbon in the combined condition as cementite, similar to steel and grey cast iron. The structure of the pearlitic malleable iron differs from that of the straight malleable iron in that the matrix consists of a pearlite-like structure of ferrite and cementite. Figs. 22 and 23 illustrate the structure found in this type of iron. It consists of graphite nodules, or temper carbon, with a matrix of spheroidized cementite in ferrite. Pearlitic malleable iron can be made by several different treatments, such as (1) modifying the composition of the original white iron from that used in the manufacture of straight malleable iron, (2) making use of a short annealing cycle, or else (3) subjecting a straight malleable iron casting to a special heat treatment. A brief discussion of these treatments follows.

Modifying Composition. By modifying the composition of the white iron, it is possible to retard the action of graphitization during the regular annealing cycle so that some combined carbon is retained in the final product. Careful control of the silicon-carbon ratio and the additions of manganese, molybdenum, and copper are common practice in securing a retention of combined carbon in the annealed iron. A lower silicon and carbon content retards the action of graphitization. Also, copper, manganese, and molybdenum have about one-fourth the graphitizing power of silicon, and addition of these elements retards graphitization during the annealing cycle.

Short-Cycle Annealing. A common practice in making a pearlitic malleable iron is to employ a shorter annealing cycle than that used when complete graphitization is wanted, as in the making of a straight malleable iron. Manganese additions can be made to the molten

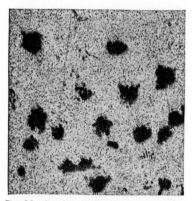

Fig. 22. Pearlitic Malleable Cast Iron. Dark Nodular Temper Carbon (Graphite). Matrix Is Fine Mixture of Ferrite and Cementite. Polished and Etched. Magnified 100 Times

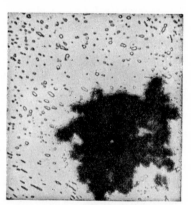

Fig. 23. Same as Fig. 22. Magnified 750 Times. Dark Nodular Temper Carbon (Graphite). Matrix Consists of Cementite Particles In Ferrite Field

metal in the ladle prior to casting as an aid in retarding complete graphitization. A typical analysis for making a pearlitic malleable iron is as follows:

Total Carbon 2.40%
Silicon 0.92%
Manganese 0.32%
Manganese added to ladle 0.63%

This iron is cast to form a white iron similar to that made for straight malleable iron. The addition of manganese to the ladle helps to retard graphitization during the casting cycle and during the annealing cycle that follows. A practice followed for this white iron requires about 30 hours at 1700° F., followed by cooling to below 1300° F. in the annealing furnace, and subsequent reheating to 1300° F. for about 30 hours, followed by cooling to normal temperature. The total time consumed by this annealing cycle is about 75 hours, as compared with five to seven days for the annealing of a straight malleable iron. The shorter annealing time prevents complete graphitization and the annealing time at the lower temperature, 1300° F., puts the combined carbon in a spheroidized condition. As a result of this treatment, a cast iron is produced containing a matrix of spheroidized cementite and ferrite in which the nodules of temper carbon are present.

Special Heat Treatments. It is possible to obtain a pearlitic type of structure in a straight malleable iron by simply reheating a completely graphitized iron to a temperature high enough to give the ferritic matrix an opportunity to dissolve some of the nodular temper carbon, i.e., by heating above the critical temperature of the iron. By controlling the cooling rate from the solution temperature, the dissolved carbon may be precipitated as a coarse spheroidized cementite or as a fine laminated pearlite. Accurate control of the complete cycle is necessary in order to obtain the desired amount of combined carbon and type of structure.

Properties of Pearlitic Malleable Iron. The properties of pearlitic iron depend upon the character of the matrix, i.e., the amount of combined carbon as cementite and the size, shape, and distribution of the cementite particles. In general, pearlitic malleable iron has a higher yield strength and ultimate strength and lower elongation than normal malleable iron. It machines less readily and has a higher Brinell hardness.

Briefly, the properties may be varied between the following limits:

	$A*$	$B\dagger$
Ultimate Tensile Strength	60,000 to 90,000 lbs. per sq. in.	
Yield Point	43,000 to 60,000 lbs. per sq. in.	
Elongation in 2 Inches	15% to 3%	
Brinell Hardness	160 to 200	

  *(A) Soft Pearlitic Malleable Iron
  †(B) Hard Pearlitic Malleable Iron

Applications include use where strength, rigidity and wear resistance are important factors, such as in gears, sprockets, air tools, brake drums, cams, crankshafts, and wearing pads.

QUIZ QUESTIONS

1. *What is the principal difference between steel and cast iron?*
2. *How does the carbon content of steel compare with that of cast iron?*
3. *Name the three classes of cast iron.*
4. *What melting methods are used to produce grey cast iron?*
5. *List the variables that influence the carbon control in grey cast iron.*
6. *What is the most important constituent in grey cast iron?*
7. *What two constituents are found in grey iron but not in steel?*
8. *What influence has the pearlitic constituent upon the properties of grey iron?*
9. *What type of structure in a grey iron is considered strongest and yet is easily machined?*
10. *What influence has the presence of free cementite in a grey iron?*
11. *Why is phosphorus undesirable in a casting? Under what conditions may it be used?*
12. *What effect has the rate of cooling upon the structure of a grey iron casting?*
13. *For what reasons are alloying elements added to grey iron?*
14. *What outstanding properties has grey iron?*
15. *How are grey iron castings classified according to the specifications of the American Society for Testing Materials?*
16. *Why are grey iron castings less susceptible to notch brittleness than most materials?*
17. *What treatment is given grey iron castings to relieve stresses?*
18. *How do the hardening and tempering of grey iron castings compare to similar treatments given steel?*
19. *What type of grey iron responds best to heat treatments such as hardening and tempering?*
20. *What are the advantages of flame-hardening of grey iron castings?*
21. *What is white cast iron?*
22. *What is chilled cast iron?*
23. *List the uses or applications of both white and chilled cast irons.*
24. *Describe the method of making malleable cast iron. Name several uses.*
25. *Describe the temper carbon condition found in malleable iron.*
26. *Describe the average properties of malleable cast iron.*
27. *What alloys may be added to malleable irons? Why are they added?*
28. *What approximate strength and ductility are developed in pearlitic malleable cast irons?*
29. *Describe the common practice used in the annealing cycle for the pearlitic malleable irons.*
30. *Describe the structure developed in pearlitic malleable iron.*
31. *What special heat treatments may be employed in order to obtain a pearlitic malleable iron?*

Rapid transformation of metal powder to part occurs here at the briquetting press. Down through the overhead tube flow the metal powders which are automatically fed into the die. Pressure is derived from upper and lower punches. Next step is the sintering furnace, where these fragile briquettes will get their strength.

Courtesy of Chrysler Corporation, Amplex Division

CHAPTER XVI

Powder Metallurgy

POWDER metallurgy is the process whereby metallic shapes are manufactured from metallic powders. The process involves the production or manufacture of metallic powders and the subsequent welding of these powders into a solid of the required shape. Although at the present time this process is making only a microscopic tonnage of metallic shapes, as compared with the tonnage produced by the usual melting, casting, and forging methods, it has created a lot of interest among metal workers and the tonnage of shapes being produced by this technique is increasing every day. Ultimately, the powder metallurgy process may become as important to the metal-working industry as the die-casting method. The powder metallurgy process has definite limitations and many difficulties to overcome, which distinctly limit its applications at the present time.

The modern metallurgist cannot claim credit for the discovery of the powder-metallurgy process. Metallic powders and solids from metallic powders have been made for many years. Powder metallurgy was used in Europe at the end of the 18th century for working platinum into useful forms. Platinum was infusible at that time. However, it is known that the early Incas in Ecuador manufactured shapes from platinum powders by a similar process long before Columbus made his famous voyage. At the present time, the powder metallurgy process is limited to the manufacture of shapes of a few pounds in weight, but some 1600 years ago the famous iron pillar in Delhi, India, weighing $6\frac{1}{2}$ tons, was made from iron particles or sponge iron similar to an iron used in the modern process. Wollaston, by 1829, had developed a technique that proved very successful in the manufacture of a malleable platinum from platinum powder that permitted forging of the resultant solid like any other metal.

The first modern application of the powder metallurgy process was the making of filaments for incandescent lamps. The first metal filament was made from metallic osmium powder, produced by mixing osmium or its oxide with a reducing material that also served as a binding material. The mixture was extruded or pressed to form a filament, which was heated to reduce the oxide and then sintered into a solid form. Similar techniques were developed using tungsten, vanadium, zirconium, tantalum, and other metals. The first successful metal filament was made from tantalum, but with the discovery by Coolidge that tungsten sintered from tungsten powder could be worked within a certain temperature range and then retain its ductility at room temperature, tungsten became the most important filament material.

METAL POWDERS. Metal powders are now available from many of the common metals and some alloys. Metals and alloys such as aluminum, antimony, brass, bronze, cadmium, cobalt, columbium, copper, gold, iron, lead, manganese, molybdenum, nickel, palladium, platinum, silicon, silver, tantalum, tin, titanium, tungsten, vanadium, zinc, carbides, boron, and tungsten, have been successfully produced in powder form. The poundage of metal produced in the powdered form is an insignificant part of the total tonnage used by the metalworking industry. However, the importance of metal powders and of shapes produced from the powders is great, as compared with the poundage, when you consider the role played by this process in the illumination field in making filaments for lamps, or the tiny contact points made by this process for use in relays, etc. Also, recent applications of this process in the manufacture of the oilless bearings and in the manufacture of metallic shapes used in machines and tools make this process very interesting to the average individual connected with the metal-working industry and to the layman who comes in contact with metals in his everyday life.

Methods of Making Metal Powders. Metal powders may be considered as raw materials for the fabrication of metal shapes and not as end products in themselves. The powders are usually made with some idea as to the requirements of the applications in which they will be used. Most of the metal powders are tailor-made to suit the requirements of each application. Due to the many requirements demanded of the metal powders, varied means of manufacture are necessary.

The metal powders may be distinguished from one another and classified by a study of the following characteristics: (a) particle size, (b) particle shape, (c) surface profile, (d) solid, porous, or spongy nature, (e) internal grain size, (f) lattice distortion within each particle, and (g) the impurities present and their location, and whether or not they are in solid solution or exist as large inclusions or as surface and grain-boundary films.

The shape of the metallic powder particles is such as to require study to determine whether or not the shape is angular, dendritic, or fernlike, ragged and irregular, or smooth and rounded. It is obvious that such a study of all these factors relating to metal powder is relatively arduous and requires skill and special technique. The manufacturer of metallic powders tries to control all of these characteristics and improve techniques so as to manufacture a uniform product in each batch. The methods used in the manufacture of metallic powders include grinding, machining, stamping, shotting, granulation, atomizing, vapor condensation, dissolving constituent, calcium hydride, chemical precipitation, carbonyl process, fused electrolysis, oxide reduction, and electrolytic deposition.

The **mechanical methods,** such as machining and milling, used in the manufacture of metal powders make a relatively coarse powder. The cost is usually high, and the powders made by these methods are usually treated to remove the cold work-hardening received in the process.

In the **shotting process** a rather coarse particle is made by pouring molten metal through a screen or fine orifices and allowing the shot to fall into water. Sometimes this process is used as a breakdown step in the production of a finer powder.

The **granulation process** depends upon the formation of an oxide film on individual particles when a bath of metal is stirred in contact with air. The molten metal is stirred vigorously while cooling, and, as it passes through a mushy state, the metal is granulated by the oxide films which form on the surfaces of the particles, preventing them from coalescing. This method produces a relatively coarse powder with a high percentage of oxide.

In the **atomization process,** molten metal is forced through a small orifice and broken up by a stream of compressed air, steam, or an inert gas. Fine powders may be made by this process, but it requires special nozzles and careful control of temperature, pressure, and the temperature of the atomizing gas. Although oxidation can be prevented by use of an inert gas, little oxidation occurs in this process if air or steam is used. Apparently, the particles oxidize and form a thin protective coating upon the surfaces, thus preventing excessive oxidation from occurring. This process may be used for such metals as tin, zinc, cadmium, aluminum, and other metals having a relatively low melting point. This process allows the production of metal powders with controlled fineness and with a uniform particle size.

Metal powders may also be made by the **vapor condensation process.** In this process, the metal is heated to the vapor state, which, upon cooling, is condensed to a solid powder state. Slight oxide films prevent coalescence of the vapor into a massive liquid state upon cooling. Zinc dust is made in large quantities by this process.

In the **carbonyl process,** metal powders are made by the formation of a carbonyl gas. Carbonyls are produced by passing a carbon monoxide gas over a sponge metal at suitable temperatures and pressures. The carbonyl formed may be a gas or a liquid at room temperature. Upon heating, these carbonyls decompose to form a metal and carbon monoxide gas. The metal formed by this reaction is a very fine dust with the particle size not over a few microns in diameter. Iron and nickel powders may be made by this process.

In the **oxide reduction process** for making a metal powder, the metal is usually in an oxide form such as iron oxide or ores of iron such as magnetite and hematite. The oxide is ground to the desired fineness and then reduced to the metallic state by passing a reducing gas over the heated oxide powder. Gases such as hydrogen and carbon monoxide have been successfully used for the reduction process. The powder formed by this process has particles of a spongelike nature, and it is ideal for cold pressing due to its softness and plasticity. Sponge iron is also made by heating iron ores in contact with charcoal at relatively low temperatures, similar to the process that was used in the production of the irons by early man. The most common metal powders produced by the oxide reduction process include powders of iron, tungsten, copper, nickel, cobalt, and molybdenum.

In the **electrolytic deposition process,** metal powders are made by depositing the metal, as in an electroplating process. By proper choice of electrolyte, regulation of the process as to temperature, current density, circulation of the electrolyte, and proper removal of the deposited metal at the cathode in the bath, a metal powder may be produced that is very pure and free from oxides. The powder produced by this method is dendritic or fernlike in particle shape and is a powder of low apparent density. The electrolytic powder is quite resistant to oxidation, and, upon storage, retains this characteristic until it has been pressed and sintered.

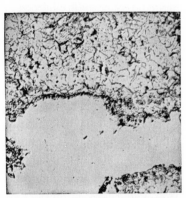

Powders made by the **chemical precipitation process** are tin, silver, selenium, and tellurium. In this process, the metal powder to be made is precipitated from a solution by another metal. Tin powder can be obtained from a stannous chloride solution, while zinc and silver can be obtained from a nitrate solution by the addition of either copper or iron.

Fig. 1. Pressed and Sintered Alloy Powder of 90% Cu and 10% Sn, Pressed at 40 Tons per Sq. In. and Sintered at 1950°F. Shows Little or No Diffusion between the Copper and Tin. Copper Is Dark and Tin Is Light. Magnified 250 Times

Production of Alloy Powders. Alloy metal powder is usually made by mixing metal powders to form an alloy and then heating the mixed powders in a reducing atmosphere to some temperature below the melting point of either powder. Upon heating, diffusion of one metal into the other occurs. The degree of diffusion and uniformity of the alloying depends upon the metals employed and the treatment they receive. Complete diffusion rarely takes place, and therefore only partial alloying occurs. Fig. 1 illustrates the microstructure of a 90% copper–10% tin powder mixture that was pressed at 40 tons per square inch and sintered at 1950° F. Very little diffusion occurred between the copper (dark) and the tin (light). To obtain a more homogeneous structure, prealloyed powder should be used. Diffusion is aided by the heating that is carried out following briquetting. If the sintering temperature is relatively high and the time cycle long, diffusion is given an opportunity to greatly increase the alloying effect. If mixed metal powders are to be prealloyed before pressing or briquetting, caking of the mixed powders may take place during the diffusion cycle, especially if the temperature is in excess of the melting point of one of the constituent metals. The caked metal may be subsequently ground to a powder, but this may produce some work-hardening and require another annealing heating so as to produce a soft plastic alloy that will press easily. Alloyed powders are harder than the pure metals and consequently are harder to press or compact into a briquette.

Characteristics of Metal Powder. The characteristics of any metal powder should receive close study because to develop intelligent specifications for any given metal powder one must understand what makes the powder behave as it does. At the present time, there are no hard and fast specifications for metal powders, as most of the specifications that are being used by the different manufacturers have been developed by purely empirical means. Some of the factors that are important to the behavior of any powder will be reviewed briefly.

Chemical Composition. The chemical composition of metal powders is not as important as their physical and mechanical properties. However, composition, and particularly impurities, will greatly influence the characteristics of any powder. The most important factor is the amount of oxygen that may be found in the powder as oxides. Oxides may be present in the powder from the method of refining and may form on the surfaces of powder that is exposed to air, as in storage or handling. The oxides found in the metal powder from the manufacturer may greatly weaken the final product. The thin oxide films that form during storage or handling may not have any detrimental effect because the powder may be cold weldable and the thin films can be reduced by the atmosphere used during the sintering operation. However, it may be found that any oxide film will reduce the ability of the powder to cold-press into a satisfactory shape; accordingly cracks and ruptures will occur in the cold-pressed shape. In iron powders, the presence of carbon (as cementite, Fe_3C), silica, sulphur, and manganese may greatly influence the plasticity of the iron powders, making them difficult to cold press. Carbon in the form of graphite may be desirable from the viewpoint of lubrication during cold pressing, and its presence during sintering may result in changing the iron to a product similar to steel. Graphitic carbon is often added to iron powders for the purpose of making a harder iron similar to steel.

Structure of the Powders. The structure of the powder greatly influences such characteristics as plasticity and ability to be cold-pressed or made into briquettes. It influences pressures required in pressing, flow characteristics, and the strength of the final product. The study of the powder will reveal whether or not the powder is angular in shape, solid, porous and spongy, crystalline, dendritic or fern-like, or ragged and irregular in shape. The type of structure that is desired in any given powder is usually determined from experience by the metallurgist.

Flow Characteristics. Powders will fill the die cavities by gravitational flow. A powder is required to flow uniformly, freely, and rapidly into the die cavity. If the flow is poor, it becomes necessary to slow down the process of cold pressing in order to get sufficient powder into the die. The flow rate of any powder is largely influenced by the size of the powder particles, distribution of size, particle shape, and freedom from even minute amounts of absorbed moisture.

Apparent Density. The weight of a known volume of unpacked powder is called its **apparent density.** It is usually expressed as grams per cubic centimeter. The apparent density is a very important factor affecting the compression ratio that is required in order to press the powder to a given density. If the apparent density of a given powder is one-third that of the required density, then three times the volume of powder is required to produce a given volume; i.e., the loose powder in a die cavity should be compressed from 3 inches in height to 1 inch, or the stroke of the punches used in the dies should close up 2 inches. It is obvious that a bulky or low apparent density in the powder will require a longer compression stroke and relatively deep dies to produce a cold-pressed piece of a given size and density.

Particle Size. Particle size is one of the most important characteristics of any powder. The most commonly used method of measuring the size of any metal powder particle is to pass the powder through screens having a definite number of meshes to the linear inch.

In the screening method, the size of the particle is measured by a square-mesh screen of standard weave which will just retain the particle. However, most powders are composed of nonspherical particles, and therefore particle size is not a concise method of measurement. Most frequently the powders as used are made up of various sizes of particles. Their size is commonly reported by screening out the coarse, then the medium, and then the fine particles and reporting thus: 66%—100 to 200 mesh; 17%—200 to 325 mesh; and 17%—325 mesh. This means that 66% of the powder by weight will pass the 100-mesh screen but not the 200-mesh screen, etc. Other methods used for sizing powders include microscopic measurement and sedimentation, both being used to determine the size of particles when they are smaller than the finest mesh size of screens.

Welding of Powders. In the process of fabricating parts from powdered metals, the most important step is the one involving the welding together of the metallic powder to form a solid which will yield the proper shape and the properties required of the finished part. We may think of this step as one comparable to that used in the process of welding two pieces of wrought iron or low carbon steel, this being accomplished by pressure and heat properly applied; this is called **pressure welding.** We are all familiar with the forge- or hammer-welding process practiced for thousands of years by man. We are also familiar with the seizure that occurs when two surfaces rub together without proper lubrication or through failure of an oil film. All this is a clue as to the action that takes place when we weld metal powders together to form a solid or so-called briquette. Although a good weld cannot be made between metals at room temperature by pressure alone, when the metal particles are relatively fine and plastic, a welding may occur that is satisfactory from the viewpoint of handling, although little or no strength will be developed. This is particularly true when metal powders such as iron, copper, etc. are used; however, gold powder can be cold-welded by pressure, producing a reasonably strong bond or weld. Under pressure at room temperature, metal powders that are plastic and relatively free from oxide films may be compacted to form a solid of the desired shape, having a strength (green strength) that allows the part to be handled. This result has been called **cold welding** or briquetting.

Molding of Metal Powders. The welding under pressure of the metal particles in order to form a solid briquette of the shape desired requires the use of pressures varying from 5 to 100 tons per square inch. Relatively light loads are used for the molding or briquetting of the softer and more plastic metals and for producing porous metal parts such as those employed in porous bearings. Pressure up to 100 tons per square inch is necessary when maximum density is needed and when pressing relatively hard and fine metal powders.

Commercial pressing is done in a variety of presses which may be of the single mechanical punch-press type or the modern double-action type of machine that allows pressing from two directions by moving the upper and lower punches, synchronized by means of cams. These machines also incorporate movable core rods, which make it possible to mold parts having long cores and assist in obtaining proper die fills and help in the ejecting operations of the pressed part. Fig. 2 illustrates a modern mechanical press used for briquetting metal powders.

Fig. 2. Double-Action Mechanical Press Used in the Pressing or Briquetting of Metal Powders

Courtesy of the F. J. Stokes Machine Company

The molding of small parts at great speeds and at relatively low pressures can be best accomplished in the mechanical press. However, large parts and parts to be molded at relatively high pressures are best molded in hydraulic presses. The rate of production of parts by the powdered metal process will vary depending upon the size of the part and the type of press used. Mechanical presses can produce parts at the rate of 300 to 30,000 per hour. To obtain a production of 30,000 parts per hour requires rotary type presses in which more than one set of dies is incorporated into the design of the machine. The single punch press with a double action can be used for production of parts up to 2000 pieces per hour. A press to prove satisfactory should meet certain definite requirements, among which are the following: (1) sufficient pressure should be available without excessive deflection of press members; (2) the press must have sufficient depth of fill to make a piece of required height dependent upon the ratio of loose powder to the compressed volume, this being referred to as the compression ratio; (3) a press should be designed with an upper or lower punch for each pressing level required in the finished part although

Fig. 3. The Change from Powder to Briquetted Part in Two to Six Seconds Is a Fitting Example of Manufacturing Speed Attainable by Powder Metallurgy

Courtesy of the Chrysler Corporation

this may be taken care of by a die designed with a shoulder or a spring-mounted die which eliminates an extra punch in the press; (4) a press should be designed to produce the number of parts required. Large presses operate on a production of 6 to 8 pieces per minute, while small single action presses can produce 60 or more parts per minute. Small rotary presses may have a production capacity of 500 per minute. Figs. 3 and 4 illustrate the changing from powder to briquetted shape in mechanical presses.

Punch and die equipment are of prime importance in any powder metallurgy application. Unit pressures are high, and the best of steels and workmanship must be used to obtain satisfactory operation and reasonable die life. Materials used for dies and punches vary from hard carbide alloys to ordinary carbon steels. The punches are usually made from an alloy punch steel that can be hardened by oil quenching. Dies are often made from air-hardening alloy steels of the high-carbon-high-chromium type. The usual method used in die design is to make an experimental die, and the knowledge gained

Fig. 4. Close-up of the Table of a Briquetting Press Showing a Part Being Ejected from the Die

Courtesy of the Chrysler Corporation

from making a part in this die is used in the final die design. Factors affecting die design include: powder mix, depth of die fill, pressures employed in briquetting controlled by the density requirements of the part, rate of production, abrasive nature of metal powders, need of any lubricant, method of ejection of part from die, volume change during sintering such as growth or shrinkage, and the necessity of re-pressing after sintering in order to produce parts within the size toler-ance allowed. By a careful study of these factors, the designer is able to make proper drawings for a production die.

Lubricants are used in the molding or briquetting of powders for the purpose of protecting the die from excessive wear and to aid in the flow and ease of pressing the powders into a briquette. Lubricants used include graphite, stearatex, and zinc, aluminum, and lithium stearate. The lubricants are usually added to the metal powder and thoroughly mixed before pressing. Aluminum stearate is used for the aluminum alloy powders, and lithium stearate or zinc stearate for the iron powders. Graphite also may be used as a lubricant with iron powders. If enough graphite is added to the iron powder, a carburization of the powder occurs during the sintering operation, resulting in the formation of a higher carbon alloy. The total carbon content of the sintered alloy can be controlled by the amount of graphite added to the original powder.

Sintering. Heating of the cold-welded metal powder is called the sintering operation. The function of heat applied to the cold-welded powder is similar to the function of heat during a pressure-welding operation of steel, in that it allows more freedom for the atoms in the crystals; it gives them an opportunity to recrystallize and remedy the cold deformation or distortion within the cold-pressed part. The heating of any cold-worked or deformed metal will result in recrystallization and grain growth of the crystals, or grains, within the metal. This action is the same one that allows us to anneal any cold work-hardened metal and also allows us to pressure-weld metals. Therefore, a cold-welded or briquetted powder will recrystallize upon heating, and, upon further heating, the new-born crystals will grow, consequently the crystals or grains become larger and fewer. If this action takes place throughout a cold-pressed powder, it is possible to completely wipe out any evidence of old grains or particle boundaries and have a 100% sound weld.

Sintering Temperature and Time. The sintering temperatures employed for the welding together of cold-pressed powders vary with the compressive loads used, the type of powders, and the strength required of the finished part. Aluminum and alloys of aluminum can be sintered at temperatures from 700° to 950° F. for periods up to 24 hours. Copper and copper alloys, such as brass and bronze, can be sintered at temperatures ranging from 1300° F. to temperatures that may melt one of the constituent metals. Bronze powders of 90%

copper and 10% tin can be sintered at approximately 1600° F. or lower for periods up to 30 minutes. Compacts of iron powders are usually sintered at temperatures ranging from 1900° F. to 2200° F. for approximately 30 minutes. When a mixture of different powders is to be sintered after pressing and the individual metal powders in the compact have markedly different melting points, the sintering temperature used may be above the melting point of one of the component powders. The metal with a low melting point will become liquid; however, so long as the essential part or major metal powder is not molten, this practice may be employed. When the solid phase or powder is soluble in the liquid metal, a marked diffusion of the solid metal through the liquid phase may occur, which will develop a good union between the particles and result in a high density.

Shrinkage During Sintering. Most cold-pressed metal powders shrink during the sintering operation. In general, factors influencing shrinkage include particle size, pressure used in cold welding, sintering temperature, and time employed during the sintering operation. Powders that are hard to compress cold shrink less during sintering. It is possible to control the amount of shrinkage that occurs. By careful selection of the metal powder and determination of the correct pressure for cold forming, it is possible to sinter so as to get practically no volume change. The amount of shrinkage or volume change should be determined so as to allow for this change in the design of the dies used in the process of fabricating a given shape.

Furnaces and Atmospheres. The most common type of furnace employed for the sintering of pressed powders is the continuous type. This type of furnace usually contains three zones. The first zone warms the pressed parts, and the protective atmosphere used in the furnaces purges the work of any air or oxygen that may be carried into the furnace by the work or trays. This zone may be cooled by a water jacket surrounding the work. The second zone heats the work to the proper sintering temperature. The third zone cools the work to a temperature that allows handling. The third zone has a water jacket that allows for rapid cooling of the work, and the same protective atmosphere surrounds the work during the cooling cycle. Fig. 5 illustrates a furnace of this type. The work may be placed on trays or suitable fixtures and pushed through the furnace zones at the correct rate either by hand methods or by mechanical pushers. A mesh-belt type of conveyor furnace can be used whenever the temperatures of sintering allow it. Such furnaces are used for sintering, operating successfully up to 2000° F., although temperatures in excess of 1600° F. may cause damage to the conveyor belt.

Protective atmospheres are essential to the successful sintering of pressed metal powders. The object of such an atmosphere is to

Fig. 5. A Sintering Furnace with Three Zones: Purging, Sintering, and Cooling
Courtesy of Westinghouse Electric and Manufacturing Company

protect the pressed powders from oxidation which would prevent the successful welding together of the particles of metal powder. Also, if a reducing protective atmosphere is employed, any oxidation that may be present on the metal powder particles will be removed and thus aid in the process of welding. A common atmosphere used for the protection and reduction of oxides is hydrogen. Water vapor should be removed from the hydrogen gas by activated alumina dryers or refrigerators before it enters the furnace. A cheap high-hydrogen gas may be generated by the dissociation of ammonia, forming a mixture of gases for a protective atmosphere containing 75% hydrogen and 25% nitrogen. The most common type of protective gas used is manufactured from partially burned hydrocarbon gases such as coke oven gas, natural gas, or propane. The gas is premixed with air in a suitable gas converter or generator and then cooled and let into the furnace. By control of the gas-air ratio, a variation in the composi-

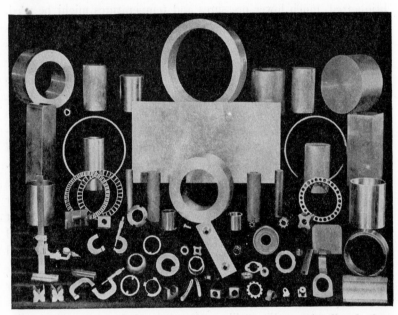

Fig. 6. Bearings, Tools, and Machine Parts Made by the Powder Metallurgy Process. Some Are Porous, Some Dense, Some Self-lubricating, Some Dry, but Nearly All of These Units Were Made Directly from Dies without the Necessity of Subsequent Machining. Some of These Parts Are Made 200 Times Faster with Features Impossible to Obtain by Standard Manufacturing Methods

Courtesy of Chrysler Corporation

tion of the manufactured gas is permitted so that a gas can be generated that will prove suitable for a given composition of metal powder. The importance of the atmosphere cannot be too highly stressed. Pure iron will oxidize in an atmosphere suitable for copper sintering; therefore, the selection of the atmosphere depends upon the composition of the pressed metal part. For sintering copper and many of its alloys, a gas on the reducing side is usually satisfactory, provided no free oxygen is present. For sintering iron at 1950° to 2100° F., a gas containing approximately 18% CO, 1% CO_2, 2% CH_4, and 32% H_2, dried to a dewpoint of 40° F. has proved satisfactory. A ratio of $5\frac{3}{4}$:1 between air and propane gas will produce an atmosphere of this composition.

Hot Pressing. If metal powders could be pressed at temperatures high enough to sinter them to a solid at the same time they are briquetted, much lower pressures and temperatures might be used. Much experimental work will be required before this method becomes

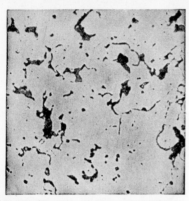

Fig. 7. Structure of a Porous Metal Bearing Made from Iron Powder. The Dark Areas Represent Voids in the Metal Bearing. Photomicrograph Magnified 250 Times

a general practice. The problems involved in hot pressing include the following: oxidation of the powders, excessive wear on dies, selection of alloys for punches and dies that will resist the temperatures employed, method of heating and control of temperature, pressures that are to be used, and annealing during or after the pressing cycle. Excellent properties have been obtained from hot pressing of iron and brass powders, using much lower pressures than those needed for

the cold-pressing and sintering process, but only in the laboratory.

Applications. Fig. 6 illustrates some of the many shapes that have been successfully made by the powder metallurgy process. The manufacture of porous metal bearings from iron, brass, bronze, and aluminum alloys has proved to be a major application of this process. Bearings made by this process are pressed and sintered at temperatures that will produce a part which is more or less porous and spongy. Fig. 7 illustrates the microstructure of a porous iron bearing showing the voids (dark) present in the finished part. The voids are more or less connected so that if the part is soaked in oil, the oil is drawn into the porous bearing and held there until pressed out by pressure from a load applied in service. Fig. 8 illustrates porous bearings made from aluminum powder, resulting in a lightweight bearing.

Some machine parts have been successfully made by the powder metallurgy process using powders of iron, iron-carbon (steel), brass, bronze, etc. Figs. 9 and 10 illustrate the type of microstructure obtained by pressing a reduced iron powder at 40 tons per square inch and sintering at 2100° F. for 30 minutes. The presence of oxides

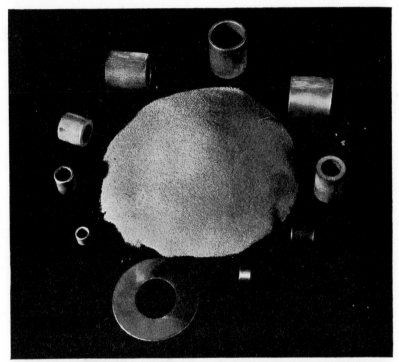

Fig. 8. Self-lubricating Aluminum Oilite Bearings, the First Ever Successfully Developed and Made. Advantages of This Product of Chrysler Corporation Are Its 77% Weight-saving over Bronze and the Elimination of Electrolysis in an Aluminum Housing which Occurs with Other Metals. Most Popular Uses of the New Bearings Are in Aircraft

Courtesy of Chrysler Corporation

shows up very clearly in these structures. Small machine parts that do not require much strength and hardness can be made from such an iron powder. If surface hardness is required, parts made from this reduced iron can be casehardened by carburization similar to that of low carbon steels. Fig. 11 illustrates the microstructure of a pressed and sintered electrolytic iron powder. The structure of this iron looks

similar to that of the regular commercial pure iron and is relatively
free from oxides. Iron-carbon alloys similar to steel can be made by
this process and can be used for the manufacture of parts that require

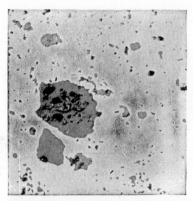

Fig. 9. Photomicrograph of a Pressed and
Sintered Reduced Iron Powder. Dark Areas
Are Oxide Inclusions.   Polished Section,
Magnified 250 Times

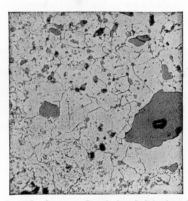

Fig. 10.   Same as Fig. 9, but Polished and
Etched to Bring Out the Iron or Ferrite
Grains. Magnified 250 Times

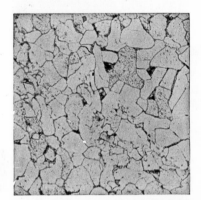

Fig. 11.   Photomicrograph of Electrolytic
Iron Powder, Pressed at 50 Tons per Square
Inch and Sintered at 2100°F. for 30 Minutes.
Shows Similarity to Structure of Commercial
Pure Iron. Magnified 250 Times

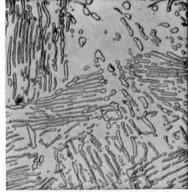

Fig. 12. Photomicrograph of an Iron-Carbon
Alloy Made by Mixing Iron and Graphite
Powders, Pressed at 50 Tons per Sq. In.
and Sintered at 2100°F. for 30 Minutes.
Shows a Pearlitic Structure Similar to That
Found in Tool Steel. Magnified 1000 Times

a certain degree of hardness. Fig. 12 illustrates the microstructure
of an iron-carbon alloy made from mixing iron and graphite powders,
followed by pressing or briquetting at 50 tons per square inch and

sintering at 2100° F. for 30 minutes. The structure is of a pearlitic nature similar to that found in annealed tool steel. A part made with this type of structure can be heat-treated by hardening and tempering in the same way used for regular carbon steel.

Tungsten wire for filaments in the lamp industry is made from pure tungsten powder which is pressed and sintered to form a bar of tungsten. This bar is hot-swaged to about 0.10 inch or less in diameter and is then drawn through tungsten carbide dies to about 0.010 inch in diameter while at a temperature of 1500° to 1750° F. The wire is then drawn through diamond dies to the finished diameter. Start-

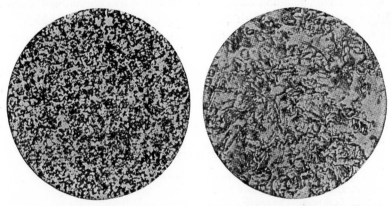

Fig. 13. Photomicrograph of Cemented Tungsten Carbide; Magnified 750 Times

Fig. 14. Photomicrograph of Cast Tungsten Carbide; Magnified 750 Times

Courtesy of American Society for Metals

ing from a powder, the unit strength of the swaged and drawn tungsten wire reaches some 850,000 pounds per square inch—more than twice that of the hardest steel—and is the strongest material known.

Another important branch of powder metallurgy is the field of hard tool materials. Hard carbides such as tungsten carbide (WC), titanium carbide (TiC), boron carbide (B_4C), etc., can be bonded together by the powder metallurgy process to form a very hard material that has proved extremely important as a cutting tool and die material. To bond these hard carbides together, a binder or metal matrix, usually cobalt, is employed. Nickel is also used in this respect. The carbide and metal binder are made into powder form by the usual mechanical methods. The prepared powder can be cold-pressed and sintered or hot-pressed to form a solid of the required shape. Manufacture of hard carbide materials by the powder metallurgy process produces much more uniformity of structure and properties than obtained by the melting process as illustrated by Figs. 13 and 14. Carbide tools and machine parts are exceedingly hard, although brittle, and find many applications in the field of cutting tools and dies.

Besides machine and tool applications, the powder metallurgy process has been successfully employed in the manufacture of contact points of tungsten, silver, or copper, clutch faces and brake linings where a mixture of a high coefficient of friction material is added to a metallic base, grinding wheels and drills made by combining diamond dust or carbide dust with softer metals, welding rods in which the necessary fluxes are incorporated with the special metallic material of the rod or bound to the surface of the metallic rod, babbitt bearings made by bonding a bearing alloy to a metallic backing strip, and many other successful applications. There are many limitations to the application of the powder metallurgy process, but, with an understanding of these limitations, success for this process will be definite and continued.

QUIZ QUESTIONS

1. State the procedure used in the powder metallurgy process.
2. How are metal powders produced?
3. Is it possible to produce alloys by powder metallurgy?
4. Describe the process of molding metal powders.
5. Describe the process of sintering.
6. Describe the atmospheres required in sintering furnaces.
7. How is tungsten wire made?
8. What problems are involved in hot pressing?

CHAPTER XVII

Titanium, Zirconium, Indium, and Vanadium

TITANIUM. Titanium is a new addition to the family of engineering metals. Only three tons of titanium were produced in 1948, but production climbed to 5,250 tons in 1954. The production of titanium may be expected to rise continually since demand for it will continue to exceed the supply. In spite of this, improved methods of reclaiming mill and consumer scrap will alleviate the condition somewhat.

Titanium-bearing ores are plentiful, but the technical difficulties in recovering, melting, and processing titanium make the metal costly. However, since titanium has a very high strength-to-weight ratio at temperatures between 300° F. and 700° F., it is widely used in airframes and aircraft engines at prices 30 to 40 times that of stainless steel.

The U.S. Air Force claims that a one-pound weight reduction in a jet engine results in an eight- to ten-pound reduction in airframe weight. Titanium thus saves 500 pounds in each of the eight jet engines of a heavy bomber and makes possible a reduction of 40,000 pounds.

The engineering world paid scant attention to the Bureau of Mines announcement of titanium at first, but men of vision in the armed forces soon found it to be a panacea for their many problems, and obtained industrial interest for the new metal.

No other structural metal presents the problems encountered in producing titanium. The liquid metal seems to be a universal solvent, which either dissolves or is contaminated by every known refractory. The contaminants acquired during the manufacturing process are generally fatal to titanium's physical properties. The metal, when molten, unites with the oxygen and nitrogen in the air with such speed that all reduction and ingot-melting processes must be carried out in a vacuum or in an inert atmosphere. No method has been found to remove contaminants acquired during processing.

Under such trying circumstances large scale industrial production is extremely difficult, and in 1951, many engineers wondered if titanium could be handled on a large enough basis to be competitive. Later technological progress has indicated that it can.

A simple and efficient continuous Kroll-type reactor was developed in 1953 which lowered the cost of titanium. In the reactor, titanium tetrachloride is reacted with magnesium to form spongy titanium and magnesium chloride. The process produces many tons of titanium.

Some progress has been made in obtaining commercial titanium by reacting purified sodium with tetrachloride, by continuous thermal decomposition of the iodide and by arc dissociation of halides (such as titanium tetrachloride). However, the major efforts are being expended on electrolytic methods. The electrolysis of molten-salt electrolyte seems to promise recovery of nonmassive deposits in sufficiently pure form to melt into ductile metal. This process will probably continue to develop but it will not replace the Kroll reactors for some time.

The first step in winning titanium metal from its ore is to chlorinate an oxide-carbon mixture to secure titanium tetrachloride. Titanium tetrachloride is reduced to titanium sponge by reduction of the chloride by magnesium. The reaction produces titanium sponge and magnesium chloride. The magnesium chloride is passed through an electrolytic cell and magnesium and chlorine are recovered and may be used again.

Production of Ingots. In the molten state, titanium reacts vigorously with the oxygen and nitrogen of the air. If the amount of these elements is kept below 0.5%, they act as hardening agents, but in amounts over 0.5% oxygen or 0.25% nitrogen they drastically reduce the ductility of titanium. Hydrogen embrittles titanium, reducing its ductility. Adequate protection from moisture and the atmosphere are therefore important. Vacuum technology or inert atmospheres of pure argon or helium can accomplish this.

The ordinary techniques of melting and casting are ruled out.

The method usually used is the von Bolten process of arc-melting in an inert atmosphere at near atmospheric or greatly reduced pressures. Electrodes may be of tungsten, carbon, or consumable electrodes of titanium. A difficulty of tungsten and carbon electrodes is that they are subject to spalling and melting particularly if they are spattered with titanium. Melting is usually done in a water-cooled copper crucible, building up each ingot individually, or by extracting the ingot through the bottom of the crucible. By using a reduced pressure and double melting with consumable electrodes, contamination is avoided and hydrogen content of the metal is kept at a low level.

Forging, rolling, and drawing present no special problems. Mills capable of handling the stainless steels and the alloy steels can handle titanium.

Properties of Titanium. Silver-gray titanium lies between aluminum and steel in strength, density, elasticity, and serviceability at elevated temperatures. It has a density of 0.16 pounds per cubic inch. It is 60% heavier than aluminum and only 56% as heavy as an alloy steel, which has a density of 0.286 pounds per cubic inch. The alloys of titanium are stronger than all aluminum alloys and most steel alloys. Titanium also has excellent ductility. The titanium alloys are superior in strength-to-weight ratios over the usual engineering metals and alloys. Titanium has an endurance ratio well above heat-treated alloy steels and nonferrous materials. Its endurance limit is always more than 50% of its tensile strength.

The coefficient of thermal expansion of titanium alloys is about 40% less than for austenitic stainless steel. Titanium's low expansion sometimes introduces thermal stresses when alloyed with other metals. Thermal conductivity of titanium alloys is about the same as austenitic stainless steel. It may vary up to 25%, depending upon alloying constituents. The electrical resistivity of titanium is approximately the same as austenitic stainless steel and increases with more alloying elements, making it easy to heat by electrical means for working.

Fatigue Resistance. Titanium and its alloys have good fatigue resistance in the unnotched condition. With very sharp notches, titanium appears to be greatly inferior to steel. The deficiency seems to disappear as the notch is made rounder and, under some notch conditions, titanium may be superior to other metals. Where notch fatigue is important, the user should conduct specific tests to determine titanium's desirability. The fatigue limit of titanium improves as the temperature is lowered to sub-zero. Not much research has been done on titanium and its alloys at low temperatures. However, what little research has been done indicates that hardness and tensile strength are increased as temperature is lowered. Elongation decreases at low temperatures, and notch sensitivity appears to increase.

Elevated-Temperatures. Titanium has excellent weight strength ratios between 300° and 700° F., but it is inadequate at high temperatures. The ultimate strength and yield strength of titanium drop fast above 800° F. Titanium readily absorbs oxygen and nitrogen from the air above 1200° F., embrittling the metal. There is hope for development of alloys which will withstand temperatures up to 1400° F.

Chemical Corrosion Properties. Titanium is almost immune to most corrosives, but when it is subject to attack, the rate of corrosion is usually severe.

So far the chemical industry has been unable to get much titanium for test purposes. One chemical concern tested titanium with sulphuric acid concentrations up to 22% at high heat, and pressure and titanium remained unaffected. The company is constructing a large operational unit entirely of titanium.

Titanium is exceptionally immune to sea water and marine atmosphere. It is the only structural metal that has a corrosion behavior in salt water identical to that in air. This places a great demand on titanium for ship building. Unalloyed titanium retained its original luster and appeared to be absolutely unaffected when exposed to rural and marine atmospheres for a period of five years. Titanium should be insulated when used with other metals by organic coating or electrical insulation, because it causes severe corrosion to metals with which it is in contact.

Commercially Pure Titanium. Titanium of the highest purity possible at a reasonable production cost is called commercially pure titanium, which is 99.5% pure. The importance and need for a standard was recognized by consumers, so commercially pure titanium was established as a composition of 0.2% maximum iron, 0.10% maximum nitrogen, a trace of oxygen, less than 0.07% carbon, and 0.02% tungsten, the remainder being titanium.

Type Ti-75A (Titanium Metals Corporation) has the following characteristics: hardness, 85–95 Rockwell B; ultimate strength, 80,000 psi minimum; yield strength, 70,000 psi minimum, and elongation, two inches, 20% minimum.

Commercially pure titanium does not respond to heat-treatment but can be cold worked to above 120,000 psi tensile and 100,000 psi yield strength with a consequent drop in ductility. Commercially pure titanium and titanium base alloys are available in the form of sheet, strip, plate, wire bar, rod, forging billets, and forgings.

Titanium Alloys. Laboratories have explored thousands of titanium alloys of various combinations. Some having very impressive physical properties are commercially available. One difficulty experienced was reproducing the alloys from heat to heat. This problem was solved by improving melting practices. The variations in raw sponge and the tremendous effect of contaminants which are readily picked up by titanium made it very difficult, if not impossible, to duplicate previous heats.

The size of the titanium atom is such that it fits well with other metallic atoms, indicating that it may make many good solid solution type alloys. Titanium also makes a physical transformation at 1625° F., thus indicating a possibility of producing various age-hardenable alloys with alloying elements whose solid solubilities decrease with temperature. Titanium shows strong tendencies toward forming interstitial solid solutions with metalloids (elements having both metallic and nonmetallic properties). Oxygen, nitrogen, and carbon dissolve in molten titanium to form solid solutions or nonmetallic inclusions (foreign matter). Binary (two-constituent) alloys of these elements do not respond to heat-treatment but are readily work-hardened. Iron, chromium, and molybdenum stabilize the high temperature beta phase of titanium, producing alloys which harden when quenched. The quaternary (four-constituent) alloys formed from titanium, iron, chromium, and molybdenum have better combinations of high strength and ductility than have been obtained from binary or ternary (three-constituent) alloys at the same strength level.

In addition to the commercially pure grade (Ti-75A) and the extra soft variation special grade, the Titanium Metals Corporation markets four different titanium-base alloys, having nominal compositions and annealed physical properties of sheet as follows: Type Ti-100A, an oxygen-nitrogen alloy, is used primarily for sheet, plate, strip, and wire—nonheat-treatable but work-hardenable. Mill products of this alloy have physical properties as follows: hardness, 30 Rockwell C maximum; tensile strength, 100,000 psi minimum; yield strength, 90,000 psi minimum; and elongation, 15% minimum.

Type Ti-140A is a two-phase, high-strength alloy sold primarily as bar and forgings, but also in experimental production as sheet and strip. This alloy has high-temperature stability and excellent impact values. It appears to be spot-weldable, but as yet fusion welds have shown only indifferent ductility values. In bar and forgings the annealed properties are as follows: hardness, 300–304 Brinell Hardness Number; tensile strength, 130,000 psi minimum; yield strength, 120,000 psi minimum; and elongation, 12% minimum.

Type Ti-150A is an alloy sold primarily as bars and forgings— heat-treatable and work-hardenable. It is moderately responsive to heat treatment and is supplied as annealed at about 1250° F. Physical properties are: hardness, 311–364 Brinell Hardness Number; tensile strength, 135,000 psi minimum; yield strength, 120,000 psi minimum; and elongation, 12% minimum.

Type Ti-155A is a very high strength forging alloy, beta stabilized by iron, chromium, and molybdenum additions and with sufficient aluminum to maintain high strength at temperatures up to 1000° F. This alloy is only in experimental production, but has already been welcomed in the jet-engine industry as an ideal composition for compressor wheels, particularly for later stages where high temperatures build up as the air is compressed. This alloy also exhibits excellent creep and impact performance. Annealed Ti-155A bars and forgings have the following physical values: hardness, 300–370 Brinell Hardness Number; tensile strength, 155,000 psi; yield strength, 140,000 psi; and elongation, 12%.

Uses. Virtually all titanium is being used today so as to take advantage of its favorable ratio of strength-to-weight between 300° and 700° F. Titanium would be used more if it cost less.

Aircraft Gas Turbines. Titanium bar stock and forgings are used in making compressor disks, spacer rings, rotating and stationary compressor blades, and vanes, through bolts, turbine housings, and liners, and miscellaneous hardware for turbo-prop engines. Titanium sheet is used for fire shields, brackets, and shroud stock.

Airframes. Titanium and titanium alloy sheet are used in airframes for both structural and nonstructural applications, primarily surrounding engines, where service temperatures are in the range from 300° to 700° F. Titanium is used in both military and commercial aircraft where even its high cost is justified by the savings in weight and the accompanying extra pay load.

Fasteners. Titanium and titanium alloy rivets, nuts, bolts, and screws have been manufactured in a variety of sizes, principally for evaluation. The high-shear type of rivet, on which stainless steel or Monel clips or collars are swaged (pressed, pulled, or hammered), has great possibilities. Shear-type fasteners may be important in design because of the relatively high-shear–tensile ratio of titanium. Titanium alloy screws, and particularly bolts, also offer possibilities for saving weight.

Other Applications. Because of superior corrosion resistance, titanium and titanium alloys are being used experimentally as seats and disks in globe valves, and metering disks in displacement-type fuel systems on ships; also, for military equipment which must be light for mobility or air transportability, and in the chemical industry for pipe and fittings to carry highly corrosive chemicals. Consideration is also being given to its use for lightweight storage tanks for liquefied gases.

ZIRCONIUM. Like titanium, zirconium had to wait for a commercial process to free it from the laboratory. Its extraordinary corrosion resistance has been known for 20 years but was of little use because of its high cost and short supply.

Zirconium was probably discovered by Klaproth in 1789. He found its oxide in a mineral from Ceylon and named the new element zirconium. Now, the mineral is called zirconia and the metal is called zirconium.

Zirconium was prepared first in 1824 by Berzelius, who reduced (broke down) potassium fluozirconate with potassium to zirconium, probably resulting in a contaminated form of the metal. In 1923, Coster and Hevesy, through X-ray examinations, discovered another element, hafnium, which always occurs with zirconium.

Pure zirconium metal was described as early as 1920, but not until the development of the Van Arkel process of iodide decomposition in 1925, in Leyden, Holland, was pure, coherent metal readily available for testing. The purest and most ductile zirconium available today is made by that process. The process is expensive and not suitable for quantity production. Its product is a metal of low strength.

The Kroll process is better than Van Arkel's for a large-scale operation. In that process, zirconium tetrachloride is broken down with magnesium to form magnesium chloride and zirconium metal. Hafnium, usually in quantities of 1.5% to 2.0%, is the chief impurity. The hafnium contamination of zirconium is in the same proportion as in the ore from which the metal was made.

Ore Supply. Until recently, zirconium was considered as one of the rare metals. Its ores, however, are widely distributed and no less available than those of better-known metals. The earth's crust is estimated to contain 0.04% zirconium more than the combined percentages for copper, lead, zinc, tin, nickel, and mercury.

Almost all the zirconium used in American industry comes from the three extensive ore deposits in Florida, Australia, and Brazil. The ores from Florida and Australia consist of seacoast sands from which zircon (zirconium silicate), rutile, ilmenite, and other minerals readily separated. Though the ore is lean, it is still cheaper to produce than if drilling, blasting, and crushing were also required. In Brazil, the chief zirconium ore is baddeleyite, an impure oxide with less silica than is contained in zircon. Although in the past large tonnages have been imported from Brazil (more than 15,000 tons in 1942), it is a less important source of zirconium than Florida. In 1946 shipments from Florida were reported to be 9,000 tons, and at present, with three or more companies in production, the output is very much greater.

In Australia, the output has been even higher, but less Australian ore is reaching this country than was formerly imported.

Deposits of zircon have been operated profitably in Madagascar and India. There are deposits in Oregon and North Carolina that could be worked if necessary.

Methods of Manufacture. The zirconium first was refined from a crude metallic powder produced by reduction of either zirconium oxide by calcium, of the tetrachloride by sodium, or of potassium fluozirconate by potassium. Such powders were often of very low purity, analyzing only 80% to 85% zirconium. They were converted to ductile metal bars by a refining operation known as the Van Arkel–de Boer process, which involves the formation and decomposition of zirconium tetraiodide in an air-free vessel. Iodine vapor in this vessel attacks the crude powder at a moderate temperature, and the tetraiodide formed is decomposed at a higher temperature. By causing the deposition to occur on a wire heated by an electric current, a rod of zirconium crystals is built up, and the iodine released by decomposition of the tetraiodide then reacts with more of the crude zirconium in a cooler part of the vessel. The process is repeated until all of the crude zirconium is used up or the rod of refined zirconium becomes so thick that it can no longer be kept at the required temperature by the electric current available. Scrap metal or impure sponge, as well as a powder, may be used as the raw material in this process.

A serious limitation of the process is the very heavy electric current necessary to maintain a thick zirconium bar at the temperature (about 2372° F.) required for decomposition of the iodide. Thus, only fairly thin bars can ordinarily be made. The starting wire, generally tungsten, remains inside the bar as an impurity, but this objection can be overcome by using a zirconium wire to start the process.

Pure zirconium bars produced by the iodide process are small, very costly, and of low strength. Swaged and annealed rods of this type are almost as weak as copper. Reported properties are as follows: tensile strength, 36,000 psi; yield strength, 16,000 psi; elongation in 1 inch, 26%; reduction of area, 32%; and Rockwell "B" hardness, 30.3.

For these reasons the Zirconium Metals Corporation bases its process for producing zirconium metal on the Bureau of Mines method, involving the reduction (breaking down into constituents) of zirconium tetrachloride by magnesium. By a method developed by the Titanium Alloy Manufacturing Company, the ore is first treated in an arc furnace to convert the silicate to a carbonitride (more commonly called cyanonitride), which in turn is chlorinated to obtain the tetrachloride. The tetrachloride is then reduced to metal by magnesium in a closed retort. Extreme care is required in the later stages of this process to avoid contamination of the metal by the oxygen and nitrogen in the air. The metal is produced in the form of a gray crystalline sponge (porous) which is melted in graphite by induction, or in water-cooled copper by an arc, to obtain ingots. An atmosphere free from oxygen and nitrogen is essential for melting operations. Carbon pickup from the graphite in induction melting is slight and not detrimental if superheating (heating above boiling point without converting into gas) and long holding in the molten state are avoided.

The ingots are forged or hot-rolled at about 1350° to 1400° F., and if higher temperatures are avoided, scaling and oxygen absorption are not sufficiently serious to impair the quality of the finished product. Annealing, prior to cold-working, may be done at 1300° F. in air. Scale-removal for cold-rolling or wire-drawing is difficult, and usually requires shot-blasting followed by pickling.

Uses. Zirconium metal was first used for priming explosives and flashlight powders. The extreme combustibility of this powder makes it very suitable for this purpose, and twenty years ago zirconium was produced chiefly as a powder. The metal produces a very bright light when ignited. The reactivity of finely divided zirconium renders it effective for combining with the last traces of oxygen and nitrogen in evacuated vessels or tubes, and thus the complete removal of these gases from the interior atmospheres. These uses are still current.

Among the other uses that have been suggested are for grid wires in vacuum tubes and parts of discharge tubes exposed to high temperatures, as an electrolytic condenser for rectifiers and high intensity electric lamp filaments, and electrodes in fluorescent tubes.

Not only is zirconium not attacked by the atmosphere or sea water at normal temperatures, but it is almost as resistant to acids as tantalum (a hard ductile metallic element). It resists alkalies better than tantalum. Zirconium is far superior to tantalum in wear-resistance and low density, as well as in abundance and economy.

Physical Properties. Like titanium, zirconium undergoes a physical transformation at approximately 1589° F. The room temperature phase, called alpha, has a close-packed, hexagonal, crystal structure. Above 1589° F. the crystal structure is body-centered cubic, called beta zirconium. The hexagonal close-packed structure in metals is generally considered to confer poor ductility because of the presence of only one plane of easy slip, but zirconium, like titanium, is an exception to this general rule and can be worked with ease at room temperature.

Mechanical Properties. Zirconium Metals Corporation metallic zirconium, hot-rolled to bar form, has about the following tensile properties, as determined from specimens having a gage-length of 1″ and 0.16″ in diameter: stress for 1% extension under load, 68,000 to 80,000 psi; tensile strength, 97,000 to 113,000 psi; elongation in one inch, 9% to 14%, and reduction of area, 10% to 30%.

The tensile and bend properties of zirconium sheet, cold-rolled to between 0.035″ and 0.11″ thickness, and annealed at 1400° F., as determined on standard specimens, are as follows: yield strength at 0.2% offset, 56,000 to 72,000 psi; tensile strength, 76,000 to 83,000 psi; elongation in two inches, 13% to 19%, and minimum bend radius, 1.8 to 3.9 times thickness.

Zirconium sheet has no directional properties. Its transverse ductility is at least as good as in the lengthwise direction; its transverse yield strength is slightly better. The tensile strength of zirconium decreases with rising temperature to 50% at temperatures from 600° to 700° F.

Hardness. The hardness of Zirconium Metals Corporation zirconium varies from about 175 to 275 Brinell, more than that of aluminum alloys but less than steel. Hardness is greatly dependent on the oxygen and nitrogen in the metal. The hardness-strength relation of zirconium differs somewhat from that of steel.

Work Hardening. Cold-working of zirconium increases its strength and hardness, and cold-rolling produces a pronounced loss in ductility of the metal, as indicated by the reduction in the percentage of elongation that occurs in cold-rolled specimens.   Fig. 1

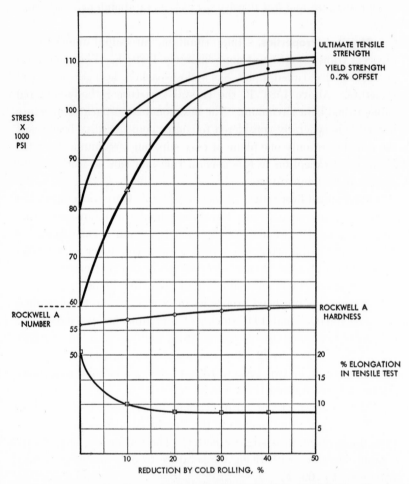

Fig. 1. Effects of Cold Rolling on the Mechanical Properties of Commercially Pure Zirconium

shows the effects of cold-rolling on the mechanical properties of commercially pure zirconium.

Effect of Annealing on Cold-Worked Zirconium Strip. Cold-rolled zirconium sheet and strip thicker than approximately 0.045″ may be satisfactorily annealed at 1400° F. in air, without damage by oxidation. In annealing gage material, however, a vacuum or inert atmosphere is necessary to prevent embrittlement of the zirconium by gaseous contamination. The reduction in hardness which takes place when cold-rolled 50% strip is heated under a protective atmosphere of argon for one hour at various temperatures is indicated on Fig. 2. The effect of air is discussed in the section on cor-

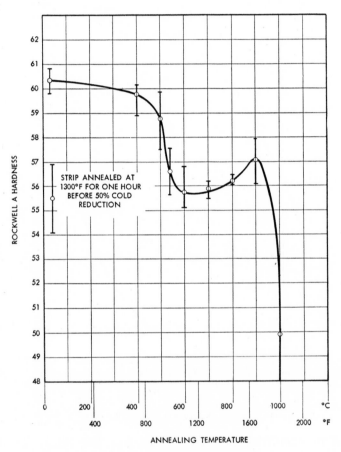

Fig. 2. The Reduction in Hardness When Cold-Rolled 50% Zirconium Strip Is Heated Under a Protective Atmosphere of Argon for One Hour

rosion resistance and illustrated by Fig. 3. The graph in Fig. 2 indicates that complete stress-relief and at least some recrystallization occur at 1172° F., with little further change in hardness up to 1652° F. However, at a temperature between 1652 and 1832° F., zirconium hardness drops very suddenly, so that full softening may be obtained by annealing at 1832° F. for one hour. Annealing at this temperature is not practical in air and must be conducted in a protective atmosphere to avoid excessive oxidation of the metal. Hydrogen should not be used because it has been found

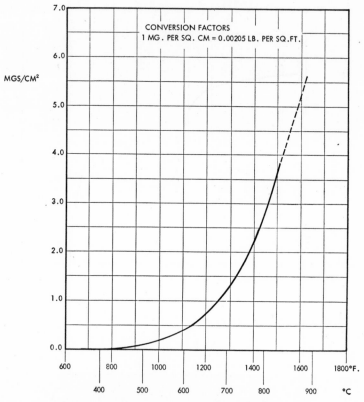

Fig. 3. Gain in Weight of Zirconium by Oxidation in Air in One Hour

to cause embrittlement. The sudden drop in hardness at about 1652° F. is believed to be related to the physical transformation from alpha to beta zirconium that takes place in this temperature range and causes complete recrystallization. The protective atmosphere used for annealing thin zirconium strip or wire must be carefully purified to remove all traces of oxygen, nitrogen, water vapor, etc. Either argon or helium is sometimes passed over zirconium sponge at about 1600° F. for such purification.

Bending or Forming. Zirconium sheet, strip, or wire may be deformed to a considerably greater angle in free bending if the initial deformation is performed at a temperature of about 400° to 600° F., instead of at room temperature. Some data on annealed zirconium sheet are included in Table 1.

Table 1. Results of Tensile, Bend, and Hardness Tests on Zirconium Sheet

Thickness (Inches)	Direction of Test	Tensile Strength	Yield Strength*	Elongation in 2 in.	Minimum Bend†	Hardness Rockwell "A"
.125	Longitudinal	83,850	53,400	10.3	R = 1.9T	54.4
	Transverse	81,950	70,700	19.25	R = 2.5T	
.103	Longitudinal	82,850	60,650	14.8	R = 1.9T	54.0
	Transverse	82,850	71,650	15.0	R = 2.5T	
.088	Longitudinal	83,050	56,050	16.0	R = 1.9T	54.9
	Transverse	82,950	65,900	16.0	R = 2.5T	
.063	Longitudinal	82,250	56,500	15.0	R = 2.5T	54.9
	Transverse	80,600	56,650	18.3	R = 2.5T	
.048	Longitudinal	78,150	.....	14.5	R = 3.8T	53.7
.035	Longitudinal	76,700	.....	13.5	R = 3.8T	50.8

Sheet width, 5½"; specimens machined to ½". Width and annealed 1 hour at 1400° F. in air.

* Determined autographically with extensometer. Yield strength determined at 0.2% offset, using E = 16,000,000.

† "T" is the ratio of pin radius to thickness of sheet. Tests made using 3D + ⅛" span, as per ASM Handbook, 1948 edition, page 124.

Zirconium Wire. Annealed, hot-rolled zirconium rods are readily cold-drawn to the form of wire, raising their strength to more

Table 2. Results of Tensile and Bend Tests on Zirconium Wire (29)

Wire Diameter (Inches)	Tensile Strength (psi)	Per Cent Elongation in 2 Inches	Per Cent Reduction of Area	BENDS AT ROOM TEMPERATURE	
				Smallest bend radius in terms of wire diameter	Number of 90° bends required for fracture
Cold drawn wire:					
0.060	103,500	3.7	.....	.....	.....
0.030	96,800	2.8	.....	.....	.....
0.015	109,000	1.0	.....	.....	.....
Wire annealed one hour at 1400° F. in argon:					
0.060	74,900	19.2	24.6	0.9T	4
0.030	83,000	13.8	26.0	0.9T	5
0.015	79,800	11.5	22.3	1 T	4

than 100,000 psi. Some properties of cold-drawn and annealed wires
of various diameters are presented in Table 2.

Notched-Bar Impact Resistance of Zirconium. The notch sensitivity or impact resistance of zirconinum for both 45° V and standard keyhole notches has been determined by Charpy test at room
temperature on hot-rolled and annealed (1,300° F. in air) bar stock.
The results of these tests are assembled in Table 3.

**Table 3. Results of Hardness and Charpy Impact Tests
on Hot-Rolled Zirconium Bars (29)**

Standard ASTM specimens with 45° V-notch 2 mm. deep, tested in
duplicate with 20 Kg.-M blow.

	TESTED AS ROLLED		ANNEALED AT 1309° F.	
Diameter of Rolled Bar (Inches)	Rockwell "A" Hardness	Impact Resistance Feet-Pounds Fracture	Rockwell "A" Hardness	Impact Resistance Feet-Pounds Fracture
1⅜	59.0–58.9	3.25 irregular	58.0–57.4	2.53–3.89 straight
1	61.0–59.6	3.88–4.34 45°	55.7–56.8	5.42–6.15 45°
¾	60.9–61.3	1.18–1.45 straight	59.1–59.6	2.17–1.81 straight

Standard ASTM specimens with keyhole notch of 2 mm. max.,
diameter 5mm. deep, tested in duplicate with 20 Kg.-M blow.

1⅜	57.0–56.5	2.89–2.89 straight	55.5–55.9	3.62–2.89 straight
1	58.5–56.7	2.53–2.53 irregular	54.7–54.3	3.26–3.62 irregular
¾	60.0–60.5	2.16–2.16 straight	58.9–58.8	2.53–2.16 straight

Impact tests on zirconium metal have been made at elevated
temperatures, using V-notch Charpy specimens. The following results indicate that a transition from brittle to ductile fracture takes
place on heating commercial zirconium metal in the vicinity of
900° F., where the impact value sharply increases from less than 15
foot-pounds at 800° F. to more than 40 foot-pounds at 1000° F.

Temperature		
Fahrenheit	Centigrade	Foot-Pounds
80	27	3.0
400	204	3.6
600	315	8.7
800	428	14.5
1,000	538	43.4

It is possible that by special heat treatment combined with vacuum annealing, according to a paper presented by W. L. Mudge, Jr., at the 1953 Western Metal Congress, the transition temperature might be lowered, or the transition on cooling eliminated, so that the notched-bar impact values would be higher at room temperature.

Fire Precautions. Solid massive zirconium is not dangerous to handle. It will not burn when forged or rolled at red heat, and can be machined as safely as stainless steel. Turnings or chips of ordinary size can be handled in air with complete safety, but very fine turnings will sometimes ignite and burn slowly with an intense white light and considerable heat. When either powder, sponge, or turnings start to burn, the fire should be extinguished only by smothering with dry sand, salt, or inert oxides such as titanium oxide or zirconium oxide. Carbon tetrachloride or carbon dioxide should not be used because they may cause explosions and more violent burning.

Zirconium powder in air is both pyrophoric (ignitable in air) and explosive, even when damp. Extreme caution should be exercised, when handling the dry powder, for friction, static electricity, or any form of heat concentration will cause the dry powder to ignite. Handling dry zirconium powder should, therefore, be done only in small isolated batches. In storing or shipping, zirconium powder should always be kept under water. Milling or screening should never be done dry. Carbon tetrachloride is a better protective liquid than water for fine milling. Drying must be done with extreme care. Drying is preferably done in air at room temperature, followed by warming to not more than 220° F.

Health Hazards. There has been no known reaction from the handling of zirconium metal. In fact, zirconium chemicals are used in medicinal salves.

Precision Casting. Zirconium metal cannot be melted and cast by ordinary methods because of its reactivity with the atmosphere and with refractories when molten. The purity of zirconium may be maintained in the molten state through melting in a closed, water-cooled copper vessel, either evacuated or filled with helium or argon. It does not wet the water-cooled copper. A method of melting in such a furnace, and pouring into an attached mold without contact

with air, was developed recently by W. E. Kuhn in the laboratories
of the Zirconium Metals Corporation. This development work has
shown that castings up to at least several pounds in weight can be
made with a large enough furnace, so that either molds or refractory
investment molds (a process wherein molds are made by surrounding a wax pattern with a refractory ceramic material, producing
molds which will sustain high temperatures) can be used. The
fluidity of zirconium metal melted by an arc in this way is sufficient
to enable rods 3″ long and only 5/32″ in diameter to be cast without
defects. Intricate castings which produce the patterns precisely in
size and detail can be obtained through the use of investment molds
of zirconia cements.

INDIUM. Indium was discovered in 1863 by Reich and Richter.
They were seeking thallium, which they discovered two years before, and, while examining a sphalerite (zinc sulphide) ore from
Freiberg in Saxony with a spectroscope, they observed prominent
indigo blue lines which had never been noted before. They identified it by the lines and named it indium because of them. It was
first believed to be a rare element, but indium, it was later learned,
is available in considerable quantities in many sections of the world.

Indium is generally found in zinc blends. There are indications
that it is found in a number of other ores, but the quantity of indium
present in all ores will vary considerably. In most ores its extraction is economically impractical. In recent years, ore has been
found in which indium occurs in greater quantities than ever before
known, changing the status of indium from a rare metal to one of
commercial importance. Indium may be extracted and purified in
many ways; treatment of indium chloride with ether precipitation
by boiling with hydroscopic sulphite; treatment of indium and tin
sulfates with hydrogen sulphide; separation of indium from tin with
sodium hydroxide; solubilization of indium in an acid solution with
sodium sulphate; treatment of indium-bearing lead or lead alloys
with sodium hydroxide and sodium chloride; treatment of leady-
residues from zinc ore smelting with sulphuric acid to form a cal-
cine; separation of indium and gallium by electrolysis, and precipitation of indium as orthophosphates.

The first patent ever issued in extraction of indium was granted to Dr. William S. Murray and his associates for work done in 1926. They worked with a complex ore containing lead, zinc, iron, copper, silver, gold, and indium. Separation of the concentrates from the gangue (waste) was made by grinding and treatment by flotation process. Concentrates of zinc and lead-silver were obtained. Indium was found in the zinc concentrate. The zinc concentrate was roasted in the presence of sodium chloride in the first refining process. Since it was found that indium chloride will fume at roasting temperature, a Conttrell precipitator was used to catch these fumes. The fumes were dissolved and the indium plated out.

Today the zinc concentrate is roasted, and the soluble portion is dissolved in sulphuric acid. From this solution indium is plated out or thrown out by neutralization of the acid. Indium from this process is again dissolved, purified, and plated out. The new process produces indium of more than 99% purity.

Physical Properties of Indium. Indium, which resembles tin, is a soft, white metal with a bluish tinge. It is ductile, malleable, softer than lead, crystalline, and diamagnetic. It appears between iron and tin in the electromotive series.

Indium does not react with water, even at boiling temperature. It will not combine with the gases in the air at normal temperatures but, when heated, it burns with a nonluminous, blue-red flame, producing indium oxide. Up to its melting point, the surface of indium remains bright but, at higher temperatures, a film of oxide appears. Indium readily combines with organic compounds which can be easily oxidized or combined chemically with water.

Indium has an atomic weight of 114.8. It is face-centered tetragonal crystal lattice in structure, very malleable and ductile, and has an approximate tensile strength of 15,980 psi. It melts at 311° F. and boils at 2642° F.

Uses of Indium. One major development in the use of indium has been the coating of metallic surfaces with indium, diffused into the base metal. This extensively prolongs the life of these moving parts by reducing friction and wear. The thicker the film of indium is, the more resistant the surface is to wear. Indium has a low coefficient of friction and over a wide range of temperatures, is slippery and changes its viscosity very slightly.

A recent development in indium's use is the combining of indium and graphite for lubrication and wear reduction, in moving parts for internal combustion engines, engine accessories, etc. The combination also reduces erosion and corrosion for electrical products.

Alloys of Indium. The addition of small quantities of indium hardens and strengthens the metal with which it is alloyed, increasing its tarnish or corrosion resistance.

Aluminum-Indium. It was found by W. H. Frankel of American Smelting and Refining Company that small amounts of indium have an influence on the age hardenability of these alloys. Additions of 0.1% of indium retard the age-hardening of duralumin, but increase both the rate and amount of hardening of 4% copper-aluminum alloys, from which magnesium is absent.

Beryllium-Copper-Indium. The addition of indium to beryllium copper alloys increases their hardness and tensile strength and lowers their melting and heat-treatment temperatures. The presence of indium increases the fluidity of the alloy.

Cadmium and indium dissolve completely in each other in the molten state in all proportions. A eutectic is formed at 75% indium and 25% cadmium with a melting point of 252.5° F. These alloys are used in the production of surfaces which are subjected to friction.

The addition of indium to gold provides sounder dental castings. Indium is softer than lead, more lustrous than silver, and as untarnishable as gold. Used as a deoxidizer and cleanser, it increases tensile strength 14% and ductility 24%.

Gold-indium alloys have some unique characteristics for brazing. The alloys of 77½% gold and 22½% indium have a working temperature of a little above 932° F. This is an ideal temperature for work on metal objects with glass inserts, since temperatures above 1112° F. are destructive to glass-metal seals, while temperatures of 932° F. must be endured, and indium prevents unwanted contamination of adjacent parts.

Lead-indium alloys are used widely in bearings and in solders. The addition of 1.0% of indium to lead doubles the hardness of the lead. The addition of indium to silver tends to limit tarnishing.

Low Melting Alloys with Indium. The earliest work on new, low-melting alloys was done by Dr. Sydney J. French in 1935. In 1938, Dr. French determined that the addition of indium to Wood's or Lipowitz Metal caused its melting point to drop approximately 1.45° for every 1% indium present. The lowest melting point reached was 47°, with an alloy containing 18% indium. The presence of indium decreases the tendency of such alloys to oxidize in the molten state. Recent development of low-melting solders available commercially today are based on these facts. These solders possess superior bonding power, better wetting characteristics, and superior corrosion resistance.

Bearing Alloys. The aviation industries were the first to recognize the value of indium-treated bearings. The Indium Corporation of America produced the first indium-treated aviation bearings.

Aviation bearings must be nearly faultless. Indium bearings have not been excelled in meeting the demands presented by high oil temperatures, generation of acid in oil, heavy loads, and the necessity of high wettability in aviation engines. Silver-lead indium bearings are the most widely used aviation bearings today.

Each of the three components of the silver-lead indium type bearing has a service to perform. Silver has the internal properties which resist failure due to fatigue but, externally, silver lacks the quality of "oiliness" needed in a good bearing surface. To fill this requirement, a thin layer of lead is applied to the silver surface. Lead, unfortunately, is soluble in the organic acids present or formed in lubricating oils. To offset this difficulty, a thin layer of indium is deposited on and diffused into the layer of lead. The addition of indium to the bearing surface accomplishes the following things: it increases the strength of the bearing material; it prevents corrosion of the bearing surface without impairing the fatigue resistance or other bearing properties; it increases bearing wettability, and thus permits the bearing surface to retain its oil film more completely.

It was felt a few years ago that, if a bearing would stand 200 hours of operation, it was a good bearing. Today indium-treated bearings are expected to last as long as the engine.

In 1938, C. F. Smart, of the Pontiac Division of General Motors

Corporation, presented Technical Paper No. 900 before a meeting of the American Institute of Mining and Metallurgical Engineers. In his paper Mr. Smart included comparative tests by one of the major oil companies. A quotation from Mr. Smart's conclusions for engine tests on plated bearings follows:

> In one engine test, connecting rod bearings lined with Cd-Ag-Cu [cadmium-silver-copper] alloy, treated with approximately 0.20% In [indium], were run for over 5,000 miles at high speed. At the conclusion of the test these bearings showed only slight evidence of etching, whereas the untreated bearings run in one of the connecting rods were replaced three times because of their badly corroded condition. The acid number of the oil used reached a value of 3.3.
>
> In another engine the fatigue life of babbitt-lined bearings ranged up to a maximum of about 60 hours, under the severe conditions used for testing (4,250 rpm, full throttle, with oil temperatures 250° to 260° F. at the bearings). Cd-Ag-Cu bearings treated with 0.4 to 0.5% indium run under these test conditions, and in the presence of oil containing 0.5% of oleic acid, were in excellent condition after 120 hours, showing no evidence of corrosion and only a very slight indication of fatigue cracks.
>
> Such tests on bearings, in engines run at high speed and with corrosive oils, verify the information obtained at laboratory tests—namely, that the indium treatments as described prevent corrosion of the Cd alloy bearings without impairing the fatigue resistance or other bearing metal properties.

One bearing manufacturer tested indium-treated copper-lead bearings against the present micro-babbitt type bearings for automobiles. Operating under a load of 6,500 psi, twice that of the micro-babbitt bearings, copper-lead-indium bearings ran for 500 hours as compared with 30 hours for the micro-babbitt bearings.

Indium-treated bearings in one instance gave 50 hours use under pressures from 10,000 to 15,000 psi, where previous bearings were destroyed after 10 hours.

Other examples are many and from varied sources, but the results all remain the same, i.e., indium treatment materially improves all bearing surfaces.

Brazing Alloys. There are two distinct classes of brazing alloys or solders. Several solders are available which have relatively low melting points (below 600° or 700° F.), but there is a very great need for a brazing alloy with good flowability and strength for heat ranges between 700° and 1100° F. Since indium melts at 311° F., and since it alloys very readily with copper, silver, and other elements, several alloys, using indium, have been produced which melt at from 795° to 965° F. Because indium adds greater wettability to brazing materials and, in larger proportions, greater strength, it becomes a very desirable constituent of some of the conventional brazing materials.

VANADIUM AND VANADIUM ALLOYS. Vanadium is one of the more important elements used in alloy with steel. The element was discovered in a Mexican ore in 1801 by Del Rio. In 1830, Sefstrom rediscovered it in Swedish iron ore and named it vanadium. The pure metal was first isolated in 1867 by Roscoe. It occurs in the mineral vanadite and in iron ores, fire clay, and granite. The richest known vanadium deposit is in Minasraga, Peru. It is difficult to produce pure vanadium, and only small amounts are produced commercially. Two methods of vanadium production often used are the reduction of vanadium dichloride with hydrogen, and the electrolysis of vanadium trioxide in fused calcium vanadate.

Vanadium is a hard, silvery-white metal but, if heated to a suitable temperature, it is sufficiently tough and malleable to be hammered and rolled into rods or drawn into wire. It can be highly polished and will not tarnish when exposed to air. The physical properties of vanadium are as follows: melting point, 3110° F.; boiling point, 5432° F.; density, 5.68 grams per cc, and electrical resistivity, 26 microhms.

Vanadium has a more powerful effect upon the properties of steel than any other element except carbon. Comparatively small amounts of it are necessary. The best results are obtained from 0.1% to 0.2% of the vanadium alloy, but if more than 0.3% is used, strength is greatly decreased. From 0.1% to 0.15% vanadium increases the tensile strength of low and medium carbon steels about 50%, with no decrease in ductility. The tensile strength of steel, with about 0.2% vanadium and 0.8% carbon, is not changed by the vanadium, but the elastic limit and ductility are increased.

Vanadium produces a very small grain size in steel. Grain-size reduction and its control by the use of vanadium are major aids in approaching perfection in steel making. The grain structure of vanadium steels can be slightly coarsened to the extent of insuring ease of machining and smoothness of the machined surface. The reheating temperature for steels of any composition is established by their vanadium content, and reheating can be accomplished at the moderate temperatures readily obtained in industrial heat-treatment furnaces. Grain structure coarseness is neither very high nor is it irregular from melt to melt. Vanadium steels return to their fine-grained condition on reheating to the temperatures customarily employed for annealing, normalizing, quenching, etc.

The fineness of structure in vanadium steels extends to the distribution of the carbide. Even in extremely low melting steels, the primary carbide is affected and more uniformly distributed in smaller particles. This is true even in steels with large amounts of free carbides. This consistent and great reduction of grain size, and subdivision of structure within the grains, are naturally reflected in many of the mechanical properties of the steel, principally in an increase in yield point and yield ratio, with a simultaneous improvement in ductility and toughness.

There is a very distinct and useful effect in the behavior of vanadium steels upon quenching. Carbon-vanadium steels, quenched from customary heat-treatment temperatures (just high enough to secure maximum surface hardness), are shallow hardening. If a carbon steel and a vanadium steel are both quenched from the same temperature, they will both have the same surface hardness, but the vanadium steel will possess lower core hardness and a much thinner, fully hardened outer layer. The grain size of the vanadium steel at 1800° F. is the same as that of the carbon steel at 1500° F., and vanadium steel coarsens slowly. The phenomena described are largely the result of fine grain size which effects more rapid transformation upon cooling and thus causes greater difficulty in the retention of hard martensite. Increase in the hardening temperature slowly increases grain size in the vanadium steel and, because of this, as well as the action of the solution of additional vanadium-rich carbides that render the matrix less rapid in its reactions, depth of hardening increases.

Observations such as these have led investigators to the conclusion that the carbides are alone responsible for the grain characteristics of vanadium steels, that is:

Vanadium-rich carbides are relatively stable and dissolve somewhat more slowly than iron carbide even at temperatures well above those usually employed in heat treatment.

At any temperature at which part of these carbides remain undissolved, they inhibit grain growth or serve on cooling as points of initial crystallization; thus they maintain fine grain size.

When temperature and time are sufficient for the carbides to become largely dissolved, the grain coarsens.

Iron and vanadium are mutually soluble in all proportions. Only up to about 1.0% vanadium content, however, are the carbon-free alloys hardenable. Beyond this amount gamma iron does not exist at any temperature and, hence, martensite, on which the hardness of quenched steels depends, cannot be formed. The introduction of carbon increases the range of compositions in which martensite is possible, so that with 1.0% carbon, for example, some degree of hardening may be obtained with slightly more than 6.0% vanadium in the steel.

When vanadium is added to carbon steels, it has a strong affinity for carbon, forming vanadium carbide. These carbides are very stable. To secure maximum hardening of vanadium steels, the carbides must go into solution. Hardening depends upon composition and heating conditions insofar as they influence the amount of carbon in solution, the amount of carbon as vanadium carbide remaining undissolved, and the formation of gamma iron as limited by the amount of dissolved carbon and vanadium.

Quenching temperatures that cause little or no vanadium carbides to enter into solution secure the maximum benefit from the grain-refining power of vanadium and produce exceptional combinations of useful strength and toughness. However, increased depth of hardness, on tempering at relatively high temperatures, may be obtained through the use of quenching temperatures high enough to partially dissolve the vanadium carbides present in the steel, yet insufficient in temperature or time to result in appreciable grain growth.

Carbon vanadium steel is the most commonly used steel except for tool steels. Most frequently it is used in large forgings, but the uses of small sections are increasing in number. The superior mechanical properties of carbon-vanadium steel, coupled with its fine machining qualities in the normalizing state, and its low degree of distortion, are responsible for this use.

In many instances, carbon-vanadium steel is tempered after normalizing, in which case the following heat treatment is generally used: Normalizing-heat at 1600° to 1650° F.; cool in still air. Tempering-heat of 1100° to 1200° F.; cool in still air or furnace.

The addition of 0.15% vanadium to plain carbon steel of this type raises the strength and load-sustaining capacities at higher temperatures.

Carbon-vanadium steel has also been made in the 0.30% to 0.35% carbon range for use in small shafts, arms, connecting rods, and other machine parts subject to impact loading. These parts are normally quenched and tempered. The use of very mild alloy steel of this type in carburized gears is possible where (1) a moderately high core hardness is needed to support the case and prevent fatigue failure by repeated deflection; (2) uniformity of case depth and of hardening of both case and core is vitally important; and (3) moderate impact strength of the carburized tooth are required.

The manufacture and use of rolled or forged steel in large sections present considerably different problems from those encountered in manufacture of small masses. The dangers of internal ruptures, insufficient hardening, and sharp hardness gradients in the finished product necessitate uniform and not too rapid heating, time to insure total diffusion for hot working and heat treatment temperatures, uniform temperature gradients in cooling, and magnitude and time of occurrence of volume changes in the transformation range in different locations in the mass. In some instances, where smaller masses are concerned, any one of many compositions might satisfy manufacturing and design requirements.

In heavier masses, the above indicated sensitivity to fabrication processes limits to a much smaller number the selection of steels suitable for a particular set of ultimate properties. This sensitiveness to steep temperature gradients, i.e., rapid cooling, often prevents the development of a desired hardness by a quenching and tempering practice.

Some forgings of moderately large section may be quenched and tempered and provide, in this hardened condition, very satisfactory service. When properties that appear to demand such treatment are called for, special consideration must be given to all pertinent details, such as composition, size, manufacturing practice, and the nature of the service.

Vanadium steel forgings have supplied heavy industrial needs for many years. Carbon-vanadium steel appeared early in the century, at the beginning of commercial vanadium history. It extended rapidly to the construction of locomotives and heavy machinery, where it still retains a preeminent position. The demand of recent years for a steel of the hardness and wear resistance of the carbon-vanadium type, with materially increased ductility and impact strength, led to the production of manganese-vanadium steel for forgings. Still more recently, a chromium-molybdenum-vanadium steel was introduced for large sections in which full penetration of high hardness and commensurately high resistance to sudden loading are required. A vanadium-molybdenum-manganese steel has been produced which has a high elastic limit, ductility, and impact strength without liquid quenching.

Vanadium Cast Steels. The tremendous growth in the size and power of heavy machinery such as that used in the fabricating industries, mining, and transportation presents the foundryman with the job of producing not only sound castings of greater size and thinner sections but articles of greater complexity and ability to sustain both static and dynamic loads.

Vanadium is among those elements whose widened use is a result of this growing appreciation of alloy cast steels. The incorporation of vanadium into the composition of steel castings results in a vast improvement of their properties. Steel castings containing vanadium have a higher elastic ratio than castings without vanadium but of otherwise like composition and heat treatment. At the same time, they possess at least equal ductility in tension and a considerably higher impact strength and wear resistance. Their grain size is markedly smaller and more uniform, while grain growth at heat-treatment temperatures is decidedly retarded.

Other components of the composition being the same, and the details of steel-making, pouring, etc., almost constant, a vanadium-containing steel will exhibit less marked dendritic segregation and greater freedom from Widmanstatten patterns within the grains than a vanadium-free steel before heat treatment.

Without advocating the use of unheat-treated alloy steel castings, it is clear that, for equal hardness and strength, the vanadium steel, with its superior distribution of microconstituents, possesses

Fig. 4. Photomicrograph of 0.50% Carbon Steel, Air-Cooled at 1800° F., Magnified 100 Times; Note Coarse Grain Structure

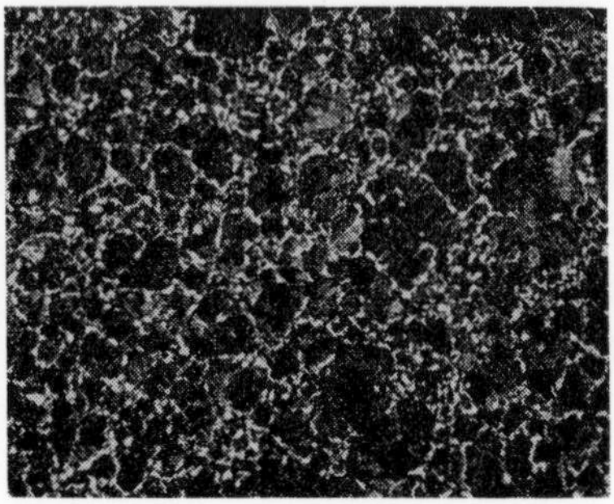

Fig. 5. Same as Fig. 4, with 0.27% Vanadium Content. Note Effect of Vanadium in Reducing the Grain Structure of the Steel

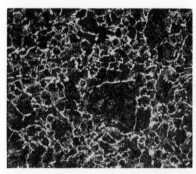

Fig. 6. Photomicrograph of 0.50% Carbon Steel, Air-Cooled at 1500° F., Magnified 100 Times; Note Coarse Grain Structure

Fig. 7. Same as Fig. 5, with 0.27% Vanadium Content; Note Effect of Vanadium in Reducing the Size of Grain Structure of the Steel

Courtesy Vanadium Corporation of America

greater ability to sustain stress or to deform rather than rupture under suddenly applied overloads. These characteristics are extremely important in avoiding the cracking of intricate castings during heating and cooling cycles in the early stages of manufacture.

Table 4. Tension and Impact Tests of Cast Alloy Steels Double Normalized and Tempered

Type	Typical Chemical Composition							Yield Point (lb. per sq. in.)	Tensile Strength (lb. per sq. in.)	Elongation (per cent in 2 in.)	Reduction of Area (per cent)	Izod Value (foot-pounds)
	C	Si	Mn	Ni	Cr	Mo	V					
Mn (a)	0.35	0.40	1.40	…	…	…	…	60,850	102,650	27.5	58.8	25.8
Mn-V (a)	0.35	0.40	1.40	…	…	…	0.10	74,500	100,700	30.5	61.8	57.5
Mn (b)	0.35	0.40	1.40	…	…	…	…	67,500	108,500	25.9	54.5	19.5
Mn-V (b)	0.35	0.40	1.40	…	…	…	0.10	77,700	103,300	27.5	57.6	52.8
Mn-Mo (a)	0.35	0.40	1.50	…	…	0.15	…	69,800	114,050	21.0	41.6	18.8
Mn-Mo-V (a)	0.35	0.40	1.50	…	…	0.15	0.10	76,050	118,650	23.0	39.1	30.5
Cr (a)	0.30	0.40	0.80	…	1.00	…	…	60,400	94,500	27.5	54.7	28.3
Cr-V (a)	0.30	0.40	0.80	…	1.00	…	0.10	64,850	94,300	27.5	57.1	59.3
Cr-Mo (a)	0.30	0.30	0.50	…	1.00	0.15	…	53,800	90,900	28.0	58.4	28.5
Cr-Mo-V (a)	0.30	0.30	0.50	…	1.00	0.15	0.10	62,800	88,800	31.0	61.5	52.3
Ni-Cr (a)	0.30	0.40	0.60	1.30	0.50	…	…	61,850	92,900	27.0	54.4	48.0
Mi-Cr-V (a)	0.30	0.40	0.60	1.30	0.50	…	0.10	69,650	94,500	28.5	55.8	71.3
Ni (a)	0.28	0.35	1.00	1.50	…	…	…	53,450	93,250	27.0	56.6	35.5
Ni-V (a)	0.28	0.35	1.00	1.50	…	…	0.10	69,900	91,200	28.5	59.4	74.3

Experimental induction furnace melts.   Average of several commercial open-hearth melts heat-treated in small furnaces.

The structure of the vanadium-containing steel exerts considerable influence upon ease of diffusion of the several constituents at heat-treatment temperatures. It also unquestionably bears a relation to the response of vanadium steels to simple heat treatment. Mechanical properties may be obtained by double normalizing and tempering that are not equaled even by the more drastic and often dangerous liquid quenching and tempering of many other alloy steels. This is of great importance in large complex castings. New uses of high-strength cast steels are available through suitable adjustment of composition, combined with even single normalizing and tempering, or through single normalizing alone.

The macrostructural advantage of vanadium steels, i.e., less marked dendritic formations, persists after heat treatment. Microstructurally, equally sharp distinctions between vanadium-containing and vanadium-free steels develop, causing or accompanied by pronounced differences in the mechanical properties.

Table 4 illustrates the influence of small amounts of vanadium upon the tension and impact values of some normalized alloy steels. The simultaneous increase in both yield point and resistance to impact is consistent with the magnitude of the changes that result from the incorporation of vanadium. No appreciable alteration of tensile strength, elongation, or reduction of area accompanies these increases. The ability to support high static loads and suddenly applied overloads without rupture, shown in these comparative tests, is responsible for numerous and diverse engineering applications. Of the several vanadium cast steels now in regular production, carbon-vanadium cast steel was the earliest produced commercially. The ASTM tentative specification for physical properties requires the following minimum values for normalized and tempered castings: yield point, 55,000 psi; tensile strength, 85,000 psi; elongation in 2″, 22%; and reduction of area, 42%.

Representative values obtained from such normalized and tempered carbon-vanadium steel of about 0.35% carbon are shown in Table 5.

The usual heat treatment employed for the development of these properties consists of normalizing at 1600° to 1650° F. and tempering at 1050° to 1200° F. In the case where double normalizing is employed, the temperatures approximate 1775° to 1850° F. and 1575° to 1625° F.

Chromium-Vanadium Steels. Table 6 shows the chromium vanadium steels which have enjoyed popularity for many years.

Lower carbon grades of chromium-vanadium steels are frequently used in the case-carburized condition. Those of intermediate carbon content are quenched and tempered to various hard-

Table 5. Mechanical Properties of Carbon-Vanadium Cast Steel

Yield Point (psi)	Tensile Strength (psi)	Elongation (per cent in 2 inches)	Reduction Area (per cent)	Izod Value (foot-pounds)
59,900	93,800	23.5	46.3	29.0
55,800	91,000	25.0	44.9	30.8
63,000	90,000	25.0	42.0	35.0*
62,300	93,400	24.5	47.8	20.8

* Double normalized and tempered.

Table 6. Chromium-Vanadium Steels of the 6100 Series, Society of Automotive Engineers

Steel No.	Carbon Range	Manganese Range	Phosphorus, Max.	Sulphur, Max.	Chromium Range	Vanadium	
						Min.	Desired
6115	0.10–0.20	0.30–0.60	0.40	0.045	0.80–1.10	0.15	0.18
6120	0.15–0.25	0.30–0.60	0.40	0.045	0.80–1.10	0.15	0.18
6125	0.20–0.30	0.50–0.80	0.40	0.045	0.80–1.10	0.15	0.18
6130	0.25–0.35	0.50–0.80	0.40	0.045	0.80–1.10	0.15	0.18
6135	0.30–0.40	0.50–0.80	0.40	0.045	0.80–1.10	0.15	0.18
6140	0.35–0.45	0.50–0.80	0.40	0.045	0.80–1.10	0.15	0.18
6145	0.40–0.50	0.50–0.80	0.40	0.045	0.80–1.10	0.15	0.18
6150	0.45–0.55	0.50–0.80	0.40	0.045	0.80–1.10	0.15	0.18
6195	0.90–1.05	0.20–0.45	0.30	0.035	0.80–1.10	0.15	0.18

nesses for axles, shafts, gears, springs, etc., while the very high-carbon steels serve for tools, ball and roller bearings, wearing plates, and other fully hardened parts.

Low-carbon chromium-vanadium steels, of the types represented by SAE 6115 and 6120, are used for case-carburized parts, such as automobile and aircraft engine gears, camshafts, and piston pins (see Fig. 8). They give a hard, tough, and strong case of high wear-resistance. The low rate of drop in the carbon content as the core is approached causes case and core to be strongly bound together so that there is little tendency to flaking, powdering, or flowing under pressure.

The usual heat-treatment procedure designed to give the very best properties is as follows: carburize at 1650° to 1700° F. and cool in the pots; oil quench from 1600° to 1650° F., water quench from 1450° to 1475° F., and temper at 375° to 425° F.

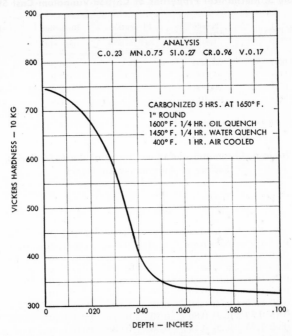

Fig. 8. Depth of Hardness Characteristics of Vanadium-Chromium Steel, SAE 6120

While this treatment is the optimum one for both case and core, many purposes are served by a single oil quench, which is carried out after reheating to 1625° F. This heat treatment, followed by tempering for stress relief, is the customary one for small automotive pinions. Chromium-vanadium steels are more applicable to single quenching than many of the other alloy steels, because of their fine grain in case and core, even after the higher temperature necessary for single quenching operation. Tempering may be employed after single quenching.

Typical tension and impact properties in the core of case-hardened parts (one inch diameter) of these low-carbon chromium-vanadium steels are given in Table 7.

**Table 7. Tension and Impact Tests of the Core
of Carburized Chromium-Vanadium Steel
(C—0.19. MN—0.68. Si—0.18. Cr—0.83. V—0.15)**

Heat Treatment (deg. F.)	Yield Point (lb. per sq. in.)	Tensile Strength (lb. per sq. in.)	Elongation (per cent in 2 in.)	Reduction of Area (per cent)	Izod Value (ft.–lb.)
Carburized 1675 (16 hr.)					
Pot Q. oil; 1520 oil; 350 air	70,700	114,300	25.0	53.6	54.5
Pot cool; 1520 water; 350 air	95,450	137,950	17.0	38.0	21.3
Pot cool; 1660 oil; 1520 oil; 350 air	62,350	111,100	25.0	52.8	57.5
Pot cool; 1540 oil; 350 air	60,450	109,150	24.0	50.8	37.0

The fabrication of welded pressure vessels is another application of chromium-vanadium steel of the SAE 6115, 6120, and 6125 ranges. They are generally arc-welded with heavily flux-coated chromium-vanadium electrodes. Most of these vessels are only tempered after welding for stress-relieving purposes, but some are fully annealed.

Steels 6120 and 6125 respond to cyanide hardening and are used for gears, bolts, washers, small stampings, and forgings. The nitrides formed are extremely fine, and there is no tendency to develop the undesirable, coarse, acicular (needle-shaped) structure, thus insuring case toughness and resistance to spalling (chipping). The transition from the hard surface to the core is gradual and, even in long-time cyaniding, there is no danger of embrittlement of the core.

Chromium-vanadium steel in the SAE 6120 and 6125 carbon ranges is also used in boiler construction, superheater tubes, tubing for the chemical industry, bolts, and pressure vessels and welding rods.

Manganese-vanadium steel combines in large masses, in the normalized and tempered condition, the properties of high strength or hardness with excellent ductility and impact resistance.

The specifications for tensile properties of normalized and tempered forgings are generally as follows:

Size	Yield Point (lbs. per sq. in.)	Tensile Strength (lbs. per sq. in.)	Elongation (per cent in 2 in.)	Reduction Area (per cent)
Up to 15 in. dia. or thickness	60,000	90,000	25	50

Typical values obtained on forgings made to this specification are shown in Table 8.

Table 8. Typical Values of the Specifications of Normalized Tempered Forgings

Part	Diameter of Thickness (in.)	Heat Treatment (deg. F.)	Yield Point (lb. per sq. in.)	Tensile Strength (lb. per sq. in.)	Elongation (per cent in 2 in.)	Reduction of Area (per cent)	Izod Value (ft.–lb.)
Billet (center)	4 × 4	1575 air	66,500	98,450	25.0	58.3	60
Billet (edge)	4 × 4	1575 air	77,400	102,150	25.5	58.6	68
Billet (center)	4 × 4	1575 air, 1050 air	76,550	96,600	29.0	63.0	55
Billet (edge)	4 × 4	1575 air, 1050 air	77,250	100,150	28.0	64.2	58
Rod (edge)	6	1600 air	78,250	102,450	25.0	54.9	36
Rod (center)	6	1600 air, 1000 air	71,350	97,400	26.0	57.3	49
Rod (edge)	6	1600 air, 1000 air	79,700	102,700	26.0	59.1	39
Crank Pin (midway)	10	1625 air	67,800	93,375	26.0	50.8	39
Crank Pin (midway)	10	1625 air, 1000 air	64,300	93,250	25.0	58.6	39
Axle (midway)	13	1615 air, 1160 air	75,500	96,400	26.0	57.8	38
Axle (midway)	13½	1600 air	64,500	95,050	25.0	56.0	66
Axle (edge)	13½	1600 air	73,700	94,850	28.0	57.3	63
Axle (midway)	13½	1600 air, 1200 air	66,250	91,000	32.0	67.5	73
Axle (edge)	13½	1600 air, 1200 air	71,250	91,250	30.0	68.4	71
Axle (midway)	14	1625 air	63,700	93,275	25.0	50.5	71
Axle (midway)	14	1625 air, 1000 air	64,000	94,000	25.0	56.0	71
Axle (midway)	14	1625 air, 1000 air	64,000	91,350	25.5	57.3	71

Some other vanadium alloy steels to meet special needs are as follows:

Chromium-Molybdenum-Vanadium steel was developed to meet the need for a steel capable of developing a uniform high hardness throughout moderately large sections and at the same time commensurately high ductility and impact strength.

Nickel-Chromium-Molybdenum-Vanadium steel produces quenched and tempered forgings of moderately large section and high strength. This composition has the advantage of low-carbon content which is possible in view of the high total alloy content.

Manganese-Molybdenum-Vanadium steels have high yield point in moderately large sections that have been given only a normalizing and tempering treatment.

Other major uses of vanadium are in the manufacture of spring steels, cast steels, cast irons, and the making of fine high-grade tool steels.

Vanadium Cast Iron. Vanadium has been added to irons for more than 20 years. Its beneficial effects were first utilized shortly following the introduction of vanadium alloy steel. Recently renewed interest in the properties of vanadium cast irons has brought a new demand for vanadium iron to meet the most severe requirements. Vanadium is used in cast iron except where resistance to structural decomposition at elevated temperatures, or uniformity of hardness and strength throughout a heavy section, is the single characteristic of importance. There is a complexity in cast-iron metallurgy caused by the existence of carbon in two distinct forms, the manner in which these forms change from one to the other, and the influence of raw materials and manufacturing methods upon carbon behavior.

QUIZ QUESTIONS

1. *In what ways is winning titanium from its ore different from winning other metals from their ores?*

2. *What effects do contaminants have upon the physical properties of titanium? Contrast these effects with the effects of contaminants upon other metals.*

3. *What are the effects of oxygen, nitrogen, and water and what means must be taken to eliminate them while producing titanium?*

4. *Discuss the various properties of titanium.*

5. *Describe the Van Arkel–de Boer process for refining zirconium.*

6. *What are the directional properties of zirconium sheet?*

7. *Describe the precautions necessary in the handling of zirconium powder, sponge, and turnings.*

8. *What properties does indium impart to alloys?*

9. *Why is indium used as an ingredient of solders and brazing alloys?*

10. *Why is indium used in bearing metals?*

11. *What does vanadium do to the grain structure of steel?*

12. *How is depth of hardness obtained in vanadium steels?*

13. *What precautions should be taken to avoid insufficient hardening and sharp hardness gradients in vanadium steels?*

14. *What are the limitations of vanadium cast irons?*

THE LITERATURE OF METALLURGY

For metallurgy, as well as for other engineering subjects, books are available which deal with more or less specialized portions of the subject. These books range from those dealing with its practical application, to those dealing with its theoretical aspects and requiring an understanding of the fundamentals of physics and chemistry. Not only are metallurgical books available, but also the publications of technical societies interested in metallurgy. Various metallurgical journals contain accounts of recent advances in metallurgical technique and theory. Metallurgy is a rapidly expanding science and the average man engaged in making, shaping or treating the metals finds it difficult to keep abreast of the times. In the following lists, some of the more important literature on metallurgical subjects is given.

General Metallurgy and Metallography

1. *Impurities in Metals*, Smithells, 1930.
2. *Introduction to Physical Metallurgy*, Rosenhain and Haughton, 1930.
3. *The Metallic State*, Hume Rothery, 1931.
4. *Metallographic Researches*, Benedicks, 1926.
5. *Metallography*, Desch, 1922.
6. *National Metals Handbook*, 1936, 1939.
7. *Practical Microscopic Metallography*, Greaves and Wrighton, 1933.
8. *Principles of Physical Metallurgy*, Doan and Mahla, 1941.
9. *Principles of Metallography*, Williams and Homerberg, 1935, 1939.
10. *Metallurgy of Copper*, Hofman and Hayward, 1935.
11. *Metallurgy of Lead*, Hofman, 1930.
12. *Electrolytic Deposition and Hydro-metallurgy of Zinc*, Ralston, 1921.
13. *The Metallurgy of Zinc and Cadmium*, Ingalls.
14. *Aluminum*, Corson, 1926.
15. *Practical Metallurgy*, Sachs, 1940.
16. *Engineering Metallurgy*, Stoughton and Butts, 1939.
17. *Engineering Alloys*, Woldman, 1936.
18. *Cast Metals Handbook*, 1940, 1944.
19. *Engineering Physical Metallurgy*, Heyer, 1939.
20. *Metals*, Carpenter and Robertson, 1939.
21. *The Working of Metals*, American Society for Metals.
22. *Handbook of Non-Ferrous Metallurgy*, Liddell, 1935.
23. *The Aluminum Industry*, Edwards, 2 vols., 1930.
24. *Non-Ferrous Metallurgy*, Bray, 1941.
25. *Engineering Alloys*, Woldman and Dornblatt, 1936.
26. *Structure and Properties of Alloys*, Brick and Phillips, 1942.
27. *Metallography*, Dowdell-Jerabek-Forsyth-Green, 1943.
28. *Metallurgy of Copper*, Newton and Wilson, 1942.
29. *Principles of Physical Metallurgy*, Coonan, 1943.

30. *Modern Metallurgy for Engineers*, Sisco, 1942.
31. *The Principles of Metallographic Laboratory Practice*, Kehl, 1942.
32. *The Structure of Metals*, Barrett, 1942.
33. *Metallography of Aluminum and Its Alloys*, Fuss and Anderson, 1936.

Iron and Steel

1. *The Metallurgy of Iron and Steel*, Stoughton, 1923.
2. *The Metallography and Heat Treatment of Iron and Steel*, Sauveur, 1935.
3. *The Book of Stainless Steel*, Thum, 1935.
4. *Cast Iron in the Light of Recent Researches*, Hatfield, 1928.
5. *High Speed Steel*, Grossmann and Bain, 1931.
6. *The Making, Shaping and Treating of Steel*, Carnegie Steel Co., 1925, 1935.
7. *Steel and Its Heat Treatment*, Bullens, 1935, Vol. 1, 1938; Vol. 2, 1939.
8. *Alloys of Iron and Carbon*, Vol. 1, Epstein, 1937.
9. *Alloys of Iron and Carbon*, Vol. 2, Sisco, 1937.
10. *Forging Handbook*, Naujoks and Fabel, 1940.
11. *Tool Steels*, Gill, 1939.
12. *Handbook of American Malleable Iron*, Malleable Founders' Society, 1944.
13. *Tool Steel Simplified*, Palmer, 1937.
14. *Tool Steels*, Gill-Rose-Roberts-Johnston-George, 1944.
15. *Alloy Constructional Steels*, French, 1943.
16. *Ferrous Metallurgy*, Part 1 and Part 2, Teichert, 1944.

Journals

1. *American Institute of Mining and Metallurgical Engineers*
2. *American Society for Metals*
3. *American Society for Testing Materials*
4. *Bureau of Standards*, United States
5. *Journal of Iron and Steel Institute*, British
6. *Iron Age*
7. *Metals and Alloys*
8. *Chemical and Metallurgical Engineering*
9. *American Iron and Steel Institute*
10. *Heat Treating and Forging*

GLOSSARY

Some of the most commonly used terms employed in the working, treating, and testing of metals and alloys are defined here. As many of the terms used in the metal industry have more than one meaning or interpretation, the student no doubt may find occasion to refer to more exhaustive treatment of definitions. No attempt has been made to cover all the applications of metallurgical terms here. For a more complete discussion, the student is referred to the pocket encyclopedia on *Iron and Steel* by Hugh P. Tieman, and to the *Metals Handbook* published by the American Society for Metals.

A

Ac$_1$: Identifies the critical temperature during heating of iron-carbon alloys where the first major change of structure takes place, i.e., pearlite to austenite.

aging: Process of holding metals or alloys at room temperature after subjecting them to shaping or heat treatment for the purpose of increasing dimensional stability or to improve their hardness and strength through structural changes, as by precipitation.

amorphous: To describe material that is noncrystalline and which has a random orientation of its atoms or molecules, resulting in no distinct cleavage planes such as those found in the crystal state.

annealing: Subjecting to heat treatment. This usually involves heating followed by relatively slow cooling of metals or alloys for the purpose of decreasing hardness and increasing the ease of machining or the cold-working characteristics. Annealing may be used to (*a*) remove effects of strain hardening resulting from cold work, (*b*) remove stresses found in castings, forgings, and cold-worked metals, (*c*) improve machineability and cold-working characteristics, (*d*) improve mechanical and physical properties by changing the internal structure, such as by grain refinement, and to increase the uniformity of the structure and correct segregation, banding, and other structural characteristics. In general, annealing practice should be carried out so as to obtain the type of structure that is required, depending upon the end-point or use to which the metal or alloy is to be applied. The type or way in which the annealing operation is to be carried out should be identified with the application and the results desired. Because of this, several types of so-called annealing may be employed; these differ both in practice and in results, depending upon the type of metal or alloy being treated. See *full annealing, malleablizing, normalizing, patenting, process annealing, spheroidizing.*

Ar$_1$: Identifies the critical temperature during cooling of iron-carbon alloys where the change from austenite to pearlite occurs.

A.S.T.M.: Abbreviation for *American Society for Testing Materials.*

austempering: Heat treatment in which the operations of hardening and tempering are combined by quenching steels, previously heated to the austenitic temperature range, in a molten salt bath maintained at an elevated temperature between the "knee" of the S-curve and the temperature where martensite forms.

austenite: A solid solution structure with the gamma iron acting as a solvent; a solid solution of carbon or iron carbide in iron, determined microscopically as a constituent of steel under certain conditions.

B

banded structure: A structure with a woody appearance caused by working a segregated alloy such as steel; the bands are commonly formed by layers of ferrite and pearlite.

binary alloy: An alloy composed of two elements.

blister: An enclosed raised spot on a surface caused by gases entrapped in metals; a defect apparent from surface appearance.

blowhole: Hole found in metals resulting when gases, entrapped during solidification, cause a porous condition to develop; a defect in an ingot or casting, caused by a bubble of gas.

box annealing, pack annealing: Annealing process in which the metal is placed in a suitable container or box, with or without packing material; this practice protects the metal from oxidation.

bright annealing: Process of subjecting metal to high heat, with subsequent cooling, during which operation the atmosphere is controlled in order to prevent any oxidation or discoloration.

briquette: A mass of metal powders or ore dust molded together under considerable pressure, with or without heat, into a brick-shaped block; also

spelled *briquet*. The process is called *briquetting*.

burning: Over-oxidation of metals with loss of ductility and strength during heating of metals under oxidizing conditions. Burning results in permanent injury to metals.

C

carbon steel: Steel whose physical properties are chiefly the result of the percentage of carbon contained in it; an iron-carbon alloy in which the carbon is the most important constituent, ranging from 0.04 to 1.40%. It is also referred to as *plain carbon steel* or *straight carbon steel*. Minor elements also present in carbon steel include manganese, phosphorus, sulphur, and usually silicon.

carbonization: Process of converting into a residue of carbon by the action of fire or some corrosive agent, as the driving off of volatile matter from such fuels as coal and wood by fire. This term is used incorrectly as referring to the operation of carburizing.

carburizing: The process of combining or impregnating with carbon, as in adding carbon to the surface of low-carbon steel for the purpose of case-hardening; also, as in heating steel to above its critical temperature in the presence of a carbonaceous gas.

casehardening: A heat-treatment process, applied to steel or iron-carbon alloys, by which a harder outside layer is obtained over a softer interior; depth of increased hardness depends upon length of treatment.

cast steel: Molten steel cooled and solidified in a mold.

cementite: Chemical compound of iron and carbon, containing 93.33% iron combined with 6.67% carbon by weight; also called *carbide of iron*. Chemical formula for cementite is Fe_3C.

cold drawing: Reducing the cross section of a metal by drawing it through a die while its temperature is below the recrystallization temperature, or usually at room temperature.

cold rolling: Reducing the cross section of a metal by means of a rolling mill while the metal is cold or below its recrystallization temperature.

cold working: The permanent deformation or crystal distortion of a metal below its lowest temperature of recrystallization, resulting in work hardening.

combined carbon: Carbon combined with iron or other alloy elements found in steel to form chemical compounds which usually exhibit great hardness and brittleness.

crucible steel: High-grade steel produced when selected materials are melted in a closed crucible and cast into a mold.

cyaniding: Casehardening of low-carbon steel by heating in contact with a molten cyanide salt, followed by quenching.

D

decalescent point: The critical temperature at which sudden absorption of heat takes place in steel or iron-carbon alloy during the heating cycle; the absorption of energy is accompanied by a transformation of pearlite to austenite.

decarburization: Loss of surface carbon when steel is heated in an oxidizing atmosphere, resulting in a soft low-carbon skin on steel.

dendrite: Crystal having tree-like shape; may be found in many cast metals.

drawing: See *tempering.*

E

elongation: Permanent elastic extension which a metal undergoes during tensile testing; the amount of elonga-tion is usually indicated by the percentage of an original gage length.

endurance limit: See *fatigue strength.*

eutectic alloy: Alloy of a composition that solidifies at a lower temperature than the individual elements of the alloy and freezes or solidifies at a constant temperature to form a fine mixture of crystals made up of two or more phases.

eutectoid steel: Steel of a composition that will form a pearlitic structure from austenite during slow cooling through its critical temperature. In plain carbon steel, its composition is approximately 0.85% carbon.

F

fatigue failure: Progressive cracking that takes place in metals that are subjected to repeated loads.

fatigue strength: Maximum repeated load a metal will carry without developing a fatigue failure.

finishing temperature: Temperature of metal at the moment it leaves the last pass in a hot-rolling mill, or any hot-forging or forming operation.

fracture: Ruptured surface ends of metals that have been broken.

fracture test: Breaking or rupturing of metals to determine their resistance to failure, to examine grain size, and to reveal any evidences of defects on the fractured surfaces.

free ferrite: Iron phase found in a steel which has less than 0.85% carbon that has been slow-cooled from above its critical temperature range; the iron phase is alpha iron, low in carbon content.

full annealing: Heating of steels or iron alloys to above their critical temperature range, soaking at the annealing temperature until they are transformed to a uniform austenitic structure, followed by cooling at a predetermined rate, depending upon the type of alloy and structure required; in general the cooling rate is relatively slow.

G

gamma iron: Face-centered, nonmagnetic crystal form of iron.

grain: Crystal made up of atom similarly orientated.

grain growth: Increase in size of a crystal by its stealing atoms from its neighboring crystals or grains; decrease in number of grains and increase in average size.

H

hardening: Operation of quenching steels from the austenitic temperature range so as to produce martensite or a hard structure.

heat treatment: Any operation involving the heating and cooling of metals or alloys for the purpose of obtaining structural changes.

high-carbon steel: Steel with carbon content above 1.0%.

high-speed steel: Special alloy steel used for high-speed cutting and turning tools, as lathe bits; so named because any tools made of it are able to remove metal much faster than tools of ordinary steel.

high-strength cast iron: Cast grey iron with a tensile strength in excess of 30,000 p.s.i.

high-sulphur steel: Steel which has a sulphur content ranging from 0.12 to 0.33% and which then exhibits free cutting properties.

homogeneous metal: A metal or alloy, as steel, of very uniform structure, as opposed to heterogeneous or segregated metal with a nonuniform structure.

hot quenching: Cooling of heated metals or alloys in a bath of molten metal or salt, instead of using water or oil cooling medium.

hot short: Metal that is brittle and unworkable above room temperature.

hot working: Plastic deformation of metals or alloys when their temperature is above the lowest temperature of recrystallization so that there will be no work-hardening or permanent distortion of crystals or grains.

hydrogen brittleness: A brittle and nonductile state resulting from penetration of metal by nascent hydrogen.

hypereutectic: Containing the minor constituent in an amount in excess of that contained in the eutectic mixture; a eutectic alloy that contains more than the eutectic ratio of composition, or one to the right of the eutectic point in the alloy diagram.

hypereutectoid steel: Steel containing more than 0.85% carbon in a plain carbon steel, or a steel containing a mixture of pearlite and free cementite.

hypoeutectic: Containing the minor element in an amount less than that in the eutectic mixture; a eutectic alloy containing less than the eutectic ratio of composition, or one to the left of the eutectic point in the alloy diagram.

hypoeutectoid steel: Steel with less than 0.85% carbon content in straight carbon steel, or steel containing a mixture of pearlite and free ferrite.

I

impact test: Measurement of the amount of energy required to rupture metals with sudden or shock loads.

inclusions: Dirt, oxides, sulphides, and silicates that become mechanically mixed with metals.

ingot: A metal usually cast in a metal mold that forms a material for the plastic shaping industry.

ingot iron: Commercial pure iron; low-carbon steel that has nearly the chemistry and properties of pure iron.

intercrystalline failure: Rupture that follows the grain or crystal boundaries of a metal.

isothermal transformation: Transformation that takes place at a constant temperature where the radiation of heat from the metal body is counterbalanced by an equal evolution of heat from the metal undergoing the transformation.

K

killed steel: Steel which has been sufficiently deoxidized during the melting cycle to prevent gases from evolving during the solidification period.

L

lamellar pearlite: Pearlite that has layers of cementite and ferrite in its structure.

lap: A folding over of surface layers of metal without welding; a surface defect or discontinuity formed from improper hot working of metal.

ledeburite: Eutectic of iron and carbon associated with some types of cast iron.

liquidus: Refers to *liquidus curve*, a freezing-point curve in an alloy diagram representing relationship of concentration to temperature for systems comprising a solid phase and a liquid phase.

lüders' lines: Lines which appear on surfaces of cold-drawn metals resulting from plastic flow and stress concentrations.

M

M-point: The temperature during the cooling of austenite where martensite begins to form from austenite, i.e., in the quench-hardening operation.

macroscopic: Large enough to be observed by the naked eye; as structural details that are visible at a low magnification, usually under 30 magnifications.

macrostructure: Structure that is visible at a low magnification or with the naked eye.

malleableizing: Annealing operation used in connection with the change of white cast iron to a malleable cast iron; this process changes the combined carbon of white cast iron to a temper or graphitic carbon form.

martempering: Hardening of steels or producing of martensite by quenching steels from above their critical temperature in a molten salt bath maintained at an elevated temperature just above or near the M-point, then slowly cooling in air to room temperature.

martensite: Structure obtained when steel is treated to achieve its maximum hardness, as by heating and quenching in the hardening operation. Martensite has a needle-like microstructure.

mechanical working: Plastic shaping of metals by any such method as rolling, forging, pressing, etc.

microstructure: Structure that is visible only at a high magnification, with the aid of a microscope after proper preparation, such as polishing and etching.

miscible: Ability of elements to dissolve or alloy with each other.

modulus of elasticity: Value obtained when the load or stress applied to a metal, expressed in pounds p.s.i., is divided by the value of elongation or deformation determined for a given gage length, when the load or stress applied is within the elastic limit of loading.

mottled iron: Cast iron with a structure consisting of a mixture of free cementite, free graphite, and pearlite.

N

network structure: Structure in which a network or cellular envelope of one constituent may completely surround the grains of another constituent.

Neumann bands: Parallel bands or lines which appear within a crystal or grain as a result of mechanical deformation by the mechanism of twinning.

nitriding: Surface treatment applied to ferrous alloys for the purpose of casehardening, obtained by heating alloys in contact with dissociated ammonia gas.

normal structure: Structure found in steel after slow cooling from above its critical range of temperatures; this structure has the usual standard appearance—free ferrite and pearlite, pure pearlite, or free cementite and pearlite, depending upon the carbon content of the steel. Steel with this structure is referred to as *normal steel.*

normalizing: Treatment usually applied to steel castings and forgings consisting of heating to above the critical temperature range of the steel followed by cooling in air.

nucleus: Center or beginning of crystal formation; central portion of an atom.

O

overheating: Heating of metals or alloys to the zone of incipient melting; heating to the point of developing a very coarse grain size.

oxidation: See *burning.*

P

p. s. i.: Abbreviation for *pounds per square inch.*

patenting: Treatment usually applied to steel wire consisting of heating to well above the critical temperature range of the steel, followed by cooling or quenching the wire in a molten lead or salt bath maintained at a temperature range of 800° F. to 1100° F. Also, air patenting is employed where the heated steel wire is air-cooled to room temperature, as in the standard normalizing operation.

pearlite: Eutectoid alloy of iron and carbon, which contains 0.85% carbon; structural constituent found in steel that has been cooled slowly from above its critical temperature range, consisting of layers or plates of cementite and ferrite and appearing colorful under the microscope.

pig iron: The product of the blast furnace cast into blocks convenient for handling or storage; iron alloy as recovered from the ore.

pipe: The cone-shaped cavity or hole found near the top of a casting or cast ingot resulting from natural shrinkage and uneven cooling during the casting and solidification period.

pit: A rough surface found on metals resulting from slight depressions on the surface.

plasticity: Ability of a metallic state to undergo permanent deformation without rupture.

powder metallurgy: Process by which shapes resembling a cast or forged metal are made from metal powders by pressure and heat.

precipitation hardening: Process of hardening by heat treatment where a hard phase is precipitated from solid solution at room temperature or at some elevated temperature.

primary crystals: The first crystals to form during solidification of a cast metal or alloy.

process annealing: Treatment applied to cold-worked steels consisting of heating to a temperature below the critical temperature range of the steel followed by slow cooling.

Q

quenching: Process of fast-cooling metals or alloys such as steel in the process of hardening, as air quenching, oil quenching, water quenching, etc.

quenching crack: Crack or failure occurring from rapid cooling of alloys such as steel in the hardening operation.

R

recalescence: The sudden liberation of heat by a metal when cooling through a certain critical temperature, as iron at 1652° F. The recalescent point in a steel occurs when it is cooled through the lower *Arl* critical temperature and liberates a small amount of heat.

red-hardness: Hardness exhibited by metals when heated to about a red heat.

red-shortness: Brittleness, lack of ductility or malleability that occurs with some metals or alloys at a red heat.

reduction of area: Diminution of cross-section area, usually expressed in percentage of the original area; reduction that a metal or alloy undergoes during a tensile test; it is also called *contraction of area.*

refractory: Capable of being heated to high temperatures without fusing or softening.

regenerative quenching: Heat treatment involving the use of a double heating and quenching of some carburized steels for the purpose of refining the grains of both the core and case.

resilience: Elastic properties exhibited by materials such as a spring; capability of a strained body to recover its size and shape after deformation, especially by compressive stresses.

rough fracture: Irregular surface resulting from the fracture of a coarse-grained metal or alloy.

S

scale: The dark oxide coating found on metals as a result of heating in an oxidizing atmosphere such as air.

seam: A longitudinal crack or surface defect resulting from a surface cavity that becomes elongated during hot rolling or forging.

season cracking: Failure by intercrystalline fracture that some alloys such as brass undergo when in a highly stressed condition and exposed to corrosive media.

secondary hardening: An increase in hardness that occurs with some high-alloy steels when subjected to tempering after hardening.

self-hardening steels: Steels that become martensitic or fully hard by air cooling from above their critical temperature or from the austenitizing temperature.

slip bands: Traces of slip planes that appear in a polished surface of metal when it is stressed so as to produce plastic flow after polishing and etching. These slip bands are the result of crystal displacement or blocks of crystal fragments which have moved with respect to the crystal orientation.

soaking: Allowing steel or alloys to remain at an elevated temperature long enough to become uniformly heated and to complete the desired change in structure.

solidification range: Range of temperature that extends from the beginning of freezing to the end of freezing or crystallization.

sonims: Nonmetallic inclusions found in metals.

sorbite: Structure found in steel resembling pearlite but of a finer and more granular mixture of cementite and ferrite than found in normal pearlite.

spheroidized pearlite or **spheroidized cementite:** Structure found in steel containing balls or spheroids of cementite in a matrix of ferrite. See *Spheroidizing* under *Annealing.*

spheroidizing: Annealing process which is applied to steel when the cementite or carbide is desired in a globular or spherical shape. In this treatment, the annealing cycle may follow that of full annealing, but the cooling rate employed from the annealing temperature is usually much slower in order to obtain the cementite in spheroidized form.

stress raiser: Notch or discontinuity on the surface of metals that produces stress concentrations.

subatmospheric treatment: Subjecting steels that are in the hardened condition to low temperatures, as low as minus 180° F., for periods up to 6 hours, for the purpose of stabilization and to aid in the transformation of austenite to martensite.

surface hardening: See *casehardening.*

T

temper carbon: The nodular graphitic carbon found in iron-base alloys of the malleable or pearlitic malleable cast type.

tempering: Application of heat to quenched, hardened steels or to steels in the martensitic condition. Temperatures employed in tempering are from slightly above room temperature to approximately 1200° F. Tempering can also be accomplished by the *austempering* or *martempering* methods. Tempering is also called *drawing.* See *austempering* and *martempering.*

ternary alloys: Alloys that contain three elements affecting the properties of the alloy.

troostite: A very fine pearlite found in steels that have been cooled at a slower rate from the hardening temperature than allowed the formation of martensite; it is a very fine aggregate or mixture of ferrite and cementite.

twin bands: The microscopic appearance resulting from twinning.

twin crystal or twinning: A crystal distortion that takes place when metals are subjected to shock loading which causes a change in orientation resulting in differently-orientated crystal fragments within a grain or crystal. See *Neumann bands.*

V

void: A cavity or hole in a metal or alloy.

W

welding: The crystallizing into union of metals or alloys by methods of fusion or pressure welding.

work-hardening: The increase in hardness and strength that takes place during any cold-working of metals.

Y

yield point: The load or stress that produces a measurable plastic deformation when metals are gradually subjected to an increasing load or stress; also known as the *commercial elastic limit.*

INDEX

441